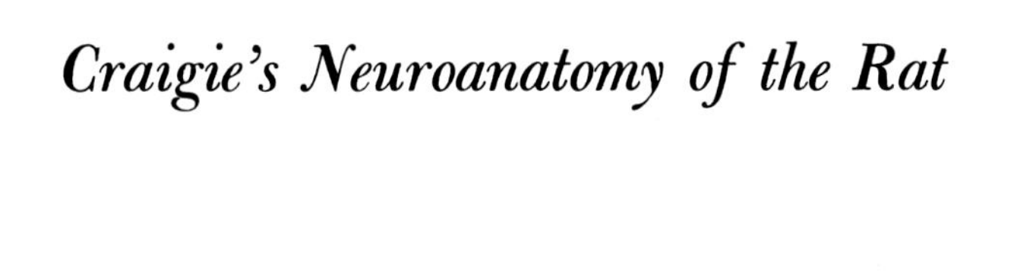

Craigie's Neuroanatomy of the Rat

Craigie's Neuroanatomy of the Rat

REVISED AND EXPANDED BY

WOLFGANG ZEMAN
Department of Pathology
School of Medicine
Indiana University
Indianapolis, Indiana

JAMES ROBERT MAITLAND INNES
Biology Department
Brookhaven National Laboratory
Upton, New York

1963 

ACADEMIC PRESS New York San Francisco London
A Subsidiary of Harcourt Brace Jovanovich, Publishers

ACADEMIC PRESS INC.
111 Fifth Avenue, New York 3, New York

United Kingdom Edition published by
ACADEMIC PRESS, INC. (LONDON) LTD.
24/28 Oval Road, London NW1

LIBRARY OF CONGRESS CATALOG CARD NUMBER: 63-16963

PRINTED IN THE UNITED STATES OF AMERICA

Preface

The unprecedented surge in biological studies involving the nervous system of small laboratory animals has made Craigie's book, "An Introduction to the Finer Anatomy of the Central Nervous System Based upon That of the Albino Rat," a prized possession among pathologists, neurophysiologists, pharmacologists, zoologists, physiological psychologists, and others. Long out of print, Craigie's book has remained the only complete account. The lack of a modern, comprehensive text on the murine nervous system, amply illustrated, was therefore a sound reason why Professor Craigie's book should be revived.

The ideas embodied in the book by Craigie have been largely retained. The progress made in neuroanatomy during the past 38 years, however, necessitated revisions and additions. Since the identification of further anatomic structures threatened to jeopardize the clarity of Craigie's original black and white drawings, made from sections stained by the Weigert method, a nearly parallel series of photomicrographs has been added. On those the more recently recognized structures, in addition to some of those which have been known for a long time, are identified. In all illustrations, the structures are fully designated by their Latin names as specified in BNA. The book consists of two mutually complementary parts: a descriptive text containing figures chosen for their didactic value, and, at the end of the book, an atlas covering the encephalon in frontal sections. All references mentioned in the text are given in the bibliographies at the end of each chapter, but in addition other important works dealing with the murine nervous system have been included.

As a result of this organization, the student is presented with a general text which introduces him to the principles of mammalian neuroanatomy by describing structures in the light of their functional significance and in respect to their ontogenetic and phylogenetic development. A glimpse at the application of this knowledge is afforded by Chapter VIII which gives an introduction to the theory of neural mechanisms.

The research worker will turn his attention to the atlas which permits the tracing of fiber tracts and nuclei. Horizontal and sagittal views complement the series of transverse sections which are arranged in a caudo-rostral order. The atlas, together with the index, was organized to cover the bulk of neuroanatomic topography requisite for work by behavioral and physiological psychologists, neurophysiologists, experimental pathologists, toxicologists, and pharmacologists, but will be of value to the general biologist. The investigator who requires more details than provided in the text will find the additional information in the original papers cited in the bibliographies.

It is hoped that this book will draw students' attention to the challenge of neurobiology. It should also enable workers in several disciplines to perform a more satisfying neuroanatomic examination on some of the millions of rodents used annually in laboratories throughout the world.

W. Z.
J. R. M. I.*

August, 1963

---

* *Dr. Innes is presently affiliated with the National Cancer Institute, Branch of Experimental Carcinogenesis, National Institutes of Health, Bethesda, Maryland.*

Acknowledgments

The authors are deeply grateful to E. Horne Craigie, Professor Emeritus of Zoology, University of Toronto, for his continuous and unqualified support. He made his plates available and permitted us to use the copyright of his former book, but much more important was his experience which he brought to bear upon the production of the book. Without his tedious efforts in correcting the manuscript and reading the proofs, the book could hardly have been assembled. Chapter II, E on the Vascular Bed was completely written by Professor Craigie and reflects his most recent studies in this field.

All the photographs are the work of Mr. Robert F. Smith, Photographic Department, Brookhaven National Laboratory, Upton, New York. The new art work and the prodigious efforts required in placing names and arrows on the drawings and photographs were by Mr. George Cox and his assistants, Miss Carol Gelhaus and Mrs. Marian Childress, Art Department, Brookhaven National Laboratory. To those people our grateful thanks are due, for without the illustrations the book would have little value.

Among the many friends with whom we discussed our plans and who helped in its progress by advice and criticism, special thanks are due to George Romanes, Professor of Anatomy, Medical School, Edinburgh University, and William DeMyer, Associate Professor of Neurology, Indiana University.

Grateful acknowledgment is made to the National Institute of Neurological Diseases and Blindness for the grant (NB 04611-01) in aid of publication.

Table of Contents

CHAPTER I

Fundamental Considerations of Neuroanatomy and Nomenclature

The theme of this book presented an onerous task of coping with the interests and background of divergent types of particular workers. At one extreme is the undergraduate starting to study comparative neuroanatomy and at the other the advanced research worker, who studies murine brains for different reasons, but who already possesses a working knowledge of neuroanatomy based perhaps upon some other species. For the student, text descriptions and illustrations are essential and some of the text must be elementary, though this part will be superfluous for many others.

The elementary student, at the beginning of any introduction to a study of the nervous system, might well ponder the question "Why study neuroanatomy?" For the student who will later enter the medical field proper, the answer will inevitably appear in his clinical years when it will become very patent that a knowledge of neuroanatomy and neurophysiology is fundamentally basic for understanding the complexities of diseases of the nervous system and their diagnosis. Knowledge of normal form and structure must always, manifestly, precede knowledge of changes of form and of the factors which produce them, and this indeed applies literally to any other organ of the body.

Research workers who use the rat as an experimental animal, and who require neuroanatomical knowledge, can have many different objectives in mind. Some study behavior after ablation or stimulation, others are concerned with study of regions or tracts, and yet others study the effect of damage by toxic or other agents to the brain, which may produce a variety of lesions differing in quality and topographic distribution. They already are aware of the importance of neuroanatomy, and all the information they require, as far as the rat is concerned, will be found in our illustrations. Chapters I and II are therefore compiled largely for the undergraduate student.

During the early historical phases of neuroanatomical studies, the medical anatomists were primarily concerned with discovering new structures existing in that great unknown of the time—the brain. The history of anatomy and embryology (see Singer, Needham, Elliot Smith) reveals how anatomy, including neuroanatomy, came into being, the most notable anatomical event of the Middle Ages being the work of the great genius Vesalius. The earlier phases were characterized by the coining of picturesque terminology, and there were similarly queer ideas on function. Names of observers in anatomy, by usage, were often tacked on to whatever new structures were discovered, and some were retained until recent times. Such eponyms have now been discarded in favor of a more logical terminology based on the structure involved and its close localization, and in an internationally understood language—Latin. The spinal cord (*medulla spinalis*) in earlier times, for instance, was compared with a tap root with rootlets emerging at intervals from the vertebral canal. The last low rootlets, which were noticed to stream away obliquely caudad before leaving the canal, were likened to the brush of a horse's tail, and hence received the name *cauda equina*. The pineal body (*corpus pineale* or *epiphysis cerebri*) got its name because of the resemblance to a pine cone, but as anatomists speculated on function and concluded that it produced cerebrospinal fluid, *penis cerebri* was a name proposed. The names amygdaloid complex (because of its almond shape), *nucleus caudatus* (because of its head and tail shape), *nucleus lentiformis* (lens-shaped), and *hippocampus* (seahorse) all testify to the predominantly, and at that time essentially, descriptive approach of the medical anatomists of yore.

Times have changed. No longer is the neuroanatomist exclusively concerned with the identification and proper nomenclature of parts. However, on this score let there be no misunderstanding; as neuropathologists who must use neuroanatomical knowledge, we must absolve ourselves from any suggestion of deprecation of the efforts of those in the history of classical neuroanatomy. Without those tedious labors of countless medical anatomists going back to Leonardo da Vinci, Vesalius, and Thomas Willis—to name but three—the requisite basic work on purely topographic anatomy could never have been achieved, and without it the current modern approach would not be possible. We comment on present anatomic nomenclature later. Without precise names for things in the nervous system, it might be necessary to use a long sentence to describe the spinal cord, such as "that long rodlike structure extending down from a hole in the skull to somewhere else lower down and from which little branches spring." Needham, in his erudite treatise on the history of embryology, shows that among the many factors which contributed to hindrance of scientific advancements in previous centuries, lack of accurate terminology was certainly one of the most important. Nowadays, it is almost impossible, as well as undesirable, to separate neuroanatomy from neurophysiology, for the facts of one (on structure) are essential for a consideration of the other (function) and vice versa. Specialized workers get labels to designate their calling, but neuroanatomists differ from neurophysiologists largely in respect to the techniques they use, not because their final objective is different in any basic sense.

Neuroanatomy has developed in width and depth. By the use of the light microscope, and now the electron microscope, a host of structures of incredible complexity have been discovered which are all related one to another. The observations of the late 19th century had their crowning achievement in the monumental studies of Ramón y Cajal, who recognized the neuron, i.e., the nerve cell body or perikaryon, its axon, and its dendrites as the functional unit of the nervous system. The neuron is a morphological and developmental unit as a cell, but it is also a trophic unit, for injury to one part will affect the entire neuron. These observations are formulated in the "neuron doctrine," which is probably the single most important concept in neuroanatomy, and which provided a basis for opening new and unprecedented vistas regarding functions of the nervous system. Cajal, whose genius created the cornerstone for modern neuroanatomy and neurohistology, and Camillo Golgi, whose method of silver impregnation made Cajal's work possible, shared the Nobel Prize for Physiology and Medicine in 1906.

Following Cajal's work, the study of the morphology of the nervous system underwent a revolution largely under the leadership of American neuroanatomists. Neuroanatomy, for a long time considered to be so static, has developed into a dynamic science. Although the great names in neuroanatomy of the last 80 years are largely European, nevertheless the solid core of research has been American, as can be seen by anyone glancing at the pages of the *Journal of Comparative Neurology.** It is obvious how interest has grown and spread from the human brain to studies of the lower animals in attempts to explain ontogenetic and phylogenetic influences. It is with this basic concept that knowledge of the animal brain has grown, not because of applied needs; and those who require such applied knowledge are fortunate in having had much work done by others. The identification of a particular morphologic structure is now seen in the perspective of its function and its functional relation to other structures. It can be considered in terms of information theory, of electronics, of biochemistry and bioenergetics, and now what has been a dreaded and lackluster subject for study by reluctant students has come into a sparkling life of its own.† This viewpoint is the subject of a recent book written by Dodgson (1962).

The foundation of this development can be traced into the latter part of the 19th century, when physiologists began to identify those gray nuclear masses and white fiber tracts subserving sensory-motor functions. It was soon realized that

* The reader is also referred to W. Haymaker, "The Founders of Neurology" (C. C Thomas, Springfield, Illinois, 1953), which contains biographical sketches on the great neuroanatomists of past generations.

† However, the widening of anatomical horizons applies not only to neuroanatomy, but to the whole of anatomy; see for example "Recent Advances in Anatomy" (Editors, F. Goldby & R. J. Harrison; London: Churchill, 1961). Chapters of this work deal with early mammalian development, placentology, epithelia and characteristics of repair, neurology and neuroanatomy, blood supply of liver, spleen, and kidneys, joints and movements, and concepts of evolution of higher primates.

the regions of the cerebral cortex, from which such sensory-motor responses could be elicited by proper stimulation, comprised a relatively small segment of the entire organ. This meant that large areas remained "white" on the functional map of the cerebral cortex and the subcortical gray structures. Only recently has it been discovered that some of the phylogenetically "older" regions of the paleocortex, the diencephalon and mesencephalon represent an integrating mechanism for the "higher" functions of the brain—namely the "mind" in its broadest sense. It is now understood that these mechanisms are indispensable for a proper function of vast and previously "uncharted" cortical regions which act as an amplifying and encoding apparatus that simplifies patterns for the integrating systems in the "old" deeper brain structures. The functional approach of the neuroanatomist along this avenue has led to the delineation of mechanisms for "affective behavior" residing in the "limbic system"—mechanisms responsible for the proper activation and function of almost the entire brain in the form of the "reticular activating system" of brainstem and thalamus, mechanisms for motivation and experience located in certain parts of the thalamus and its cortical projection areas, mechanisms for homeostasis or vegetative control located in the hypothalamus, etc. The importance of these discoveries upon such fields as psychology, psychiatry, neurology, endocrinology, human engineering, and other social sciences can hardly be overestimated, nor is the tremendous impact of these theories upon the pharmaceutical industry (discovering drugs which act on the nervous system) to be taken lightly. For generations to come, we can expect that identification of neuroanatomic structures in relation to psychological observations, to toxicity studies, to classical neuropathology, and in terms of functional representation, will keep scores of scientists busy.

In contrast to the correlation between functions and their anatomically defined mechanisms, a somewhat less spectacular but perhaps equally important development has taken place almost unnoticed. Some 34 years ago the famous research couple Cécile and Oskar Vogt (1929) published a series of articles on the "Site and Nature of Diseases" in which they elaborated a new hypothesis termed "pathoclisis."* This hypothesis, in a nutshell, proposes that certain anatomically defined systems of nervous parenchyma possess a differential vulnerability to various pathogens. Owing to a somewhat obscure German style and to the use of newly created terms,† this hypothesis has never been widely accepted although some of its facets are common-day experience. We might cite here the peculiar vulnerability of the anterior horn cells and some other neuron

* See W. Haymaker's essay: C. & O. Vogt on the occasion of her 75th and his 80th birthday, *Neurology* **1**: 179-204 (1951); and C. & O. Vogt, Importance of neuroanatomy in the field of neuropathology, *Neurology* **1**: 205-218 (1951).

† For example, a *topistic unit* (in Vogt's terminology) is a collection of nerve cell bodies (perikarya) either in the form of a *nucleus* or of a cytoarchitectonically delimited field of cerebral cortex supposed to form a biologic unit and to reveal a stable ontologic and phylogenetic pattern (see also Scholz, 1953).

bodies to succumb to the poliomyelitis virus, which is much more widely distributed throughout an infected nervous system than the extent of the lesions suggests. Attention is also drawn to the highly selective pattern of damage ensuing from such different pathogens as hypoxemia, viruses, and numerous toxins (vegetable, chemical, and bacterial).

In the field of comparative neuropathology (Innes and Saunders, 1962) this concept is equally manifest, for there we see not only that certain regional structures of the nervous system are affected in specific animal diseases, but that what may happen in one species may not apply to any other. For example, Californian star thistle is not poisonous to sheep but it is to horses, affecting selectively the *substantia nigra* and *globus pallidus* of the latter animals. In the different domesticated animals, topographic distribution of lesions in neurotropic viral infections can be highly specific and can help to identify the various encephalitides. Innes and Saunders (1962) also cite some unique examples of the specific toxic effects of drugs on the brain, of prime significance in human medicine; e.g., the effect of certain antibiotics on the 8th nerve and vestibular and cochlear systems; or, even more exceptional, the specific nonfatal, but tragic, effects of certain chemicals on the retina of man, but not on that of animals. Recently, the concept of pathoclisis has received considerable support by the demonstration of marked gradients in enzymatic activity from one anatomically defined nervous structure to another. For instance, we can now correlate the vulnerability of certain parts of the hippocampus to hypoxidosis with their content of zinc, which indicates the presence of a certain enzyme. Moreover, it has been shown that the pyramidal tracts are peculiarly vulnerable to ionizing radiation because their low oxidative enzyme activity permits free oxygen to accumulate, a fact which enhances the radiobiologic effectiveness of certain radiations. Deficiency of vitamin B_1, the pyrophosphate of which is the coenzyme cocarboxylase, is particularly detrimental to the vestibular nuclei of the rat.

These examples could be augmented *ad libitum*, yet they all document the same principle, namely that selective vulnerability is but the expression of metabolic peculiarities of the respective vulnerable structures. Accordingly, neuroanatomists have teamed with neurochemists and produced elaborate maps of graded enzyme activity. Owing to its wide use, easy accessibility, and widespread distribution as an experimental animal in research, the rat has been extensively studied by histochemical methods. Pertinent data on the brain may be found in articles published in the *Journal of Neurochemistry*, or, in the form of references, in the standard work by A. G. E. Pearse (1960).

It is not difficult to see that the correlation of the biochemical organization of a particular structure with its vulnerability to a specific pathogen will ultimately provide insight into many disease processes. Likewise, the involvement of certain systems in degenerative diseases when considered in the light of their metabolic properties should eventually make possible the discovery of the respective pathogenesis.

In summary we can say, first, that knowledge of neuroanatomy has an intrinsic value, for we must continue to expand information on the nature of the brain of man and animals. It has an equally indispensable value in applied studies to form a basis for understanding the biology of behavior, locomotion, and sensation; it is hence a prerequisite of such scientific disciplines as neurophysiology, clinical neurology, neuropathology, psychiatry, and psychology. All of these can be studied by direct observation on man and animal, but also on experimental levels, and it is in this last sphere that comparative neuroanatomy becomes important—in our case, the neuroanatomy of the rat. It is further needed for study of neurophysiologic mechanisms, be it by the naked eye or at microscopic or electron microscopic levels. Last, but not least, neuroanatomy continues to play an ever-increasing role in the identification and elucidation of disease mechanisms occurring in man and animals in terms of topographic biochemical pathology.

A presentation of histologic staining techniques is clearly beyond the scope of the present account, and the student is referred to standard texts on staining and histochemical techniques. On the other hand, a short note on the histologic stains used in the illustrations will facilitate their correct interpretation.

Neural tissues are made up of neurons which are considered to be the specific elements of nervous activity. These neurons are metabolically dependent upon the supporting tissues, the neuroglia, and the vascular bed. In the present account we are primarily concerned with the neuron, which consists of a cell body commonly called nerve cell, or more correctly perikaryon. From the perikaryon extend a number of short protoplasmatic processes—the dendrites, generally considered to conduct impulses toward the perikaryon, and a single long process, the axon, considered to conduct impulses away from the perikaryon. The axon of many nerve cells is surrounded by a lipid cover, the myelin sheath, considered in part to serve as an insulator. These various components of the neuron are chemically different and therefore can be more or less selectively stained by appropriate histologic techniques. The perikarya contain large quantities of ribonucleic acids (RNA) and therefore are easily stained with basic aniline dyes. Thus, if the arrangement of perikarya is the prime concern of the study, one would apply a cell stain; any one of the modifications of the Nissl stain (Fig. 27, page 91) is appropriate. The myelin sheath of the myelinated nerve fibers requires a different staining technique which is based on the formation of a metal-dye linkage with the lipoprotein component of the myelin sheath. The first successful staining of myelin sheaths was achieved by Weigert. His techniques have been modified, but the original principle has been left intact. Such preparations permit the tracing of myelinated fiber systems, but they do not show perikarya. It was therefore a most welcome innovation when Klüver and Barrera succeeded in developing a staining technique (using copper phthalocyanines) which demonstrates both cell bodies and myelin sheaths, the so-called luxol fast blue-cresylviolet stain (Fig. 27). This method was employed on all sections from which the photomicrographs in the present text were made.

Not all nerve fibers are myelinated, and in some areas, such as the hypothalamus, the great majority of the fibers are unmyelinated. Obviously, myelin stains will not demonstrate such fibers, and another technique for their demonstration is thus required. Unmyelinated nerve fibers can be demonstrated by impregnation with silver salts reduced to metallic silver, and it is by means of this technique, originated by Golgi and extensively modified subsequently, that most of the information on the course of unmyelinated fiber tracts has been obtained. Incidentally, this technique is the only one that will demonstrate dendrites.

In going over this text, the student might wonder how the information on the fiber connections of the various parts of the central nervous system has been obtained, considering their abundance and their three-dimensional arrangement. Clearly, a morphologic study of normal tissues would pose unsurmountable difficulties, if this was the only method available.

Knowledge of fiber connections is being obtained by three different approaches. The first is a morphologic one which entails the operative destruction of a mass of nerve cells or the section of a fiber tract. According to the neuron doctrine, all the structures distal to the lesion, i.e., the distal segments of axons or the entire axons emerging from the destroyed perikarya, will undergo a secondary degeneration. This secondary degeneration can be demonstrated by the occurrence of myelin breakdown products, provided that the nerve fibers are myelinated, or by demonstrating a disintegration of unmyelinated axis cylinders with the silver impregnation method of Nauta and Gygax (1954). The other approach is a physiological one in which a particular neural structure, such as an accumulation of nerve cells or a fiber tract, is electrically or chemically stimulated and the possible projection areas of the system are scanned for the occurrence of evoked potentials. This method is called neuronography. It is also possible to delineate fiber tracts on a developmental basis, because various fiber systems myelinate, i.e., acquire myelin sheaths at different stages of embryologic and postnatal development, and which can be stained by Weigert's method.

NOMENCLATURE AND ABBREVIATIONS USED IN THIS BOOK

The B.N.A. (Basle Nomina Anatomica, 1895) originated from the admirable efforts of medical anatomists on a worldwide basis to achieve uniformity in terminology as applied to the whole of human anatomy, including neuroanatomy. Eponyms, obsolete terms, and different views on the value of different names, some 300 years after Vesalius, were rendering anatomical nomenclature in different languages almost incoherent. The 1895 edition of the new anatomical nomenclature was later revised by a Conference in Oxford in 1950 (printed in 1956 by Williams & Wilkins Co., Baltimore, Maryland). The recommendations of the 1950 Conference were adopted at the International Congress in Paris in 1955 (printed in 1956 by Oostooek Publishing Company, Utrecht; Editor, Dr. M. W. Woerdeman). We realize that there is no B.N.A. with reference to nomenclature of the anatomy of the quadruped (nonerect animal). However, we have followed the above publications as far as possible, even though there may be objections by some human neuroanatomists to the use of certain terms, in the transferring of the names from man to lower animals. Consequently, many of the names used in Craigie's (1925) text no longer appear. We have followed suit in deletion of eponyms and synonyms in the text and illustrations, and all the names attached to the latter are in Latin. To make for greater availability of the text to all categories of readers, in the Index we have listed names of structures in English as well as Latin and also included many obsolete names and many eponyms. For practical considerations we have used abbreviations in the plates, but these have been kept to a minimum; they include the following terms:

Com.	*Commissura* (Commissure)
Decus.	*Decussatio* (Decussation)
Fasc.	*Fasciculus* (Fascicle)
Fis.	*Fissura* (Fissure)
Form.	*Formatio* (Formation)
G.	*Gyrus* (Gyrus)
N.	*Nervus* (Nerve); Nn., *Nervi* (Nerves)
Nuc.	*Nucleus* (Nucleus)
Ped.	*Pedunculus* (Peduncle)
Subs.	*Substantia* (Substance)
S.	*Sulcus* (Sulcus)
Tr.	*Tractus* (Tract)

As the English and Latin of the above are similar, or much alike, there should be no difficulty. However, as the text and plates are perused, the likeness between Latin and English names in many cases is absent, and the terms may on occasion seem needlessly cumbersome. For universal understanding by anatomists of all nations and all languages, this must be endured as the only practical method available.

At this stage, it should be emphasized that the two separate series of illustrations—viz., the black and white drawings made by Craigie of Weigert preparations, and the low power photomicrographs of the sections stained with luxol fast blue—were obtained from entirely different series of sections cut in different planes and that these planes differ also from that seen in the stereotaxic atlas of De Groot (1959) (see Figs. A1 and A2). This is not without advantage; the authors feel that for the average users of this book the planes of their sections will never be uniform and may differ from any of those represented.

All this, however, should aid the acquisition of a three-dimensional visual picture of that complicated structure—the brain.

For those who may have been brought up in the older tradition with other anatomic names for parts of the nervous system, a reading of the footnotes at the end of the Williams & Wilkins publication of the Oxford Conference nomenclature may be of value. Therein, for example, it will be found that (a) *formatio reticularis* replaced *substantia reticularis,* (b) the word *fasciculus* signifying individual bundles of nerve fibers with the same functional significance has been replaced almost entirely (but not quite) by *tractus,* (c) *pedunculus cerebellaris inferior* and *superior* replace *corpus restiforme* and *brachium conjunctivum,* respectively; these are only a few of the numerous changes from anatomical texts of years ago. As far as the quadruped is concerned, clearly other changes are necessary; for example, posterior (human) becomes dorsal, and anterior becomes ventral as far as the animal trunk is concerned, but anterior and posterior can be used on the animal head for cranial or rostral and caudal, and may also replace superior and inferior as applied to the human brain. Since "dorsal" and "ventral" refer to anatomical structures (back and abdomen) independent of the position of a body in physical space, the B.N.A. now correctly recommend dorsal and ventral also for human anatomy. Adoption of this rule will certainly alleviate many problems of terminology.

It probably is helpful at this stage to add a few explanatory remarks on the anatomical terms decussation (*decussatio*) and commissure (*commissura*), for we ourselves have been confused. Both refer to fiber systems invariably found in a midsagittal position where fibers cross from one side of the neuraxis to the other. The term commissure is used to designate fiber systems which connect structures represented bilaterally; for instance, the corpus callosum provides connections of homotypic regions of the telencephalic cortex. In contrast, decussations are crossings of fibers which connect heterotopic structures; for example, the *decussatio pyramidum* is made up of fibers which connect the motor cortex with contralateral ventral horn nerve cells in the spinal cord. Some of the structures originally identified as commissure or decussation have been shown in the meantime to contain both commissural and decussational fibers. For example, the anterior commissure contains commissural fibers for the olfactory bulbs, also decussational fibers from the amygdala to the contralateral hypothalamic nuclei and to the contralateral *nucleus proprius striae terminalis.* Vice versa, the tegmental decussations contain commissural fibers connecting the heterolateral ventral and dorsal tegmental nuclei. Consequently, there is a tendency to use either commissure or decussation for systems which contain both types of connection. In analogy to general anatomic terminology, commissural fibers may be referred to as intrinsic systems, inasmuch as they connect structures of identical functional significance. Decussational systems are extrinsic ones which provide connections between structures located at different planes of functional and anatomical significance.

References

ANDREW, W. The Nissl substance of the Purkinje cell in the mouse and rat from birth to senility. *Z. Zellforsch.* **25**: 583-604, 1936–1937.

ANDREW, W. Structural alterations with aging in the nervous system. *Res. Publ. Ass. Nerv. Mental Dis.* **35**: 129-170, 1956.

ARIËNS KAPPERS, C. U., G. C. HUBER & ELIZABETH C. CROSBY. The Comparative Anatomy of the Nervous System of Vertebrates, Including Man. 2 Volumes. New York: Macmillan, 1936.

CAJAL, S. RAMÓN Y. Histologie du système nerveux de l'homme et des vertébrés. Paris: Maloine, 1909–1911. (Reprinted by C. S. I. S., Madrid, 1952.)

CRAIGIE, E. H. An Introduction to the Finer Anatomy of the Central Nervous System Based upon that of the Albino Rat. Toronto: University Press, 1925.

DODGSON, M. C. H. The Growing Brain. Baltimore: Williams & Wilkins, 1962.

FRIEDE, R. L. A Histochemical Atlas of Tissue Oxidation in the Brain Stem of the Cat. New York: S. Karger, 1961.

GREENE, EUNICE C. Anatomy of the Rat. New York: Hafner, 1955.

GROOT, J. DE. The rat forebrain in stereotaxic coordinates. *Verhandl. Koninkl. Nederl. Akad. Wetensch. afd. Natuurkunde,* Tweede Reeks, Deel LII, No. 4, 1959.

HERRICK, C. J. Brains of Rats and Men. A Survey of the Original and Biological Significance of the Cerebral Cortex. Chicago: Univ. of Chicago Press, 1926.

HERRICK, C. J. An Introduction to Neurology. 5th Ed. Philadelphia: Saunders, 1931.

INNES, J. R. M. & L. Z. SAUNDERS. Comparative Neuropathology. New York: Academic Press, 1962.

KLÜVER, H. & E. BARRERA. A method for the combined staining of cells and fibers in the nervous system. *J. Neuropath. Exp. Neurol.* **12**: 400-403, 1953. (See also, for further developments, MARGOLIS, G. & J. P. PICKETT. New application of the Luxol fast blue stain. *Lab. Investig.* **5**: 459-474, 1956.)

LEWIS, W. B. On the comparative structure of the brain in rodents. *Phil. Trans. Roy. Soc. London* **173**: 699-749, 1882.

NAUTA, W. J. H. & P. A. GYGAX. Silver impregnation of degenerating axons in the central nervous system. A modified technique. *Stain Technol.* **29**: 91-93, 1954.

NEEDHAM, J. A History of Embryology. London and New York: Cambridge Univ. Press, 1934.

PEARSE, A. G. E. Histochemistry: Theoretical and Applied. 2nd Ed. Boston: Little, Brown, 1960.

PHALEN, G. S. & H. A. DAVENPORT. Pericellular end-bulbs in the central nervous system of vertebrates. *J. Comp. Neurol.* **68**: 67-81, 1937.

RANSON, S. W. On the medullated fibers crossing the site of lesions in the brain of the white rat. *J. Comp. Neurol.* **13**: 185-207, 1903.

RANSON, S. W. Retrograde degeneration in the corpus callosum of the white rat. *J. Comp. Neurol.* **14**: 381-389, 1904.

RANSON, S. W. Retrograde degeneration in the spinal nerves. *J. Comp. Neurol.* **16**: 3-31, 1906.

SCHOLZ, W. Selective neuronal necrosis and its topistic patterns in hypoxemia and oligemia. *J. Neuropath. Expr. Neurol.* **12**: 249-261, 1953.

SINGER, C. The Evolution of Anatomy. London: Knops, 1925.

SMITH, C. G. The specific gravity of the brain of the male albino rat. *J. Comp. Neurol.* **50**: 97-108, 1930.

SMITH, G. ELLIOT. The significance of anatomy. *Brit. Med. J.* **II**, 815-818, 1926.

VOGT, CECILE & O. VOGT. Ueber die Neuheit and den Wert des Pathoklisenbegriffes. *J Psychol. Neurol.* **38**: 147-154, 1929.

CHAPTER II

The Central Nervous System and Its Topographic Relation to the Body

A. SKELETAL COVERINGS

The central nervous system is entirely enclosed in a bony cavity. From the system to all parts of the body run peripheral nerves which leave the bony cavity through small openings (*foramina*). The brain (*encephalon*) is located within the cranial cavity formed by the various bones of the skull. The communicating cranial nerves (*nervi craniales*) leave via foramina, which are invariably located in the base of the skull. At the posterior end of the cranial cavity is the large *foramen magnum* through which the caudal extension of the central nervous system—the spinal cord (*medulla spinalis*)—passes down into the vertebral canal. Between two adjacent vertebrae, on each side, there is a small foramen (*foramen intervertebrale*) through which the segmentally arranged spinal nerves pass to become the spinal peripheral nerves. Some of the foramina also accommodate blood vessels which connect with the vascular bed of the central nervous system (pages 30–41).

Knowledge of the skeletal coverings of the brain and spinal cord is important for the removal of the central nervous system and is indispensable for studies involving ablation and stimulation experiments by stereotaxic instrumentation.

We omit any lengthy descriptive text because the accompanying plates are sufficient for all practical purposes to show relevant anatomic relations.

Figure 1 is a lateral view of a macerated specimen of an intact skull and the vertebral column in its natural curvatures. The vertebral column consists of seven cervical, thirteen thoracic, six lumbar, four sacral, and from twenty-seven to thirty caudal or coccygeal vertebrae. The first and second cervical vertebrae (*atlas* and *axis* or *epistropheus*) can be distinguished by their broad winglike dorsal process. The second thoracic vertebra is extremely conspicuous, for it possesses the longest spinous process of any of the bones.

Figure 2 is a dorsal view of a macerated skull of a mature adult rat. Attention is drawn to the longitudinal, bregmatic, and lambdoid sutures (also Fig. A1)

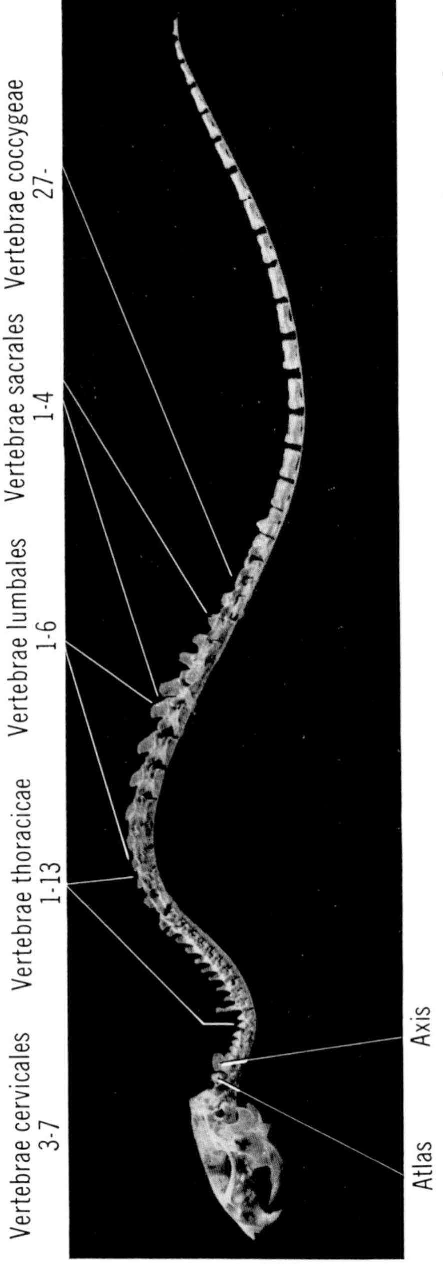

FIG. 1. Skull and vertebral column. Macerated specimen. About half natural size. Coccygeal vertebrae (*vertebrae coccygeae*) is a term used commonly in veterinary anatomy, and caudal in zoology; coccyx refers to the four fused vertebrae which form the terminal bone in man.

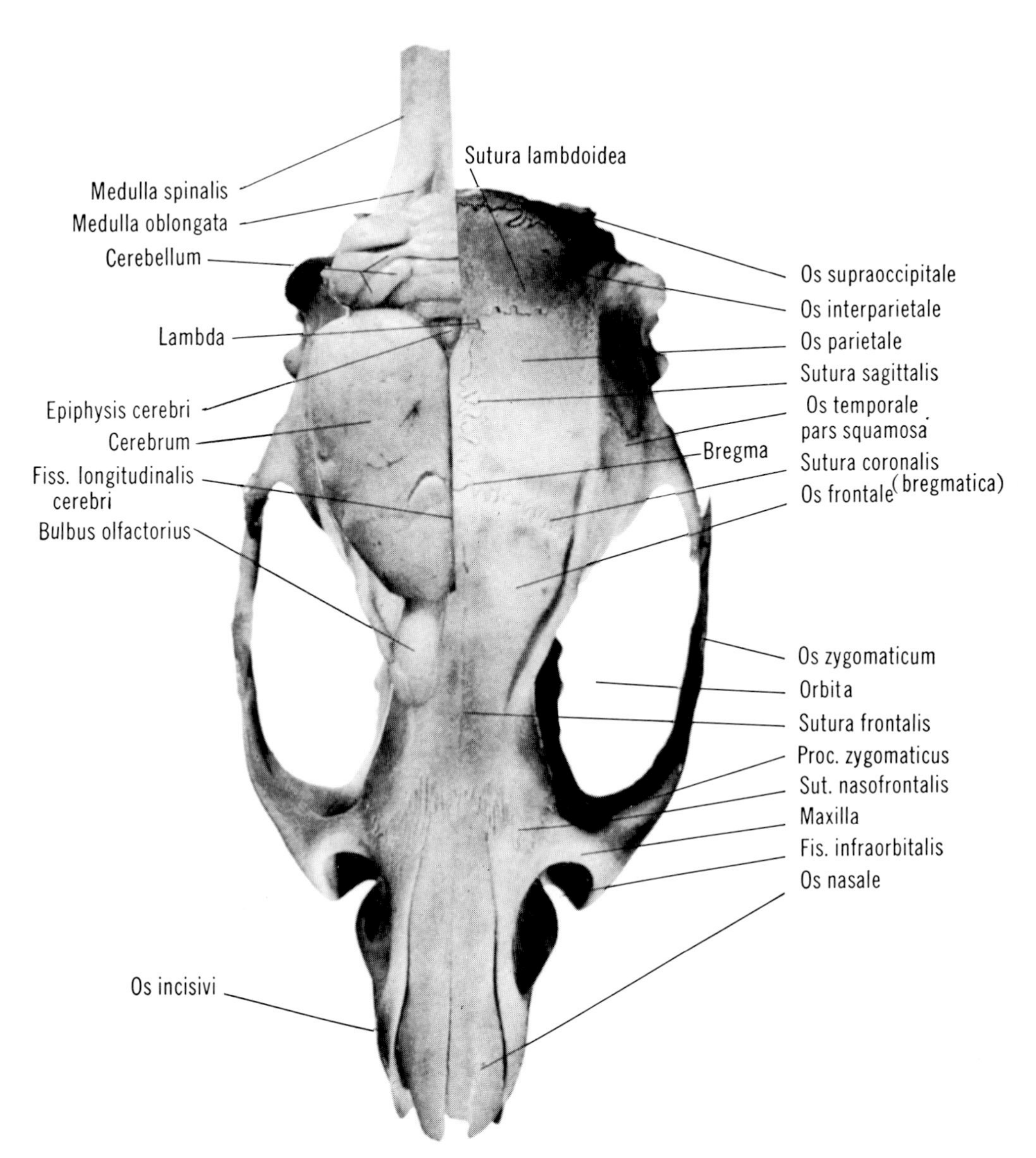

Fig. 2. **Skull**, dorsal aspect. Macerated specimen with one half of a brain superimposed. × 3. *Proc. malaris* is sometimes used for *proc. zygomaticus* and premaxilla in zoology for *os incisivi. Os temporale* in man is a complex, the elements of which remain separate in the rat.

which form important landmarks for the underlying brain. The right half of the latter is superimposed on the skull. This gives only an approximate idea of the parts of the brain as they are related to the calvaria because, as can be seen from Fig. 6, the olfactory bulbs are tilted slightly upward, there is a slight obliquity ventrally of the pons, cerebellum, and medulla, and a distinct downward kink as the medulla passes through the foramen magnum to become the spinal cord.

Figure 3 represents a ventral view of the skull. Figure 4 shows the internal

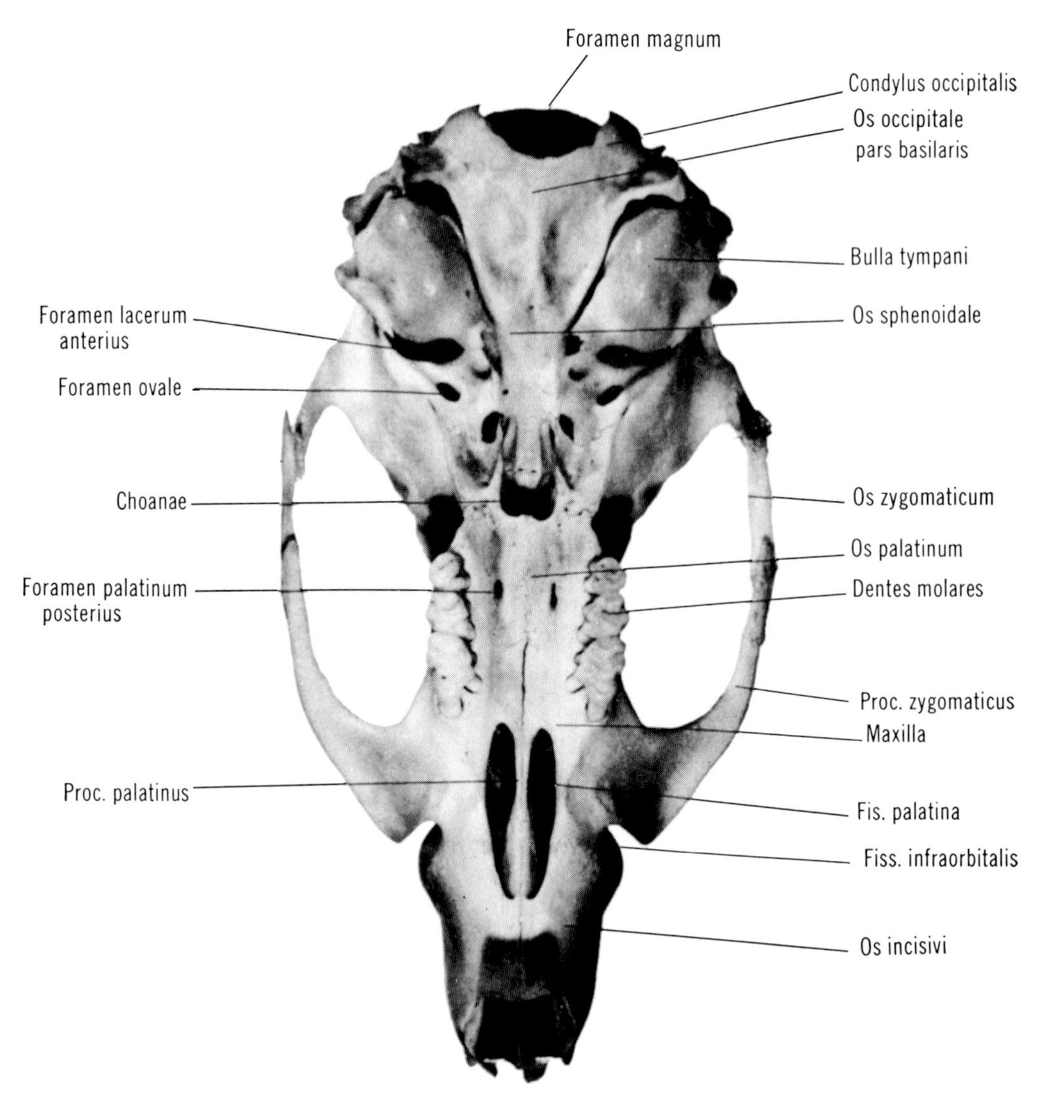

FIG. 3. Skull, ventral aspect. Macerated specimen. × 3.

aspects of the cranium, the *basis cranii,* after all the bones forming the *calvaria* have been removed to expose the brain. Figure 5 is a lateral view of the skull, and Fig. 6 gives the topographic relations between skull and brain at the sagittal plane. This figure should be compared with Fig. A1 which exhibits all the landmarks of De Groot's coordinate system in relation to the planes at which our frontal sections were cut.

Familiarity with all the anatomic features designated in these figures is important so that the various cranial nerves and vessels which enter and leave the skull can be identified.

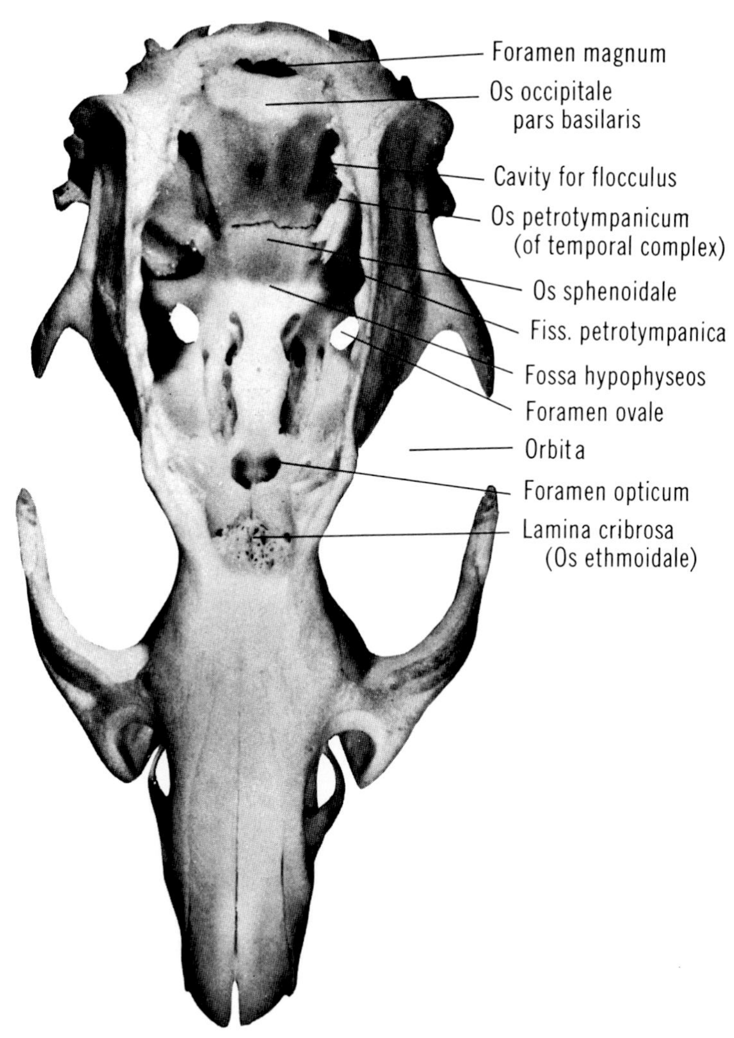

FIG. 4. Skull, internal aspect of *basis cranii.* × about 3.

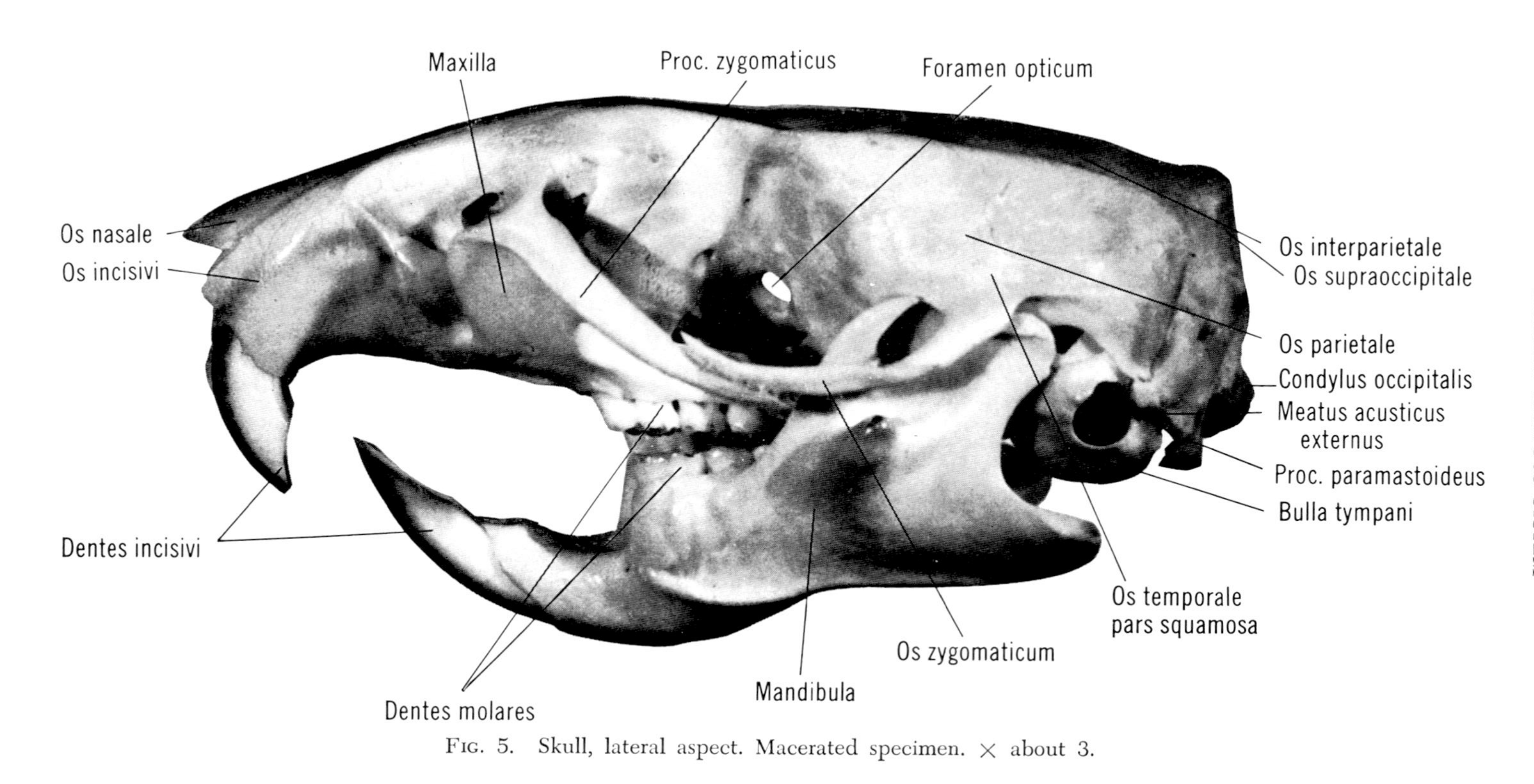

Fig. 5. Skull, lateral aspect. Macerated specimen. × about 3.

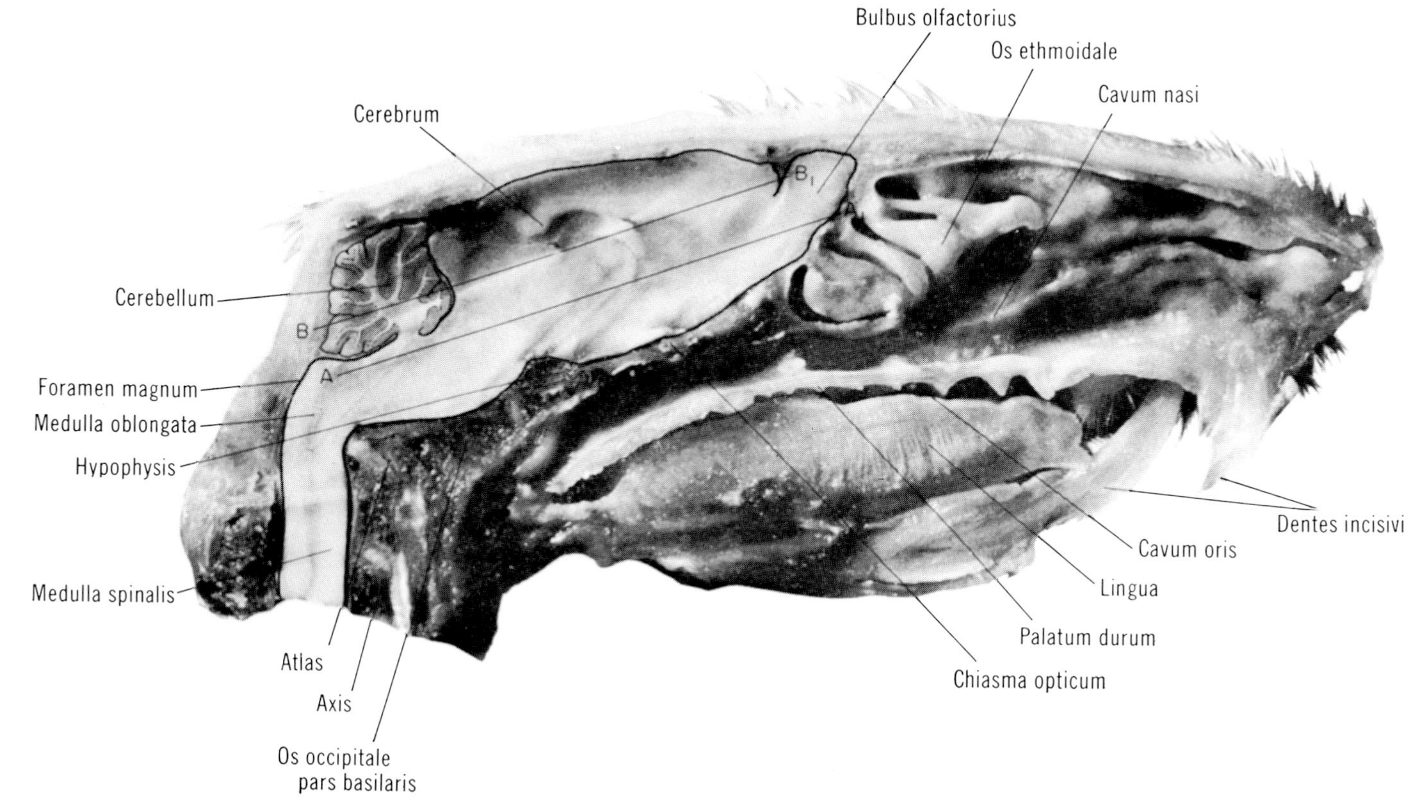

FIG. 6. Sagittal section of whole head showing anatomic relations of brain to skull. Note uptilt of forebrain and olfactory bulbs. A–A_1 is the horizontal plane of section in Fig. A37. B–B_1 is the horizontal plane of section in Fig. A38. × about 3.

B. THE MENINGES*

The entire central nervous system is covered by membranes—the meninges. Because of the small size of the rat brain, little of these is apparent to the naked eye, but they will be obvious in histologic sections.

The membranes form the meninges which, from without inward, are the *dura mater, arachnoid mater,* and *pia mater.* The dura mater (or pachymeninx) is adherent to the cranial periosteum (endosteum) except at points where there are venous sinuses. Consequently, sometimes the cranial endosteum has been called the outer or periosteal layer of dura mater, and the true dura mater regarded as an inner layer, which is continuous with the spinal dura. The latter is not adherent to the surrounding vertebral canal. Vessels which lie between the layers of the cranial dura mater are thus in the same anatomical plane as those which lie outside the spinal dura mater.

A fold of dura mater extends deep and along the whole length of the longitudinal fissure as the *falx cerebri,* and a similar fold, the *tentorium cerebelli,* is also formed by a reduplication of the inner layer of dura mater; it separates cerebral from cerebellar hemispheres and supports the occipital lobes of the cerebrum. The relations (in man) between the falx and tentorium are well demonstrated in Figs. 87 and 88 of Millen and Woollam (1962). With careful removal of the top of the skull and the arches of the vertebrae, the dura mater can be kept intact even in the rat. The arachnoid mater is a delicate lacelike membrane attached to the dura mater; between it and the pia mater extends a continuous space—the subarachnoid space—filled with cerebrospinal fluid. Together, the pia mater and arachnoid form the leptomeninges. The pia mater is a fine and highly vascular membrane which follows closely every contour of the brain and spinal cord; it forms the adventitial coat of vessels and is carried into the neural substance. In the case of the larger vessels the pial sheath is separated from the vessel wall by a prolongation of the subarachnoid space which produces a perivascular space, but this is finally obliterated as the vessel gets smaller and the pial tissue finally blends with the vascular wall.

Millen and Woollam (1962) rightly consider that there has been some confusion about the structure of the pia mater. It really consists of two layers: (a) a delicate reticular tissue which is closely applied to all surfaces of the brain, and (b) above this the network of vessels which supplies neural tissues. They state that if the term *intima pia* is used for the former layer no difficulty arises,

---

* The reader should refer to a delightful classical exposition by Millen and Woollam (1962) entitled by the enticing label "The Anatomy of the Cerebrospinal Fluid." This covers a consideration of the anatomy of all the structures which are implicated in the formation, circulation, and absorption of the fluid. Although fundamentally concerned only with man, manifestly much they say about human anatomy has indisputable relevance to the whole of the animal kingdom. Exceptions are noted in this section and in that on the ventricular system.

for the vascular tissue above can be more properly termed epipial tissues. It is the former, which, on invagination of the brain and spinal cord, along with penetrating vessels forms the perivascular space (Virchow-Robin). In this same connotation, they deal conclusively with the long-debated perineuronal spaces, which in substance are artifacts.

The functions of the meninges are twofold. The subarachnoid space filled with fluid offers by hydraulic suspension maximum protection to the delicate central nervous system against mechanical injury. The pia mater serves as a vehicle for the vascularization of the neural tissue.

C. SURFACE ANATOMY AND GENERAL TOPOGRAPHY

Before dealing with the separate divisions of the brain, as a general introductory survey, we must consider the organ system as a whole and note outstanding features seen on the surface and after some superficial dissections. These features have repeated reference as we proceed from one part (chapter) to another. It is advantageous, while considering surfaces to have available transverse, horizontal, and sagittal histologic sections of the entire brain and even of the intact head.

The vertebrate central nervous system, when seen by the naked eye, is composed of white matter (*substantia alba*) and gray matter (*substantia grisea*). The latter is made up of nerve cells and their processes, amid a framework of neuroglia and their processes and a vascular bed. The white matter is made up of nerve fibers, many of which are covered with a myelin sheath, and also of neuroglial and vascular tissues. A group of nerve cells, which may subserve a particular physiological function, is a "center" now called a nucleus. Groups of nerve fibers form a tract or fascicle.

The essential lines for cutting the skull to expose the brain will be evident by examination of Fig. 2. The anterior extremity of the brain (olfactory bulb) lies at a plane which crosses the skull directly in front of the eyes. From this it will be apparent that the occipital, interparietal, parietal, and frontal bones must be cut away to obtain a good view of the dorsal surface. For complete removal of the brain, without causing laceration or without leaving certain parts *in situ,* the whole of the top, sides, and back of the skull should be gently nipped away, a procedure which is very easy in heads which have been fixed in formalin and decalcified (see page 41). Because of the deep insertion of the olfactory bulb into the cribriform plates of the ethmoid bones, of the paraflocculus of the cerebellum into the periotic capsule, and of the hypophysis into a shallow fossa but closely surrounded by dura mater, all of these will certainly be left behind unless great care is taken.

The main divisions of the central nervous system are shown in Scheme 1.

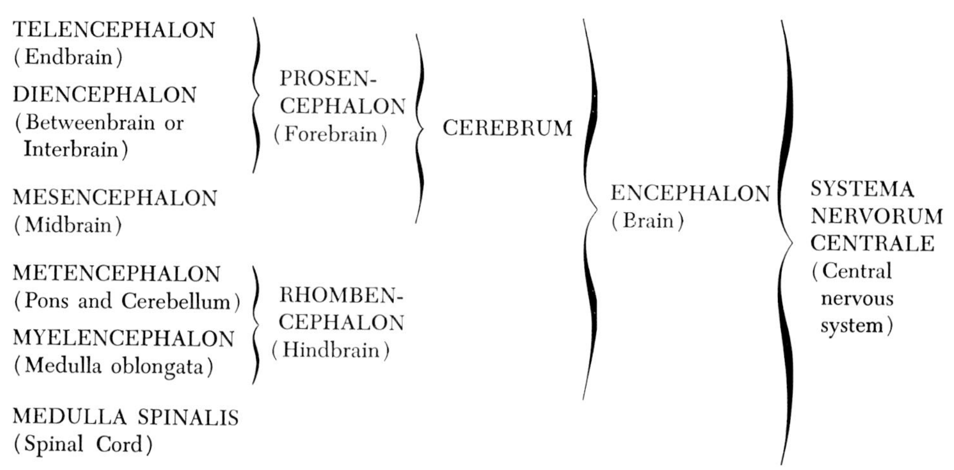

SCHEME 1

Nomenclature of the central nervous system based on ontogenesis. The term "brainstem" is applied to the encephalon (brain) from which most of the cerebral hemispheres are excluded, or it may designate the encephalon without the entire telencephalon. Sometimes the cerebellar hemispheres are excluded. Obviously, the term "brainstem" is ill defined.

We confine our consideration at this stage to the appearance of the brain from the dorsal and ventral aspects, and to a few minor dissections where parts are removed to expose deeper structures—all illustrated in Figs. 7–10.

Viewed from above (Fig. 7), the most striking features of the rat brain are the very notable development of the olfactory bulbs and the smoothness of the remaining surface of the forebrain which is totally devoid of gyri (convolutions). The latter brains are named lissencephalic. The whole forebrain is somewhat pear-shaped, the apex pointing forward. Most conspicuous are the two smooth cerebral hemispheres, bilaterally symmetrical, which are separated by a deep longitudinal fissure (*fissura longitudinalis cerebri*). At the caudal end, a deep transverse fissure, which is occupied by dura mater forming the *tentorium cerebelli,* separates the cerebrum from the cerebellum.

The cerebral hemispheres diverge somewhat from each other posteriorly. In the midline at the junction of the longitudinal and transverse fissures is a small grayish body—the pineal gland (*corpus pineale,* or epiphysis)—which projects between the caudal extensions of the hemispheres. Immediately caudal to the cerebrum is the cerebellum (the "diminutive of cerebrum") which covers the pons and much of the anterior part of the medulla oblongata. The latter is a stalklike structure which gradually narrows backward in passing through the foramen magnum to become the spinal cord.

If the pineal gland and the posterior parts of the cerebral hemispheres are removed, the roof (*tectum*) of the midbrain is revealed (Fig. 9). At this stage all we need note are the four distinct rounded protuberances, two on each side, separated by an anteroposterior furrow (*sulcus crucialis*) in the midline and a

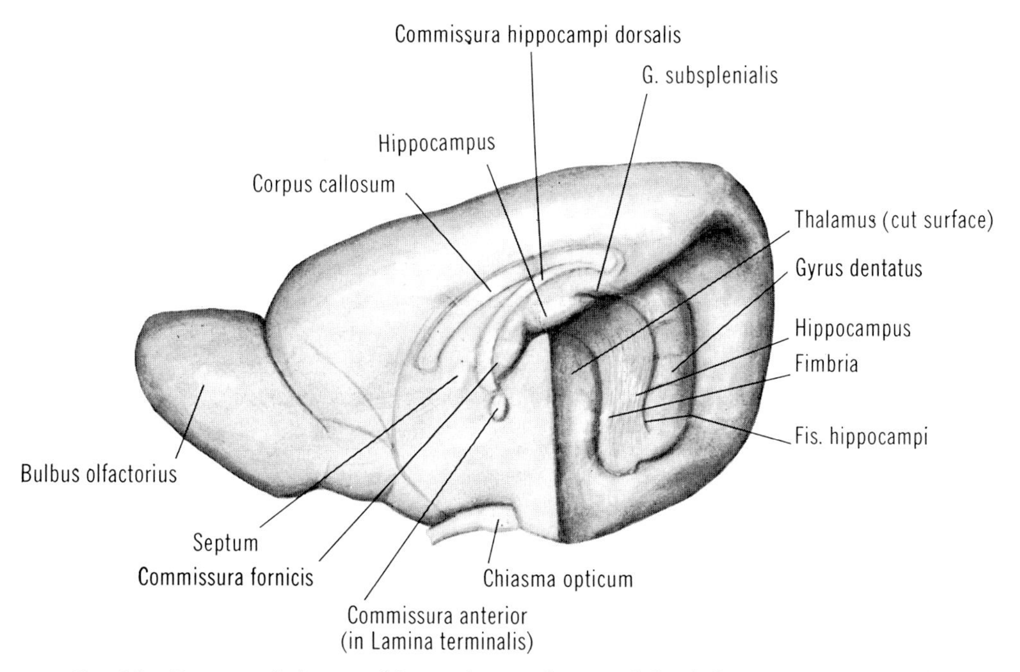

FIG. 10. Brain, medial view of hemisphere with most of the thalamus cut away. The hippocampal formation (hippocampus plus dentate gyrus) forms the outer wall of *fissura chorioidea.* × about 5.

D. VENTRICULAR SYSTEM

Reference here should be made to Millen and Woollam (1962), for apart from dealing with fundamental anatomic facts, they give a historical introduction which is full of interest. They trace observations back to Galen, who gave an extraordinary detailed account of the ventricular system as we know it today. As there was no human dissection from his time until the 16th century, further observations were not made until that time. However, Galen dissected animals (not human beings), and in the case of the ventricles he apparently used the ox. Millen and Woollam point out a very pertinent fact (not found in veterinary text books of anatomy) that in this species, because of the large *massa intermedia,* there is literally no true third ventricle, but only a series of interconnected tubes.

The cavity of the embryonic neural tube expands to become the ventricular system. In all our photographs and drawings of coronal and horizontal sections of the brain, parts of the ventricles will be found. Such disconnected views—transverse or horizontal—make it difficult to reconstruct the system of cavities as a whole. This is best illustrated by a diagram which, however made, still fails to give a three-dimensional perspective. The only methods by which the cavities can be properly depicted are those in which casts are made, or ventriculograms, after filling the cavities with air. Most illustrations in textbooks are reproductions of pictures of human specimens made by Retzius in 1900 (see Ariëns Kappers *et al.*). In the entire vertebrate kingdom the same basic ventricular pattern exists, but the extensions of the lateral ventricles, and of certain recesses, vary appreciably from species to species, as to both form and extent, but without materially altering topographic anatomic relations. The size of the lateral ventricles correlates with the general development of the cerebrum.

The divisions of the ventricular system are as follows (Fig. 11). The central canal of the spinal cord of the rat is seen as a minute hole in the center of the gray matter in transverse sections. (In adult man, the canal is very small and frequently shows no lumen.) It widens out anteriorly into the medulla oblongata to form a more capacious fourth ventricle (*ventriculus quartus*). This narrows

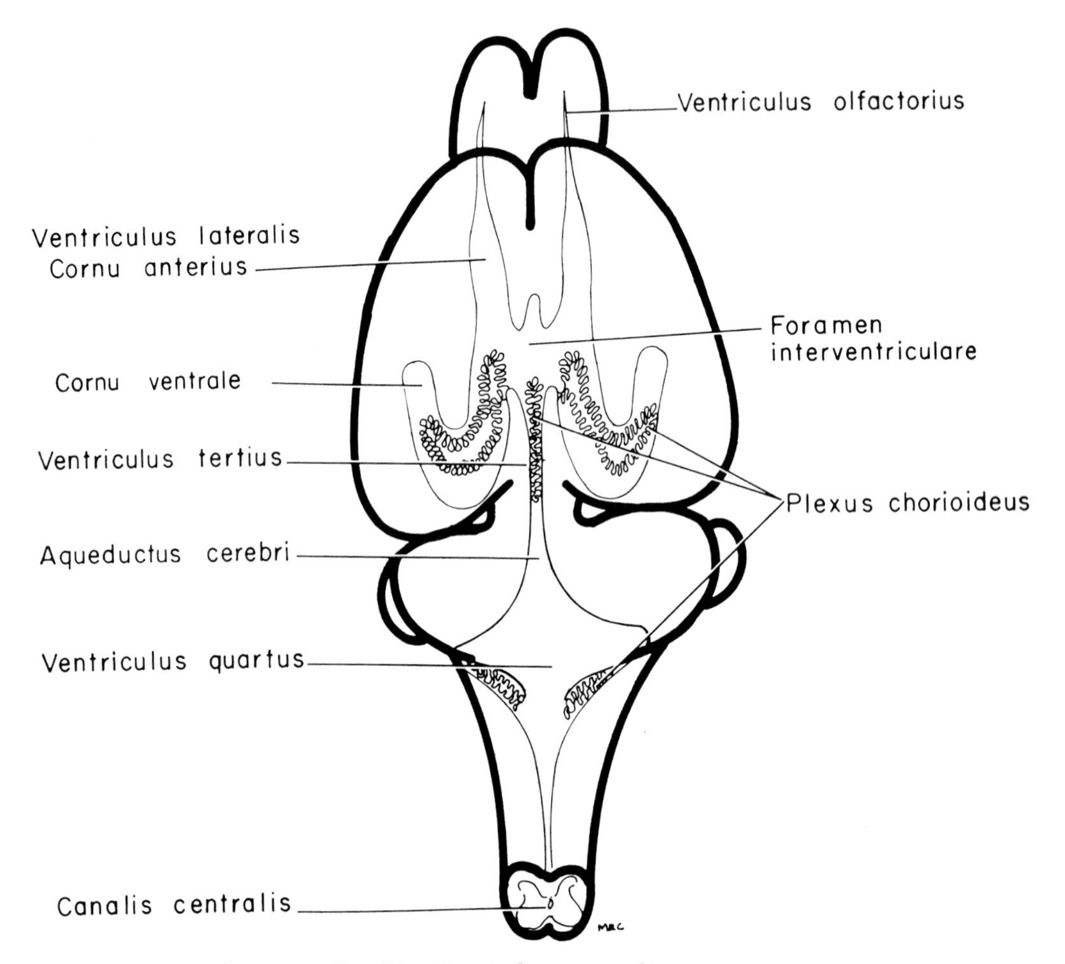

Fig. 11. Ventricular system, diagram.

forward into a canal in the dorsal third of the midline of the midbrain as the cerebral aqueduct (*aqueductus cerebri*) and continues as the third ventricle (*ventriculus tertius*) in the diencephalon. It then extends into each half of the cerebrum as the lateral ventricle (*ventriculus lateralis*) through the interventricular foramen (*foramen interventriculare*). Each division is now described separately, although it is advisable to leave consideration of important paraventricular structures to other parts of the book as we deal with different parts of the brain.

The fourth ventricle is the cavity of the *rhombencephalon* (Fig. 9). It is rhomboid in shape, elongated in a rostrocaudal direction, and narrowest behind, where it continues as the central canal. The floor (*fossa rhomboidea*) is formed by the medulla oblongata and pons. The lateral wall is formed by the anterior and posterior cerebellar peduncles, and the middle part of the roof by the vermis of the cerebellum. This leaves a small space both rostral and caudal which is not covered by more solid neural parenchyma. These spaces are filled by a thin lamina of white matter covered by pia arachnoid—the anterior and posterior medullary vela (*velum medullare anterius* and *posterius,* respectively), the lines of attachment of which are seen in Figs. 12, A8, and A35. Along the floor runs a narrow deep sulcus (*sulcus medianus*) in the midline. For about half the length of the ventricle there is a narrow low ridge (*eminentia medialis*) which bounds the sulcus on either side and which in turn is marginated by the limiting sulci (*sulci limitantes*). In front of the ridge is the *colliculus facialis,* which overlies the genu of the facial nerve. The limiting sulci at their anterior ends form a slight pit—the anterior fovea, and the lateral depression at the posterior end of each eminence is the posterior fovea. Other important structures are best identified by examination of the figures of transverse sections dealing with the medulla. From these figures it will be seen that, transversely, the fourth ventricle is roughly rhomboid in shape with the base above, and as we proceed caudal-rostral-wise the base widens to form a lateral recess on each side. In the rat, Wislocki and Leduc (1954) described a diverticulum of the fourth ventricle which extends upward into the caudal part of the posterior colliculi (Fig. 12). The ependyma of this recess is thrown into folds and differs somewhat from the general ependyma. In the rat there is also a small ventral recess.

The cerebral aqueduct passes sagittally through the upper third of the midline of the midbrain. Its shape changes as we pass forward (cf. Figs. A9–A12). It is surrounded by gray matter (*substantia grisea centralis*).

Millen and Woollam (1962; pp. 48, 49; their Figs. 23 and 24) indicate that in man the aqueduct changes its shape and diameter from the superior to posterior direction. It is thus composed of a *pars anterior,* a dilated *ampulla,* and a slowly widening *pars posterior.* Examination of the figures in relation to the mesencephalon (given in the Atlas) would indicate some parallel in the case of the rat.

The third ventricle is a high narrow slit with a rather thin floor, a mem-

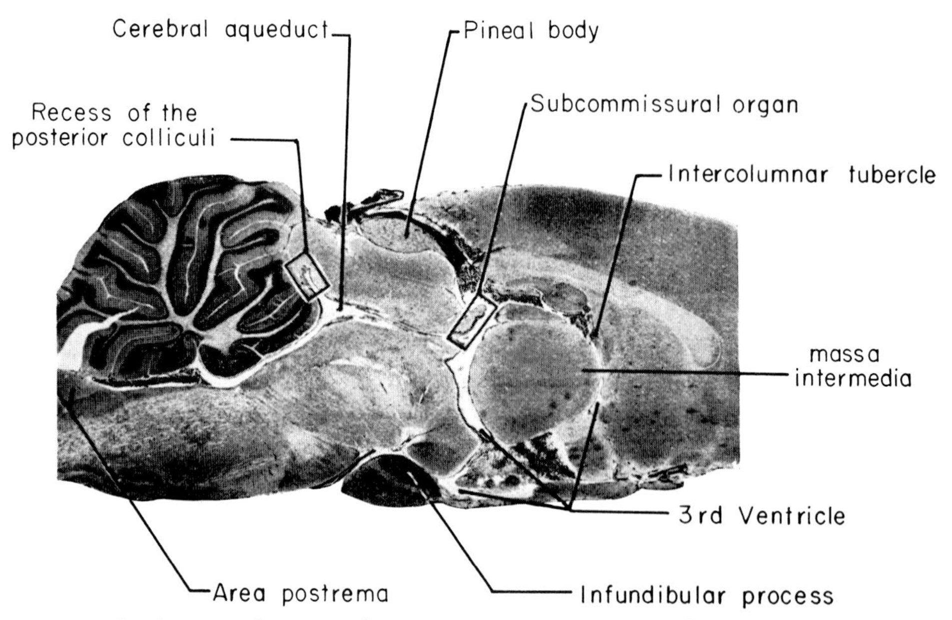

FIG. 12. Brain, median sagittal section. Various structures bordering cerebral ventricles; note particularly the recess of the posterior colliculus and the subcommissural organ. × about 5. [Rephotograph of Fig. 1, Wislocki and Leduc (1954), by courtesy of the *Journal of Comparative Neurology*.]

branous roof, and a massive lateral wall formed by the thalamus and the hypothalamus on each side. There are three recesses—optic, infundibular, and pineal. The first lies above the optic chiasma, the second extends through the infundibulum to the hypophysis, and the pineal recess passes into the stalk of the pineal body. In front, the third ventricle communicates with the lateral ventricle on each side through the interventricular foramen.

The lateral ventricles in the rat have not been studied in particular by making casts. As will be seen from the diagram, each lateral ventricle possesses a body and anterior, inferior, or ventral horns. In the rat, the anterior horn—which transversely is a crescentic triangular slit—curves rostrally and laterally around the caudate nucleus to terminate in the olfactory bulb (so-called *ventriculus olfactorius*). The inferior horn curves in a caudolateral direction around the thalamus, the floor being formed by the hippocampus. It then curves backward, outward, downward, then forward and inward; on transverse section it appears as a crescentic slit, the convexity pointing laterally.

At the opposite end of the ventricular system, the central canal (*canalis centralis*) of the spinal cord shows in some animals and man a pronounced irregular dilatation—the ventricle of Krause (*ventriculus terminalis*). In the rat, in the specimens we have seen, this is not the case (Fig. 13). However, Wislocki *et al.* (1956) in a study of the ending of Reissner's fiber (see under

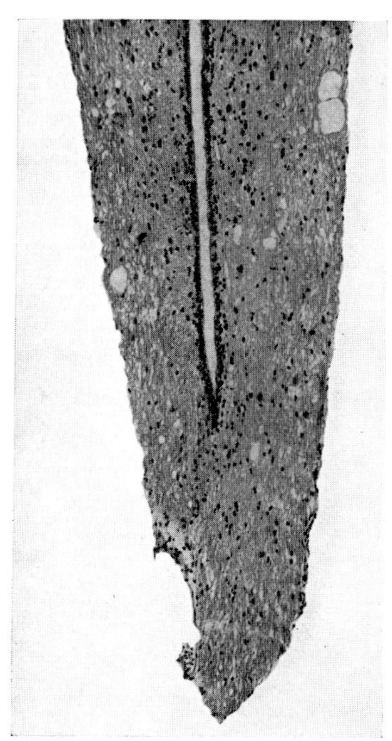

FIG. 13. Spinal cord, sagittal section showing termination of the central canal. Hematoxylin-eosin. × about 110.

subcommissural organ, pages 113) state that in the rat the canal actually ends in the *filum terminale* and may communicate with the subarachnoid space through a neuropore.

The whole ventricular system is lined by a layer of columnar ciliated epithelium (the ependyma), resting on an underlying layer of neuroglia and neural tissue. At the level of the fornical and posterior commissures, the ependyma forms highly specialized structures covering accumulations of curious cells. The structures known as the subfornical and subcommissural organs may discharge substances into the cerebrospinal fluid. Their topographical relations are discussed, with their bordering structures, in other chapters (see pages 113, 149). The ependyma is continuous with the layer of short cuboidal epithelium which covers the chorioid plexuses with their chorioidal villi. In the development of the brain from the primitive neural tube, there are four parts which remain thin and non-neural, the so-called epithelial plates (*laminae epitheliales*). The pia mater which covers these plates forms the *tela chorioidea.* Arteries which are thrust into the ventricles form sprouting convolutions, which, with the covering of cuboidal epithelium, form a chorioid plexus (*plexus chorioideus*). There are four chorioid plexuses: in the roofs of the fourth and third ventricles and on the medial wall of each lateral ventricle. The tela projects "fronds or villi" into the cavity of each ventricle, and in the rat and rabbit, near the caudal curve of the lateral ventricle, there is a larger process projecting laterally, for which the name lingula has been suggested (Woollam and Millen, 1953). The chorioid arteries anastomose in a tortuous network, and the venules in the plexus of the lateral ventricle mostly converge rostrally into one large chorioid vein. Arteries and veins are connected by a net of capillary loops richest in the villi, and there are also direct arteriovenous anastomoses.

It is now generally accepted that the cerebrospinal fluid originates in part from the chorioid plexuses. The fluid leaves the ventricular system through apertures in the posterior medullary velum. In man there are a single median aperture (*apertura mediana ventriculi quarti*) and two lateral ones (*aperturae laterales ventriculi quarti*), but in many animals there is no median foramen. We do not know what the situation is in the rat. The fluid flows around the subarachnoid space of brain and spinal cord and leaves through the arachnoid granulations (in man) to enter the dural sinuses into the venous system. In many animals, including the rat, there are no arachnoidal granulations (Pacchionian bodies), so resorption of fluid is probably by way of the meningeal pockets which form around the nerve roots as they enter and leave the spinal dural sac.

E. VASCULAR BED*

Blood reaches the brain through two main pairs of arteries, the internal carotid (*arteria carotis interna*) and the vertebral (*a. vertebralis*).

The internal carotid artery rises from the common carotid (*a. carotis communis*) near the level of the caudal end of the thyroid gland and passes along the base of the skull to enter the carotid canal between the tympanic bulla and the basioccipital bone. It thus reaches the base of the brain lateral to the *tuber cinereum* and there continues cephalad a short distance, giving off small branches to the base of the brain, a laterally directed anterior chorioid artery (*a. chorioidea*), and a branch to the optic nerve, and then dividing into anterior and middle cerebral arteries (*a. cerebri anterior* and *media*).

The anterior chorioid artery gives branches to the cerebral peduncle as it passes dorsad, and other branches to the hippocampus and to diencephalic structures including the lateral geniculate body, before entering the postero-inferior part of the chorioid plexus of the lateral ventricle. In this it anastomoses with a lateral posterior chorioid artery.

The middle cerebral artery is the largest branch of the internal carotid

* In an animal the size of the rat, clearly, the naked eye is insufficient in dissections to define either the arterial or venous systems of the brain and spinal cord. Injection methods are necessary so that with thick sections the vascular tree can be visualized. Another difficulty concerns the differentiation of arteries from veins. Millen and Woollam (1953) described a method whereby, using red and blue dispersion media, after injection into the heart or aorta, the red media filled veins and capillaries, whereas the blue pigment introduced immediately afterward did not itself enter capillaries thus filling only the arteries.

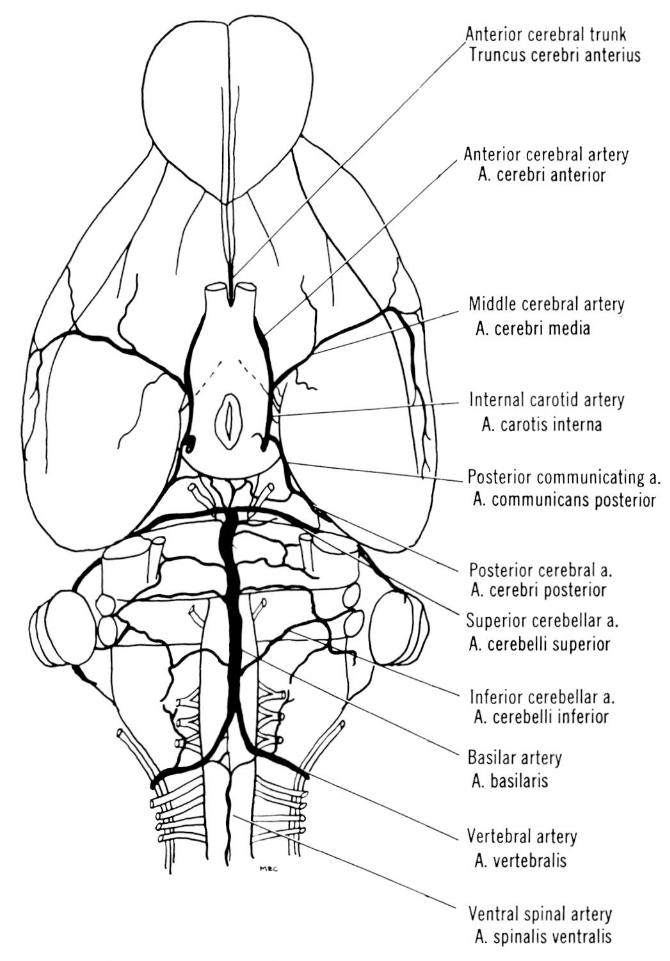

FIG. 14. Brain, ventral aspect, arterial system. × about 4.

and supplies the greater part of the cerebral hemisphere, ramifying over its lateral and dorsal surfaces (Fig. 14).

The anterior cerebral artery runs cephalomediad to unite with the corresponding vessel of the other side, forming an unpaired anterior cerebral trunk (*truncus cerebri anterior*) that curves over the genu of the corpus callosum and passes caudad over its dorsal surface, supplying this body and the adjacent cerebral cortex. From near the beginning of the trunk, slender branches run along the ventral surface to the rostromedial parts of the rhinencephalon. In man the paired anterior cerebral arteries remain separate and are connected by a transverse anterior communicating artery, but this is not normally true of the rat.

When the internal carotid artery reaches the brain, it at once gives off a posterior communicating artery (*a. communicans posterior*). Terminology used by different authors varies here. The posterior communicating artery joins the posterior cerebral artery (*a. cerebri posterior*), which is distributed to the medial, ventral, and lateral surfaces of the occipital portion of the cerebral hemisphere. Some authors prefer to consider that the pair of posterior cerebral arteries diverges from the anterior end of the basilar artery (*a. basilaris*), while others regard the two posterior communicating arteries as joining in the basilar and giving off the posterior cerebral as a side branch. The latter view seems the more in keeping with embryonic development. In the rat the posterior communicating artery is much smaller caudal to the origin of the posterior cerebral than in front of it, and is notably tortuous.

The posterior cerebral artery passes dorsad between the cerebral hemisphere and the brainstem, giving off branches to the dorsal parts of the mesencephalon, a rather large medial posterior chorioid artery, and a lateral posterior chorioid artery, before finally being distributed to the cerebral cortex. The medial posterior chorioid artery supplies the anterior part of the chorioid plexuses of the third and lateral ventricles, and the lateral posterior chorioid artery spreads through a great part of the plexus of the lateral ventricle.

From the foregoing account it is evident that the two anterior cerebral arteries, the two internal carotid arteries, the two posterior communicating arteries, and the connection with the basilar, however named, together constitute a complete anastomotic ring on the base of the brain, the circle of Willis (*circulus arteriosus cerebri*). This may be considered as an arrangement that provides, at the same time, a margin of safety and a more uniform distribution of blood through its branches.

Blood reaches the circle of Willis not only through the internal carotid arteries, but also by the basilar artery, a median ventral vessel formed by the union, about the caudal margin of the pons, of the paired vertebral arteries. The latter spring, usually, from the anterior walls of the subclavian arteries, run cephalad through the transverse foramina of the first six cervical vertebrae, and pass cephalomediad through the foramen magnum. (Developmentally, the basilar artery is formed by fusion of the caudal branches of the internal carotid, joined later by the vertebral.)

From the basilar artery, an irregular series of transverse branches supplies the parts of the hindbrain, the largest and most anterior being the superior cerebellar artery (*a. cerebelli superior*) which quite commonly rises from the circle of Willis just in front of the bifurcation of the basilar. This vessel curves dorsad and gives off small branches to the midbrain before dividing into anterior and posterior rami for distribution to the surface of the cerebellum. About half way along the basilar artery, a pair of considerably smaller inferior cerebellar arteries (*a. cerebelli inferior*) runs transversely from it and reaches the caudoventral part of the cerebellum.

Just before the two vertebral arteries meet, each usually gives off a caudomedial branch and the pair of these fuse to constitute the ventral spinal artery (*a. spinalis ventralis*) running back along the midventral aspect of the spinal cord. The ventral spinal artery is really an anastomotic chain formed by a series of ventral radicular arteries, which enter the vertebral canal in company with the ventral roots of the spinal nerves and bifurcate near the midline into ascending and descending branches. There are three or four large ventral radicular arteries in the cervical region, but in the thoracic region usually only two or three smaller and inconstant ones. The most caudal ventral radicular artery present is a markedly enlarged, unpaired vessel running along the root of the second or third lumbar nerve, usually on the right side. This is the great ventral radicular artery (of Adamkiewicz, 1882, in man), which appears to be the sole source of arterial supply to the lower lumbar and sacral parts of the spinal cord.

The ventral spinal artery varies in diameter at different levels, being notably slender in the thoracic region. It sends small lateral branches into the pial reticulum on the ventral surface of the cord and larger central arteries into the ventral median sulcus, where they pass dorsad to ramify in the bases of the ventral horns of the gray matter, usually passing alternately to the right and left sides. Whether occasional central arteries may bifurcate to both sides, as shown in Fig. 15, is a matter of dispute, though the corresponding veins apparently do so not infrequently. In the cervical region of the spinal cord of the rat, about twelve central branches are distributed to each side in each centimeter of its length; in the lumbar region, there are about seventeen per centimeter to each side; and in the thoracic region, only about seven.

Besides the ventral radicular arteries, there are also variable and irregular dorsal radicular arteries, which form slender, dorsolaterally situated, anastomotic chains, the dorsal spinal arteries (*a. spinalis dorsales*), near the dorsolateral sulci of the cord. Branches from these penetrate the dorsal horns of gray matter, but the basal parts of these horns as well as the lateral horns and the whole of the ventral horns are supplied from the ventral central arteries.

The arteries mentioned all send small branches into the pia-arachnoid and their smaller branches anastomose extensively, though Woollam and Millen (1955a) (who give the only detailed account of the arteries of the spinal cord in the rat) appear to imply the absence of such branches. Numerous small rami penetrate the nervous parenchyma, usually approximately perpendicular to the surface, and rebranch with very few anastomoses until they reach capillary size. Woollam and Millen, however, make the surprising statement that in the spinal cord of the rat, where conditions exactly parallel those in man, "the capillary bed appears to receive no arterioles in the white matter, the white matter being supplied from the capillary bed of the grey matter."

Though intraneural arterial or arteriovenous anastomoses are rare, the capillaries anastomose freely so as to constitute a three-dimensional network that is perfectly continuous throughout the nervous system. Under most patho-

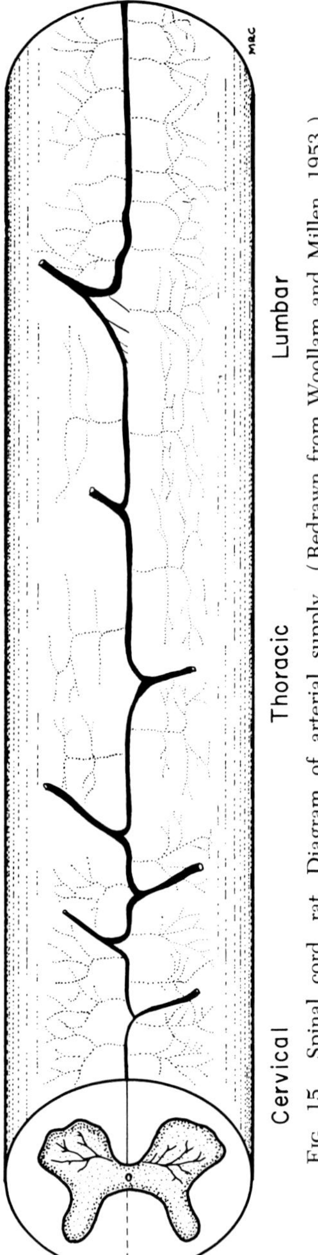

Fig. 15. Spinal cord, rat. Diagram of arterial supply. (Redrawn from Woollam and Millen, 1953.)

logic conditions, this continuous vascular bed has a high measure of safety. For instance, unilateral carotid ligation in the rat practically never reduces blood flow sufficiently to result in ischemic damage (Levine, 1960). Whether obliteration of smaller branches causes focal necrosis in the brain of the rat has not been experimentally established.

Though the endoneural capillary network is continuous, it is by no means uniform. The shapes of the meshes are related mainly to the form and disposition of the tissue elements among which they lie, and their size is almost certainly related to the metabolic requirements of the surrounding nervous substance. The caliber of the capillaries in the brain and spinal cord is fairly uniform in any one species, being slightly less than the diameter of an erythrocyte, but the total length of the vessels in a unit volume of tissue is much greater in gray matter than in white matter and differs greatly in different gray regions. In general, sensory and correlation centers tend to be more richly vascular than motor ones, though the distinction is not clear cut. In the hindbrain of the rat, the richest region is the dorsal cochlear nucleus, with almost 1200 millimeters of capillaries in one cubic millimeter of tissue; the poorest gray center is the dorsal motor vagus nucleus, with a little over 500 millimeters. Cerebral cortex and cerebellar cortex have capillary beds that lie within the quantitative range of those in the richer centers in the medulla oblongata, though their various laminae differ markedly. The ventromedial nucleus of the hypothalamus is the least richly vascular area of gray matter observed in the whole brain and the paraventricular nucleus is the richest, the latter having over 2000 millimeters of capillaries in one cubic millimeter of tissue. Charts I, II, and III, and Table I show the differences in vascularity in different layers of the cerebral cortex and the changes between birth and maturity.

Comparisons of capillary richness in the brains of wild Norway rats and laboratory albinos showed that differences in most regions are not great, but the supply is markedly and uniformly less in all the main visual centers of the wild animals, less even than in adult albinos blinded at birth. The greatest change in blinded rats is in the anterior colliculus, which receives a large proportion of the terminations of the retinal fibers and suffered an average reduction of vascularity in the gray cap of nearly 19%. In the dorsal nucleus of the lateral geniculate body, which receives collaterals from retinal fibers, the reduction in vascularity in blinded rats averaged about 10% in both binocular and monocular areas. There was no observed change in the striate area of the cerebral cortex which receives relay fibers from the geniculate body.

There has been much difference of opinion as to whether capillaries in the brain open and close with changing physiological conditions, as they do in other parts of the body. It has usually been held that they are probably all permanently open, but recent studies on hibernating ground squirrels make this unlikely.

The area of capillary wall over which one cubic millimeter of blood is

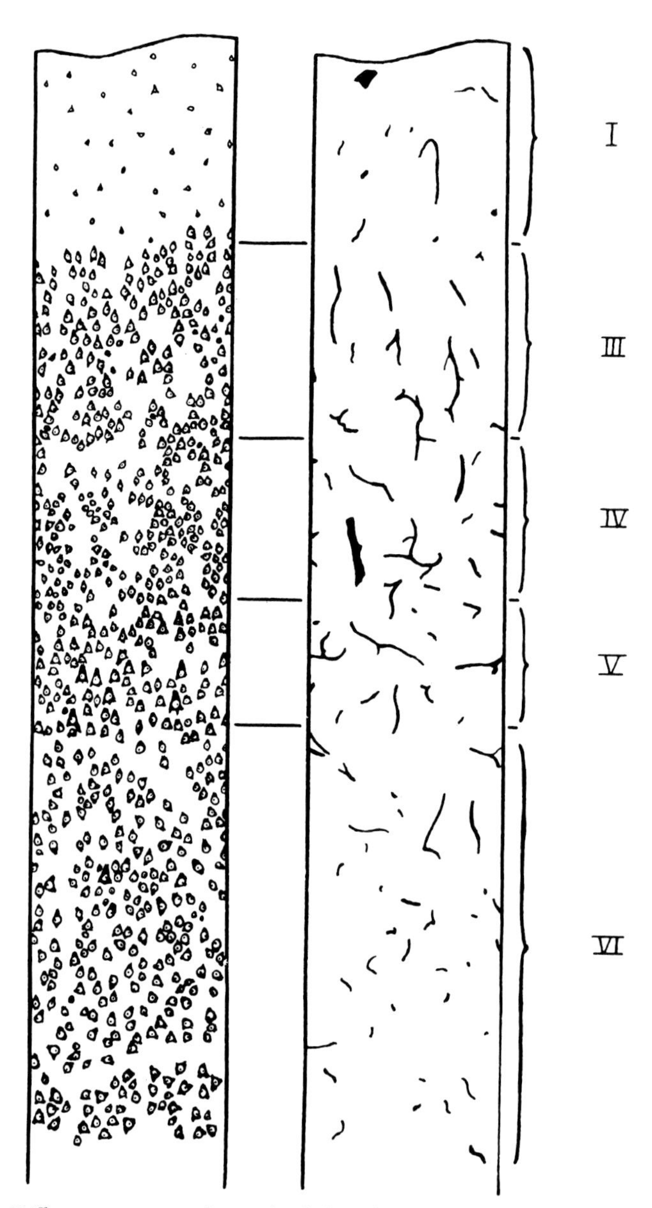

CHART I. Differences in vascularity (right) of layers of occipital cerebral cortex as seen in a thin section with cell lamination (left) of the same small part of the cortex. (Diagram × 112.)

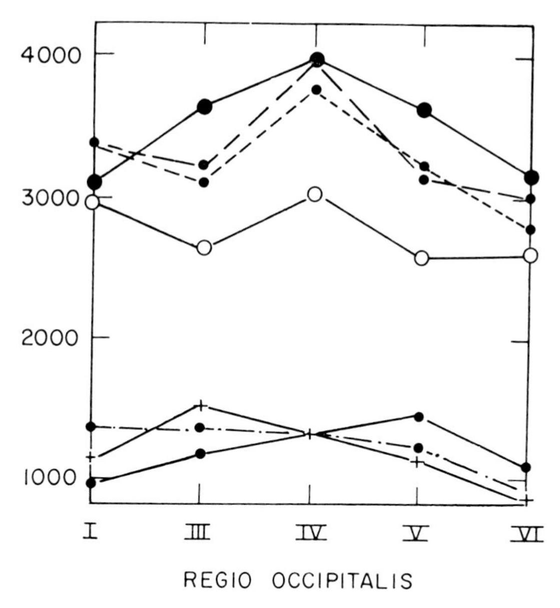

CHART II. Relative vascularity (in millimeters of capillaries per cubic millimeter of fresh tissue) of the laminae of the associative part of the occipital cortex of rats at different ages. Birth •———•; 5 days old +———+; 10 days old •—·—•—·—•—·—•; 20 days old ○———○; 90 days old • - - - •; 140 days old • – – – •; 390 days old ●———●.

spread in the brain of a rat averages over 1200 square millimeters. In man it is probably about 500 square millimeters.

The veins within the central nervous system usually do not accompany arteries but are scattered among them. Each is formed by the confluence of capillaries within the spongy capillary reticulum, and, as it runs toward the surface, it is joined by other capillaries. At the surface it enters into an extensive venous plexus in the pia-arachnoid. Here also the main channels do not follow the course of arteries, and the plexus as a whole tends to lie deep to the arterial plexus.

On the spinal cord the intraneural veins are distinguished from the arteries by receiving their tributaries at angles more obtuse than those of arterial branching. There are usually six rather indefinite longitudinal channels in the venous plexus, including a median ventral spinal vein (*vena spinalis ventralis*), a somewhat larger median dorsal spinal vein (*v. spinalis dorsalis*), and dorsolateral and ventrolateral vessels. The plexus tends to be denser on the dorsal surface. Drainage from it is entirely through radicular veins accompanying nerve roots, and these in turn empty into vertebral plexuses in the loose epidural connective tissue.

The veins of the brain empty into a system of sinuses enclosed in the dura mater. The superior sagittal sinus (*sinus sagittalis superior*) is a median vessel

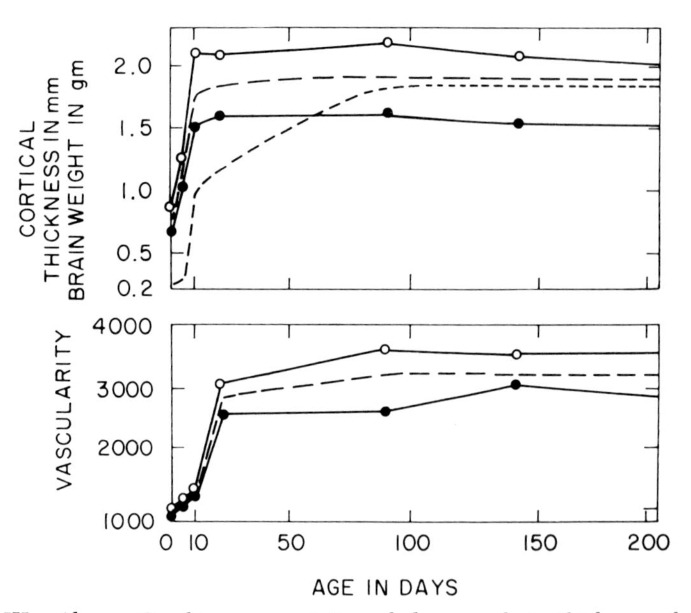

CHART III. Above: Graphic representation of the growth in thickness of the cerebral cortex with age and growth in brain weight with age. (Based upon data of Sugita, 1917.) Parietal area o———o; insular area •———•; average thickness of all parts of cortex studied — — —; brain weight - - - -.
Below: Graphic representation of changes in vascularity in corresponding parts of cortex with age. Parietal area o———o; insular area •———•; average vascularity of all parts of cortex studied - - - - -.

lying in the dorsal margin of the dural fold (*falx cerebri*) between the dorsomedial edges of the cerebral hemispheres. The inferior sagittal sinus (*s. sagittalis inferior*) is a smaller vessel in the free ventral border of the same fold, connected caudally with the straight sinus (*s. rectus*), which lies in the line of junction of the fold with that (*tentorium cerebelli*) between the hemispheres and the cerebellum. The caudal ends of the superior sagittal and the straight sinuses unite in the confluence of the sinuses with paired transverse sinuses (*s. transversus*), which extend laterad along the attachment of the tentorium to emerge from the skull behind the articulation of the mandible and empty into the internal maxillary vein (Fig. 16).

Ventrally, a paired cavernous sinus (*s. cavernosus*) is formed by union of an anterior cerebral vein with an ophthalmic vein accompanying the trigeminal nerve. The two cavernous sinuses are connected by a broad transverse anastomosis, and each cavernous sinus divides caudally into a superior petrosal sinus (*s. petrosus superior*) connecting with the ventrolateral part of the transverse sinus and an inferior petrosal sinus (*s. petrosus inferior*) running caudad and leaving the cranial cavity to join the internal jugular vein.

Into these sinuses run the veins in the pia-arachnoid. A series of superior

TABLE I
Total Length in Millimeters per Cubic Millimeter of Capillaries in Fresh Tissue in the Rat[a]

Tissue	Length	Tissue	Length
Fasc. cuneatus	148	Lateral geniculate body:	
Tr. pyramidalis	280	monocular (blinded)	907
Fasc. long. medialis	340	Cerebellum: granular layer	981
Ventromed. hypothalamus	491	Lat. genic. body:	
Nuc. motorius dorsalis X	517	monocular (normal)	1030
Nuc. mot. VII	586	Superior collic. (normal)	1041
Nuc. mot. XII	642	Nuc. vestib. principalis	1091
Nuc. sensorius X	630	Nuc. mamillaris lateralis	1148
Ventral horn: spinal cord	720	Nuc. cochlearis dorsalis	1178
Nuc. spinalis V	738	Lat. genic. body:	
Nuc. vestibularis lateralis	748	binocular (blinded)	1293
Cerebellum: molecular layer	797	Lat. genic. body:	
Dorsal horn: spinal cord	807	binocular (normal)	1451
Superior colliculus (blinded)	864	Nuc. supraopticus	1960
		Nuc. paraventricularis	2023
Occipital cortex (associative)		Parietal cortex	
Lamina zonalis I	870	Lam. zonalis I	941
Lam. pyramidalis III	1024	Lam. pyram. III	1175
Lam. granularis interna IV	1118	Lam. gran. int. IV	1351
Lam. ganglionaris V	1021	Lam. gangl. V	964
Lam. multiformis VI	888	Lam. multif. VI	790
Average	984	*Average*	1044

Striate cortex	Normal (Christie)	Normal (Rao)	Blinded (Rao)	Wild rat (Christie)
Lam. zonalis I	931	927	909	589
Lam. pyram. III	1170	1287	1206	723
Lam. gran. int. IV	1188	1341	1330	806
Lam. gangl. V	1009	1071	1008	634
Lam. multif. VI	848	846	873	579
Average	1029	1094	1065	666

[a] Data assembled from Craigie, from Rao, and from Christie (see Craigie, 1961).

cerebral veins drains blood from the lateral and dorsal parts of each hemisphere into the superior sagittal sinus, the most caudal ones entering the transverse sinus. The most anterior of the superior cerebral veins at each side anastomoses round the frontal pole of the hemisphere with inferior cerebral veins (*vv. cerebri inferiores*), which receives tributaries from the ventrolaterial part of the hemisphere and continues caudad into the superior petrosal sinus. The paired anterior cerebral veins (*vv. cerebri anteriores*) parallel the unpaired artery on the dorsal surface of the corpus callosum, run ventrad, and join the cavernous sinus.

The ventromedial parts of the forebrain, the chorioid plexuses, the corpus striatum, and the walls of the diencephalon and midbrain are drained by tribu-

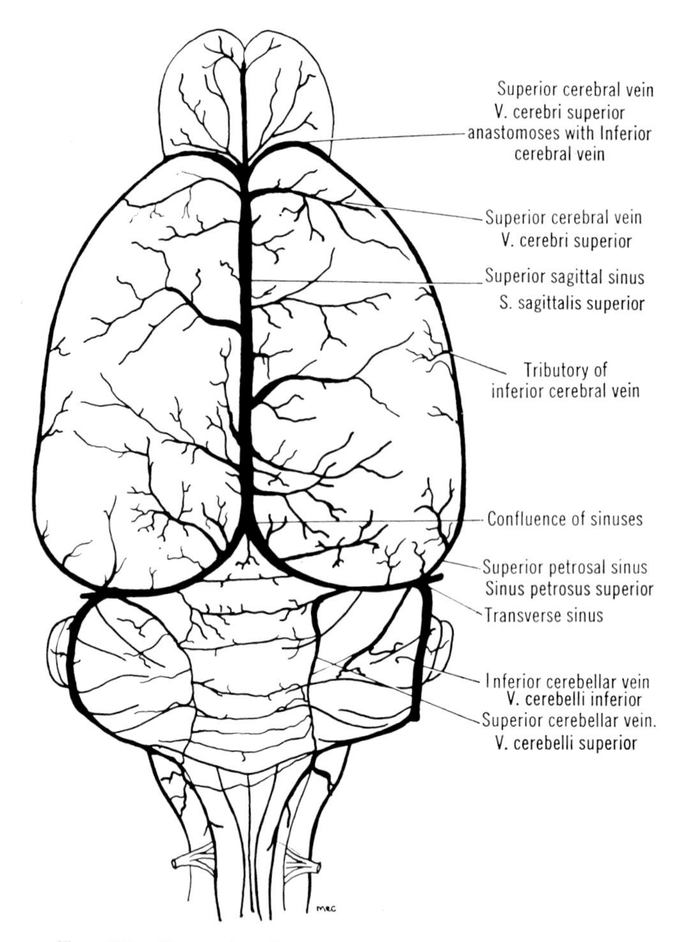

FIG. 16. Brain, dorsal aspect, venous system. × about 4.

taries of the basal cerebral vein (*v. basalis*), which accompanies the circle of Willis and empties into the superior petrosal sinus.

The straight sinus receives blood from the medial surfaces of the cerebral hemispheres through the inferior sagittal sinus and from the roofs of the diencephalon and the midbrain—including drainage of the chorioid plexuses through the great cerebral vein (*v. cerebri magna*).

Paired superior and inferior cerebellar veins (*vv. cerebelli superiores* and *inferiores*) enter the transverse sinuses, as do also the basilar veins of the medulla oblongata. The latter are continuous caudally with the ventral spinal vein. The dorsal spinal vein is continued laterorostrad, usually on one side only, and also empties into the transverse sinus.

In general, it is to be noted that the main arterial supply of the brain reaches it from the ventral aspect, but that the more extensive venous drainage tends to be dorsal.

The nervous system lacks lymphatic vessels, though it is sometimes considered that the perivascular spaces may be compared with these. Such spaces surround each blood vessel penetrating the brain or spinal cord and are continuous with the subarachnoid space. They have a definite, delicate lining, which, however, does not extend along the capillaries, so that they are ultimately continuous with pericapillary spaces traversed by glial fibers, but with no anatomical barrier between the lining of the blood vessel and the nervous tissue.

F. GROWTH, WEIGHTS, AND MEASUREMENTS

Rats are born hairless, with eyes closed and without locomotor control. Within 12 days from birth the animals can see, are covered with hair, and can moved around rapidly. All this is dependent on the development of the central nervous system. Although embryological development is an essential part of neuroanatomy, and some occasional reference is made to important ontogenetic and phylogenetic influences, a complete discussion is beyond the scope of this book. Figure 17 is an illustration of the growth and development of the rat brain from birth up to 60 days. This should be correlated with the only data on myelination in the rat we could find in some composite form (Table II).

Donaldson's classic reference text (1924) on the entire anatomy of the rat has been used by workers all over the world for more than 40 years. Many workers may have occasion to make measurements of weight and size of brain and spinal cord. Merely for convenience, and to be tied in with any consideration of anatomy, we have included thus a few excerpts from Donaldson's tables, all of which are self-explanatory and require no comment (Tables III and IV).

G. METHODS OF EXAMINATION

Because of the small size of the rat central nervous system, and on account of its soft consistency in the fresh state, it may be preferred to fix the tissue by perfusion prior to removal. Obviously, this is not possible if unfixed tissue must be obtained for histochemical and biochemical studies. Under those circumstances, the skeletal coverings must be removed prior to fixation. A small pair of bone forceps, nail clippers, and tweezers can be used for this work. Dexterity in the use of these instruments and prevention of laceration of neural tissue simply comes from experience. Unless the greatest care is taken, the olfactory bulbs, the hypophysis, and the paraflocculus of the cerebellum will be torn and left in the skull because they are almost completely embedded in bone and surrounded by dura mater.

The following perfusion technique* has been used by us for rats and mice with good results. Nembutal sodium, intraperitoneally (8–10 mg for an adult

* This technique is essentially the same as proposed by Cammermeyer (1960).

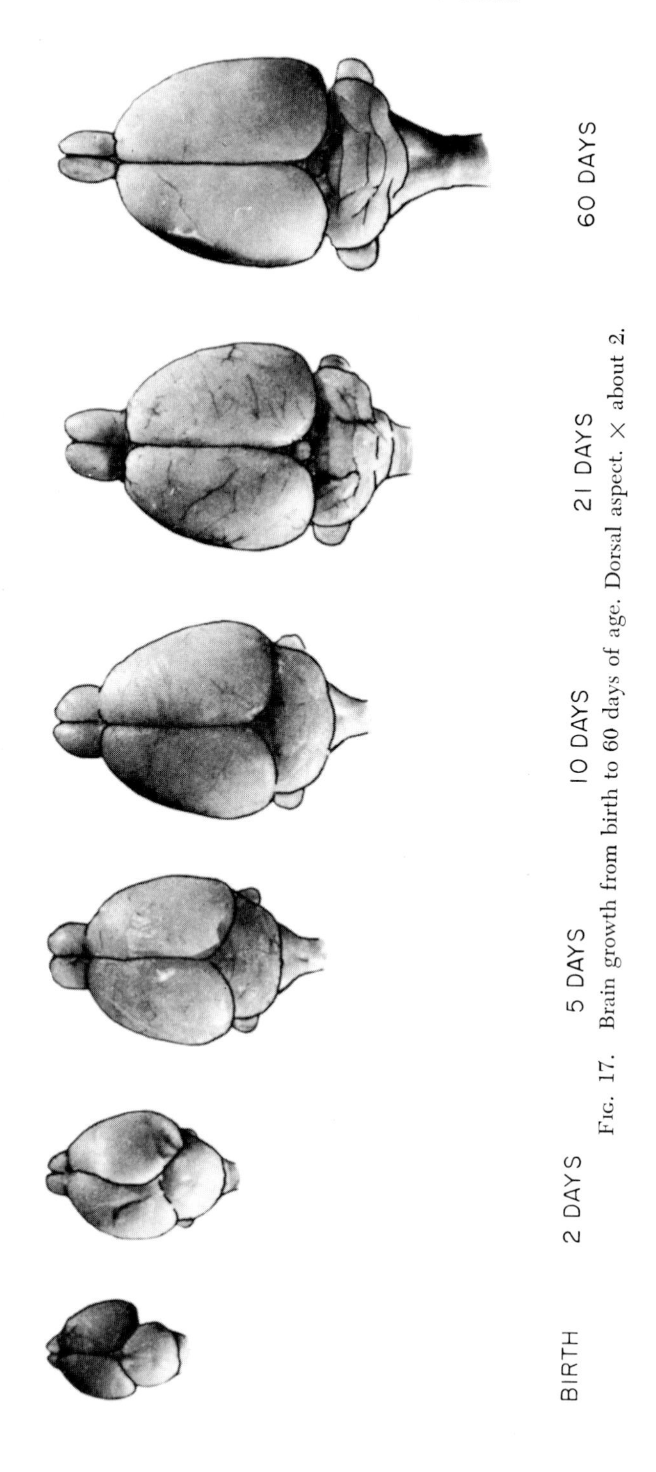

FIG. 17. Brain growth from birth to 60 days of age. Dorsal aspect. × about 2.

TABLE II

Order of Development of Myelination of the Central Nervous System of the Rat[a]

Divisions	Myelination begins (days) Cervical region	Thoracic region	Lumbar region	Speed of myelination process
Spinal cord				
Funiculus ventralis	2	3	3	Rapid
Funiculus lateralis	2	3	3–6	Rapid
Ventral roots				
Extramedullary	2	3	3	Very rapid
Intramedullary	8	8	8	Rapid
Funiculus dorsalis				
Fasciculus cuneatus	3	3	4–6	Rapid
Fasciculus gracilis	4–6	3	6	Slow
Pyramidal tract	6	10	11	Very slow
Dorsal roots				
Extramedullary	3	3	4–6	Slow
Intramedullary	8	8	8	Slow
Cerebellum				
In stem of central white substance		8		Development more rapid than in the cerebrum
In laminae: caudal and dorsal		11		At 15, 16, and 17 days fibers reach the granular layer
In laminae: cephalic		13		
In laminae: nodulus		14		
Cerebrum				
Capsula externa		11		Rapid
Fibrae longitudinales dorsales		13		Slow
Stria olfactoria lateralis		14		Very rapid
Corpus striatum		14		Rapid
Corpus callosum		14		Very slow until after the 24th day
Radiations into the cortex		14		Development extremely slow
Commissura anterior		17		Very slow until after the 24th day
Thalamus		17		Slow
Lamina zonalis I of cortex		Unknown, but certainly not before the 42nd day		

[a] After Watson (1905).

TABLE III
BODY WEIGHT RELATED TO AGE OF THE RAT[a]

Age (days)	Males		Females	
	Number of rats	Body weight (grams)	Number of rats	Body weight (grams)
Birth	129	5.39	140	5.12
1	118	5.96	136	5.55
2	120	6.42	139	6.30
3	125	7.24	155	7.00
4	130	8.33	137	8.06
5	134	9.47	137	8.92
6	134	10.67	152	10.21
7	115	11.90	125	11.37
8	126	13.61	138	12.95
9	122	14.65	140	14.31
10	137	15.47	157	14.90
11	131	16.97	134	16.58
12	127	18.13	133	17.01
13	126	18.80	139	18.02
14	116	20.44	126	19.15
15	111	21.64	124	20.09
22	51	26.43	69	26.38
25	56	32.98	56	32.25
30	45	41.83	54	39.22
37	35	54.50	39	50.44
52	32	80.85	37	73.63
67	30	112.04	33	102.23
82	25	145.73	31	137.05
97	22	169.02	29	157.85
120	52	240.40	69	179.58
150	68	263.92	80	191.72
182	108	289.61	115	198.67
212	107	303.32	109	209.36
242	106	318.88	106	220.51
272	104	328.70	108	224.61
295	100	337.05	104	235.65
325	95	338.46	104	238.82
356	95	341.46	94	246.14
384	83	349.06	85	254.25
415	79	353.86	84	256.62
450	70	369.32	87	263.84

[a] From Donaldson (1915; 2nd Ed., 1924).

rat), gives deep anesthesia. The animal is spread out on its back with the legs tied. The chest is opened and the heart exposed. An intracardiac injection of 2 mg of heparin in distilled water 1 minute before perfusion prevents blood clotting. An 18-gauge needle (about 1 inch long) with a blunt end, attached to a clear plastic tube connected to the bottle with the perfusate, is thrust into the left ventricle and from there into the aorta. The entire assembly must be

TABLE IV
BODY WEIGHT AND LENGTH RELATED TO WEIGHT OF BRAIN AND, SPINAL CORD FOR MALE AND FEMALE RATS[a]

	Males				Females			
Body length (mm)	Tail length (mm)	Body weight (gm)	Brain weight (gm)	Spinal cord weight (gm)	Tail length (mm)	Body weight (gm)	Brain weight (gm)	Spinal cord weight (gm)
47	14.9	4.9	0.226	0.033	15.4	4.7	0.211	0.033
60	29.6	7.5	0.498	0.055	31.5	8.0	0.532	0.061
70	40.7	11.4	0.803	0.088	42.8	12.0	0.846	0.095
80	51.5	15.9	1.051	0.121	54.0	16.8	1.064	0.129
90	62.0	21.3	1.188	0.155	65.0	22.4	1.193	0.165
100	72.3	27.5	1.289	0.189	75.7	29.1	1.289	0.201
110	82.4	34.9	1.371	0.225	86.2	36.9	1.368	0.238
120	92.4	43.5	1.442	0.261	96.6	46.0	1.438	0.276
130	102.3	53.6	1.505	0.297	106.8	56.8	1.500	0.314
140	112.1	65.4	1.563	0.335	117.0	69.5	1.557	0.353
150	121.7	79.3	1.618	0.372	127.0	84.4	1.611	0.392
160	131.3	95.6	1.670	0.410	137.0	102.0	1.662	0.432
170	140.9	114.8	1.719	0.448	146.8	122.7	1.711	0.472
180	150.4	137.0	1.767	0.486	156.7	147.1	1.759	0.512
190	159.8	163.3	1.813	0.525	166.4	175.7	1.805	0.552
200	169.2	194.1	1.858	0.564	176.1	209.4	1.850	0.593
210	178.5	230.2	1.903	0.603	185.8	249.1	1.894	0.634
220	187.8	272.5	1.946	0.642	195.4	295.8	1.938	0.675
230	197.1	322.1	1.989	0.681	205.0	350.7	1.981	0.716
240	206.3	380.3	2.031	0.721	214.5	415.4	2.023	0.757
250	215.5	448.5	2.073	0.760	224.0	491.5	2.065	0.798

[a] From Donaldson (1915; 2nd Ed., 1924); only excerpts are given.

completely filled with fluid since air bubbles will cause airlock by emboli and prevent proper perfusion. With a ligature hook, the needle is tied into the aorta. The right atrium is opened by scissors to permit drainage and the perfusion is started at once. In order to prevent kinking of the aorta, it is advisable to keep the needle in place by a clamp.

The first perfusate aims at flushing out the blood; the perfusion solution is made up of 5.6 gm gum acacia and 0.9 gm sodium chloride in 100 ml of distilled water or simply physiological saline solution. The second perfusion solution is the fixative, and this follows immediately the flushing rinse; connection between the two separate bottles is established by a three-way stopcock. For routine purposes 10% neutralized formaldehyde in water is best, but any other fixative can be used. Both perfusion solutions are administered in an amount of about 14% of the total body weight of the animal, i.e., about 40–50 ml for an adult rat. The bottles with the solutions are kept about 90–100 cm above the level of the animal, corresponding to a pressure of approximately

70 mm Hg. Criteria for a successful perfusion are the drainage of the clear rinsing solution from the right atrium and a change in color of the liver, which quickly becomes a stippled white during administration of the fixative. After completion of the perfusion the *truncus vascularis* of the heart is ligated to prevent reflux, the animal is covered by wet towels to prevent drying and is left untouched for 3–4 hours. The rat can then be skinned and the brain and spinal cord removed if that is desirable at that time, or the skinned head and vertebral column may be left in fixative for any length of time.

In a study of neuroanatomy, no matter of what species, it will be brought home very early to the student that a three-dimensional view of the brain is essential. In the larger domesticated animals and primates, much neuroanatomy can be seen and understood by naked eye examination of surfaces and of cuts made transversely, horizontally, sagittally, and parasagittally. This will be apparent by consultation of standard texts on anatomy of man and animals. Built-up semidiagrammatic models of different neuroanatomic systems as they pass from the higher centers to lower ones or vice versa, and with all their interconnections, are a popular method of anatomic illustration. In the case of the rat, or any of the smaller laboratory animals, because of size, far less can be accomplished by naked eye studies. The dissection microscope can be used to advantage, but in the end a combination of naked eye observations plus a study of a series of sections cut in different planes is the only means whereby the regions, areas, and systems—which we illustrate later—can all be adequately understood.

For a first macroscopic approach to the rat brain and cord, after perfusion fixation, we have thus preferred to skin the entire head and vertebral column to the root of the tail, and to submerge the specimen in any standard decalcifying fluid. A few days in the latter provides a specimen with the bones softened; after washing in running water, the overlying parts of the skull and vertebral column, i.e., dorsal surface, can be removed by the use of forceps, scalpel, and fine scissors.

For many purposes, however, once an acquaintance with normal rat neuroanatomy is achieved, it may be found that macroscopic examination of the nervous system can be entirely dispensed with. This is certainly so as far as pathology may be concerned. Rather than remove the brain and spinal cord after decalcification, we prefer to leave the brain and cord intact inside the bony coverings. A series of 1–2 mm transverse slices can be made from the olfactory bulbs to the end of the spinal cord and can be embedded and cut in a numbered series and stained by whatever methods are indicated. This method has the advantage that the relationship of neural tissues to meninges, vessels, and bony coverings remains intact, and that in the vertebral canal the spinal cord, meninges, nerve roots, and ganglia can all be identified and examined if necessary.

References

ARIËNS KAPPERS, C. U., G. C. HUBER & ELIZABETH C. CROSBY. The Comparative Anatomy of the Nervous System of Vertebrates, Including Man. 2 Volumes. New York: Macmillan, 1936.

BRIGHTMAN, M. W. Perivascular spaces in the brains of Necturus maculosus Rafinesque and Mus norwegicus albinus. *Anat. Rec.* **117**: 427-448, 1953.

CAMMERMEYER, J. A critique of neuronal hyperchromatosis. *J. Neuropath.* **19**: 141-142, 1960.

CLARK, S. L. Nerve endings in the chorioid plexus of the fourth ventricle. *J. Comp. Neurol.* **47**: 1-21, 1928.

CRAIGIE, E. H. On the relative vascularity of various parts of the central nervous system of the albino rat. *J. Comp. Neurol.* **31**: 429-464, 1920.

CRAIGIE, E. H. The vascularity of the cerebral cortex of the albino rat. *J. Comp. Neurol.* **33**: 193-212, 1921.

CRAIGIE, E. H. Changes in the vascularity in the brain stem and cerebellum of the albino rat between birth and maturity. *J. Comp. Neurol.* **38**: 27-48, 1924.

CRAIGIE, E. H. Postnatal changes in the vascularity in the cerebral cortex of the albino rat. *Anat. Rec.* **29**: 354, 1925b.

CRAIGIE, E. H. The vascularity of the vagus nuclei and of the adjacent reticular formation in the albino rat. *J. Comp. Neurol.* **42**: 57-68, 1926.

CRAIGIE, E. H. The vascularity of parts of the spinal cord, brain stem, and cerebellum of the wild Norway rat (Rattus norwegicus) in comparison with that in the domesticated albino. *J. Comp. Neurol.* **53**: 309-318, 1931.

CRAIGIE, E. H. The vascular supply of the archicortex of the rat. I. The albino rat (Mus norwegicus albinus). II. The albino rat at birth. III. The wild Norway rat (Mus norwegicus) in comparison with the albino. IV. Inbred albino rats. *J. Comp. Neurol.* **51**: 1-11, 1930; *ibid.* **52**: 353-357; 359-364, 1931; *ibid.* **55**: 443-451, 1932.

CRAIGIE, E. H. The vascularity of parts of the cerebellum, brain stem, and spinal cord of inbred albino rats. *J. Comp. Neurol.* **58**: 507-516, 1933.

CRAIGIE, E. H. Measurements of vascularity in some hypothalamic nuclei of the albino rat. *Res. Publ. Ass. Nerv. Mental Dis.* **20**: 310-319, 1940.

CRAIGIE, E. H. Vascularity in the visual centres of the brain of the rat. *Plzeň. lék. Sbornik*, Suppl. 3: 95-104, 1961.

DONALDSON, H. H. A comparison of the albino rat with man in respect to the growth of the brain and of the spinal cord. *J. Comp. Neurol.* **18**: 345-392, 1908.

DONALDSON, H. H. On the relation of the body length to the body weight and to the weight of the brain and of the spinal cord in the albino rat (*Mus norvegicus* var. *albus*). *J. Comp. Neurol.* **19**: 155-167, 1909.

DONALDSON, H. H. The rat. Reference tables and data for the albino rat (*Mus norvegicus albinus*) and the Norway rat (*Mus norvegicus*). *Mem. Wistar Inst. Anat. No.* **6**, 1915. (Second edition revised and enlarged, 1924.)

DONALDSON, H. H. On changes in the relative weights of the viscera and other organs from birth to maturity—albino rat. *Amer. J. Physiol.* **67**: 1-21, 1923.

DONALDSON, H. H. & S. HATAI. On the weight of the parts of the brain and on the percentage of water in them according to brain weight and to age, in albino and wild Norway rats. *J. Comp. Neurol.* **53**: 263-307, 1931.

DONALDSON, H. H., S. HATAI & H. D. KING. Postnatal growth of the brain under several experimental conditions. Studies on the albino rat. *J. Nerv. Mental Dis.* **42**: 797-801, 1915.

DONALDSON, H. H. & G. NAGASAKA. On the increase in the diameters of nerve cell bodies and of the fibers arising from them during the latter phases of growth (albino rat). *J. Comp. Neurol.* **29**: 529-522, 1918.

DUNN, E. H. The influence of age, sex, weight, and relationship upon the number of medullated nerve fibers and on the size of the largest fibers in the ventral root of the second cervical nerve of the albino rat. *J. Comp. Neurol.* **22**: 131-157, 1912.

DUNN, E. H. The size of the medullated axons of the Purkinje cerebellar neurons in the albino rat. *Anat. Rec.* **10**: 196, 1916.

EAYRS, J. T. Vascularity of cortex in normal and cretinous rats. *J. Anat. (London)* **88**: 164-173, 1954.

EAYRS, J. T. & B. GOODHEAD. Postnatal development of the cerebral cortex of the rat. *J. Anat. (London)* **93**: 388-402, 1959.

FREDE, M. Untersuchungen an der Wirbelsäule und den Extremitätenplexus der Ratte. *Z. Morph. Anthrop.* **33**: 96-150, 1934.

GREENE, EUNICE C. Anatomy of the Rat. New York: Hafner, 1955.

GROOT, J. DE. The rat forebrain in stereotaxic coordinates. *Verhandl. Koninkl. Nederl. Akad. Wetensch. afd. Natuurkunde,* Tweede Reeks, Deel LII, No. 4, 1959.

HAMMETT, F. S. Correlations and variability of the central nervous system and body size of the albino rat. *Biol. Bull. (Wood's Hole)* **50**: 509-524, 1926.

HATAI, S. Studies on the variation and correlation of skull measurements in both sexes of mature albino rats (Mus norvegicus var. albus). *Amer. J. Anat.* **7**: 423-441, 1907.

HATAI, S. On the brain weights of rats descended from the cross between the wild Norway (Mus norvegicus) and the domesticated albino (Mus norvegicus albinos). *J. Comp. Neurol.* **25**: 555-566, 1915.

KING, H. D. On the postnatal growth of the body and of the central nervous system in albino rats that are undersized at birth. *Anat. Rec.* **11**: 41-52, 1916.

LEVIN, G. Z. On the relations between the fissures of the brain and the cortical arteries from the standpoint of their development. *Arkh. Anat. Gist. i Embr.* **20**: 100-108, 1939.

LEVINE, S. Anoxic-ischemic encephalopathy in rats. *Amer. J. Pathol.* **36**: 1-17, 1960.

LEWIS, O. J. The form and development of the blood vessels of the mammalian cerebral cortex. *J. Anat. (London)* **91**: 40-46, 1957.

MILLEN, J. W. & D. H. M. WOOLLAM. Vascular patterns in the choroid plexus. *J. Anat. (London)* **87**: 114-123, 1953.

MILLEN, J. W. & D. H. M. WOOLLAM. The reticular perivascular tissue of the central nervous system. *J. Neurol. Neurosurg. Psychiat.* **17**: 286-294, 1954.

MILLEN, J. W. & D. H. M. WOOLLAM. The Anatomy of the Cerebrospinal Fluid. London and New York: Oxford Univ. Press, 1962.

MOFFAT, D. B. The development of the hindbrain arteries in the rat. *J. Anat. (London)* **91**: 24-39, 1957.

MOFFAT, D. B. The development of the anterior cerebral artery and its related vessels in the rat. *Amer. J. Anat.* **108**: 17-29, 1961a.

MOFFAT, D. B. The development of the ophthalmic artery in the rat. *Anat. Rec.* **140**: 217-221, 1961b.

MOFFAT, D. B. The development of the posterior cerebral artery. *J. Anat. (London)* **95**: 485-494, 1961c.

PING, CHI. On the growth of the largest nerve cells in the superior cervical sympathetic ganglion of the albino rat—from birth to maturity. *J. Comp. Neurol.* **33**: 281-311, 1921a.

PING, CHI. On the growth of the largest nerve cells in the superior cervical sympathetic ganglion of the Norway rat. *J. Comp. Neurol.* **33**: 313-338, 1921b.

REINIŠ, S. Changes in the relative vascularity of various parts of the central nervous system after the elimination of neocortex. *Acta Anat.* **46**: 73-80, 1961.

RHINES, R. & W. F. WINDLE. Early development of fasciculus longitudinalis medialis and associated secondary neurons in rat, cat and man. *J. Comp. Neurol.* **75**: 165-189, 1941.

Riese, W. Structure and function of the mammalian cerebral cortex at the time of birth. *Virginia Med. Mon.* **71**: 134-139, 1944.

Smith, C. G. The volume of the neocortex of the albino rat and the changes it undergoes with age after birth. *J. Comp. Neurol.* **60**: 319-347, 1934.

Smith, C. G. The change in volume of the olfactory and accessory olfactory bulbs of the albino rat during postnatal life. *J. Comp. Neurol.* **61**: 477-508, 1935.

Smith, L. A. A comparison of the number of nerve cells in the olfactory bulbs of domesticated albino and wild Norway rats. *J. Comp. Neurol.* **45**: 483-501, 1928.

Strong, R. M. & H. Alban. The development of the lateral apertures of the fourth ventricle in the albino rat brain. *Anat. Rec.* **52**: 39, 1932 (Suppl. Feb.).

Tamaki, K. On the sectional areas and volumes of the largest motor cells and their nuclei in the lumbar cord of the albino rat, according to sex. *Anat. Rec.* **56**: 229-240, 1933.

Tilney, F. & L. Casamajor. The development of the hemal channels in the central nervous system of the albino rat. *Anat. Rec.* **11**: 425-428, 1917.

Tilney, F. & H. A. Riley. The Form and Functions of the Central Nervous System. New York: Paul B. Hoeber, 1921. Rat: pp. 27, 31, 34, 35, 43, 46, and 47.

Unger, K. H. Über Altersveränderungen in der Grenzstrang-Ganglien der Ratte. *Anat. Anz.* **98**: 13-23, 1951.

Watson, J. B. Quoted from Donaldson, The Rat (from Animal Education, Contrib. from the Psychol. Lab., Univ. of Chicago, Vol. 4, pp. 5-122, 1905; (see Table II showing myelination of the nervous system of the various ages of the rat). (Original not traced.)

Windle, W. F. & R. E. Baxter. The first neurofibrillar development in albino rat embryos. *J. Comp. Neurol.* **63**: 173-187, 1936a.

Wislocki, G. B. & Elizabeth H. Leduc. The cytology of the subcommissural organ, Reissner's fiber, periventricular glial cells, and posterior colliculus recess of the rat's brain. *J. Comp. Neurol.* **101**: 283-309, 1954.

Wislocki, G. B., Elizabeth H. Leduc & A. J. Mitchell. On the ending of Reissner's fiber in the filum terminale of the spinal cord. *J. Comp. Neurol.* **104**: 493-517, 1956.

Woollam, D. H. M. & J. W. Millen. The arterial supply of the spinal cord and its significance. *J. Neurol. Neurosurg. Psychiat.* **18**: 97-102, 1955a.

Woollam, D. H. M. & J. W. Millen. Perivascular spaces of mammalian central nervous system: relation to perineuronal and subarachnoid spaces. *J. Anat. (London)* **89**: 193-200, 1955b.

Zhukova, T. P. Multiplication of capillaries in different parts of the brain in the postnatal period. *Biull. Eksptl. Biol. i Med.* (translation) **51** (6): 87-93, 1961 (*Biol. Abstr.* **38**: Abstract No. 10387).

CHAPTER III

Medulla Spinalis (Spinal Cord)

In neuroanatomy it is traditional to begin a study of the central nervous system with the spinal cord. Ontogenetically and phylogenetically the cord retains its segmental character and partial independence from other parts of the central nervous system. Consequently, the spinal cord of all mammals possesses the same basic anatomic pattern, the main differences being dimensions and topographic relations to vertebral column and canal. Other differences relate to the localization of neuron groupings in the gray matter and of fiber tracts. These comparative neuroanatomical problems are elaborated upon by Ariëns Kappers *et al.* (1936), and by Bullard (1912), who made a comprehensive neuroanatomic study of the cervical, thoracic, and lumbar regions of the spinal cord of a large series of domesticated, wild, and laboratory animals, all with diagrams to scale of transverse sections, from which basic similarities between different species are obvious.

The skeletal and meningeal coverings of the spinal cord of the rat are shown in Figs. 18 and 19. In transverse section the cord is composed of two bilaterally symmetrical halves partly joined in the midline. Separation of the two halves is effected ventrally by the ventral median fissure (*fissura mediana ventralis*), and dorsally by the dorsal median sulcus (*sulcus medianus dorsalis*); the latter continues toward the central canal as a septum of connective tissue. In transverse sections the central canal appears as a small hole lined by ependyma (ciliated columnar epithelium). The canal is surrounded by a butterfly-shaped area of gray matter, which is divided into dorsal, lateral, and ventral horns (*cornu dorsale, laterale, ventrale*). The dorsal horn is capped by the very massive *substantia gelatinosa* in the rat. The two halves of gray matter are joined by commissures which run ventral and dorsal to the canal. The gray matter has an encircling mass of white matter which is divided into columns or funiculi —dorsal, lateral, and ventral. As the ventral fissure does not reach the central canal, the white matter on each side is continuous in the ventral part.

A diagram of the rat spinal cord throughout its length, drawn to scale from an actual dissected specimen, is shown in Fig. 20. It is an elongated rod-like structure slightly flattened dorsoventrally, which stretches from the foramen magnum to its termination at about the third and fourth lumbar vertebrae.

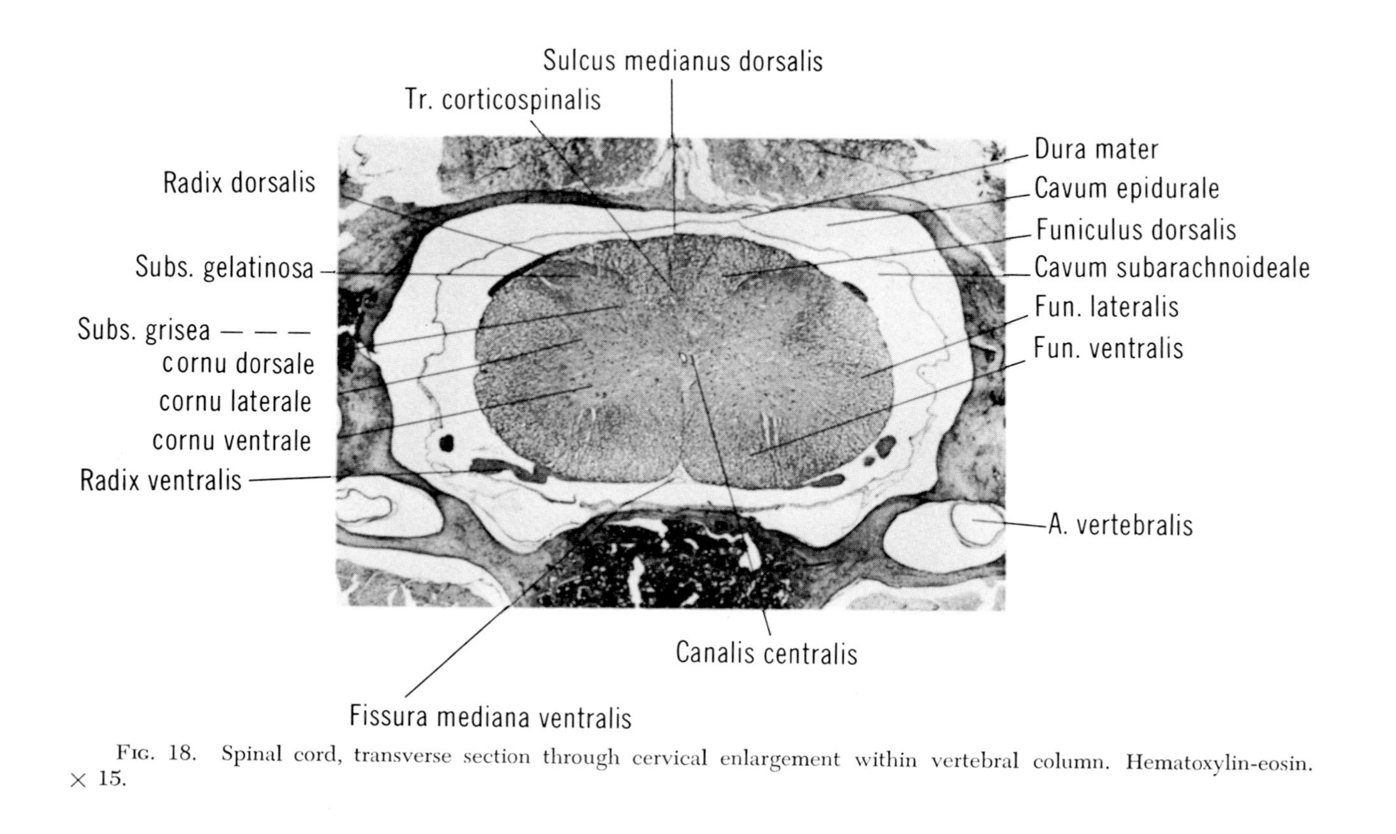

Fig. 18. Spinal cord, transverse section through cervical enlargement within vertebral column. Hematoxylin-eosin. × 15.

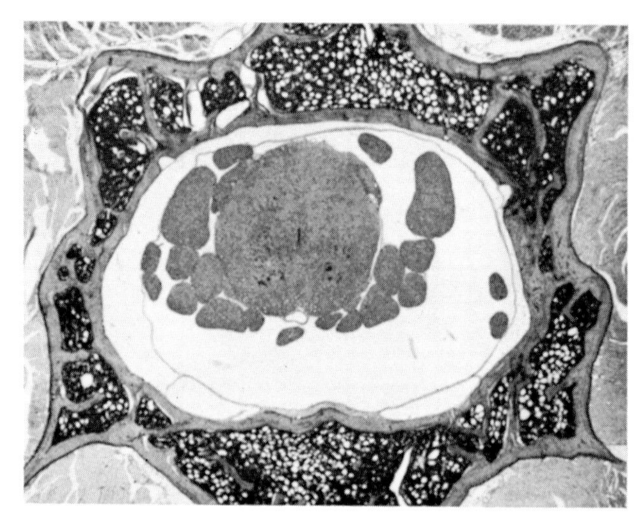

FIG. 19. Vertebral column, transverse section through lower lumbar region; termination of cord and cauda equina. Hematoxylin-eosin. × 15.

Figure 1 affords a lateral view of the vertebral column showing the natural vertical curves, and the spinal cord follows these horizontal deviations. Although not so marked as in some other mammals, a slight swelling of the cord starts at about the fourth cervical segment and subsides by the eighth, and another swelling starts about the last thoracic segment and terminates by about the third lumbar one. These are the cervical and lumbar enlargements (*intumescentia cervicalis* and *lumbalis,* respectively) which harbor the neurons innervating the fore and hind limbs. Figure 21 is a scale drawing of microscopic sections of a rat spinal cord cut transversely; it illustrates the differences in shape, and in area covered by gray and white matter at all segmental levels. From the conical termination of the spinal cord—the *conus medullaris*—extends a fine glistening white thread—the *filum terminale* (which can be identified only under the dissection microscope); this thread is finally anchored to the roof of the vertebral canal in the coccygeal region.

The discrepancy in length and termination between the spinal cord and the vertebral column is important. In man, the spinal cord terminates between the first and second lumbar vertebrae. Until the third month of intrauterine life, the spinal cord occupies the full length of the vertebral canal, but from this period on the vertebral column grows much faster than the cord. At birth the cord then seems to have been retracted further up into the canal. This feature is less marked in simian primates; in carnivores the *conus medullaris* reaches the end of the lumbar region and in ungulates it reaches the middle of the sacral region. As a consequence, the segments of spinal cord always lie higher than the corresponding vertebrae. In the rat the cord ends at the third to fourth lumbar vertebrae.

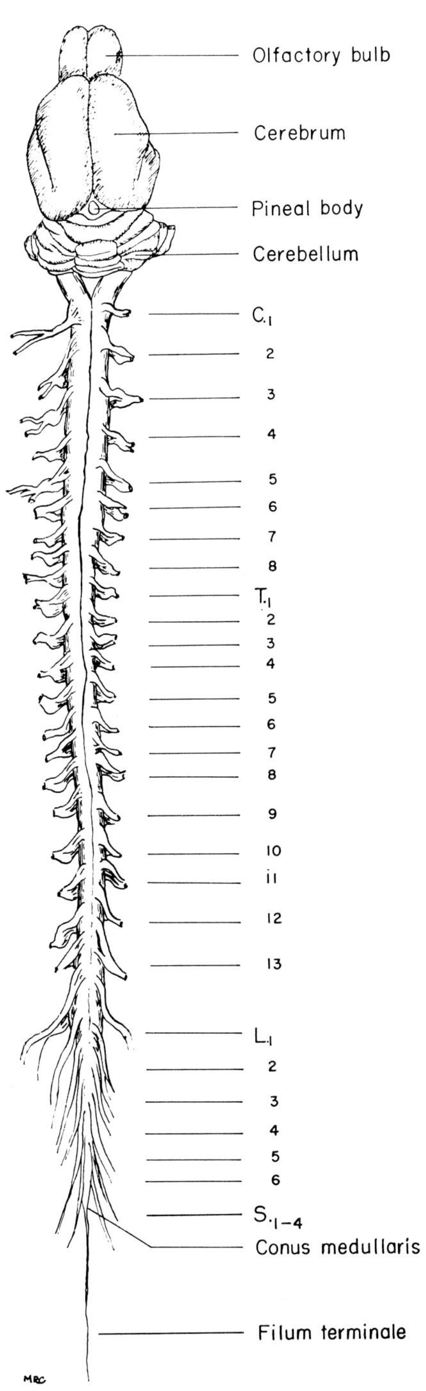

FIG. 20. Spinal cord, diagram of dissected specimen.

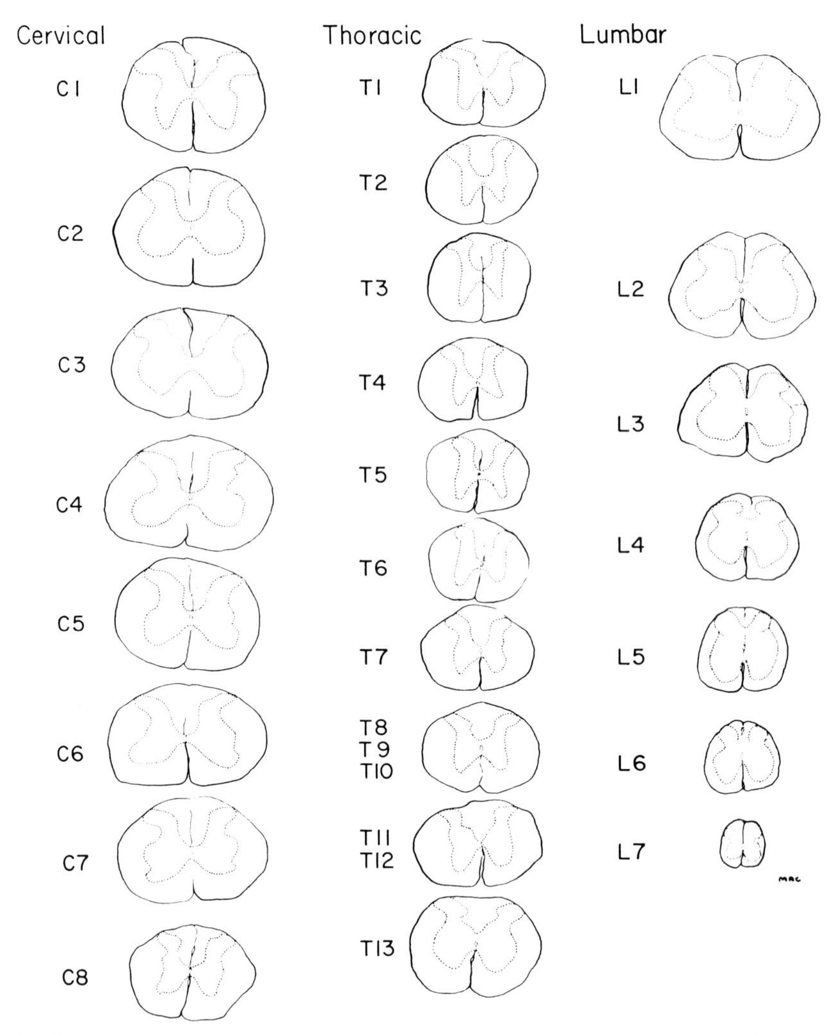

FIG. 21. Spinal cord. Drawings made from histologic sections, to scale, showing areas of gray and white matter at segmental levels. × about 7.

The spinal cord is divided into cervical, thoracic, lumbar, and sacral regions. Its length in relationship to body length, growth rate, and body weight is given in Table III (Chapter II). These divisions are recognized by their spinal nerve attachments and not by the corresponding vertebrae. From each segment of the spinal cord arises a pair of spinal nerves; each nerve is attached by dorsal and ventral roots splayed over an area near the tips of the dorsal and ventral horns of gray matter, respectively. In the cervical and lumbar regions these rootlets are close to each other, whereas in the thoracic region there is a decided gap between successive rootlets. Figure 20 shows that each nerve root must travel some distance before leaving the vertebral canal. Because of the retraction of the spinal cord in its growth up into the vertebral canal, the lumbar roots have a longer way to travel than have the others in an obliquely caudal direction—like a leash—to form the *cauda equina,* which conceals in its center, the *conus medullaris* and *filum terminale.*

On each dorsal spinal root there is a very small swelling—the spinal ganglion—visible under the dissection microscope. In the rat, apart from the ganglia of the second cervical nerves which are in the angle between the atlas and axis, all ganglia lie within the vertebral canal outside the dura mater.

There are eight pairs of cervical, thirteen thoracic, six lumbar, four sacral, and three caudal, or coccygeal, nerves. The eight cervical nerves, as opposed to the seven cervical vertebrae, are accounted for by the fact that the nerves of the first pair emerge between the skull and atlas.

As can be seen from Fig. 18, the diameter of the cord is much smaller than that of the vertebral canal in which it lies. There is a wide interval between its surface and its meninges and the bony wall, but the spaces vary in different species and also at different levels. The epidural space (between dura mater and bone) is not so marked at the enlargements as in the midthoracic region. The liberal space is a necessary provision to allow for flexion and extension of the vertebral column without causing jarring injury to the spinal cord and its roots.

Like the brain, the cord is surrounded by a close investment of pia mater, an arachnoid membrane with its wide subarachnoid space, and a much thicker dura mater, all of which are best seen in transverse histologic sections. Within the tubular meningeal sheath the spinal cord is suspended slinglike by a series of slips of tissue from the pia to dura mater—the *ligamenta denticulata*—which are spaced between individual nerve roots. The lateral margins of these are serrated and the attachments to the dura mater are at the points of the saw-like edge.

Arrangement of spinal cord neurons in the gray matter is in terms of nuclear groups the delineation of which is based largely on a study of transverse sections. In longitudinal sections these groups of nerve cells are seen to occupy long columns parallel with each other. There is a similar common pattern for all mammals (see Ariëns Kappers *et al.* for details on comparative anatomy), although exact comparison between any two different species is very difficult. A functional division of the nerve cells can be made in that the large multipolar nerve cells in the ventral horns of gray matter are motor and most of their axons emerging by way of the ventral roots terminate in the motor end plates of muscle fibers. Most of the cells in the dorsal horns are sensory in function in that they receive impulses from the incoming sensory (dorsal) nerve roots, and then transmit to higher centers in the brainstem or cerebellum. These groups account for less than half the total number of nerve cells in the spinal gray matter. Most nerve cells are internuncial in function (intercalated neurons), having connections with both sensory and motor nerve cells; those around the central canal are homologous to the cells in the reticular formation in the brainstem. Often perikarya are not arranged in the form of nuclei, but are diffusely spread throughout in homogeneous areas. In the base of the dorsal horns, for instance, ventral to the substantia gelatinosa, is an ill-defined accumulation of scattered stellate cells and richly branched neurons, known as the dorsal funicular gray. Notice that gray is used here as a noun. Slightly ventral is another area of scattered nerve cells known as the secondary visceral gray. This terminology is also often applied to the accumulation of nerve cells in the periventricular and periaqueductal tissues of the brain, generically referred to as periventricular gray.

The various functional pathways or fiber tracts within the funiculi of the white matter in the cord cannot be distinguished as such in histologic sections of normal adult rat material. They have been traced in other animals by making experimental hemisection of the spinal cord and following the subsequent degeneration in either ascending or descending directions. Another method has been to study sections of the spinal cord of fetal and young animals at different stages of development. As the onset of myelination varies in the different tracts, they can be followed in their development in myelin-stained sections.

Just as there are sensory and motor nerve cells in the gray matter dealing with impulses coming in, or going out, there are sensory and motor fiber tracts in the white matter which ascend to or descend from the brain. In the rat there is little anatomical information available on the spinal tracts other than the corticospinal one (*tractus corticospinalis* or *pyramidalis*), and the *tractus dorsolateralis.* We have, therefore, chosen the rabbit spinal cord to explicate the various tracts, the diagram being a redrawn and renamed version of the illustration in Winkler and Potter. For comparison with the tracts of the human spinal cord, references can be made to any standard textbook on human anatomy.

It is well to emphasize that, although the diagram gives the impression of homogeneous compact bundles of fibers, this in effect is not so, for fibers of one type are scattered and intermingled with fibers of another. Hence the diagram presents at best an approximate localization of tracts or fascicles (Fig. 22).

Starting from the top of the diagram and working around clockwise we encounter the *fasciculus gracilis,* which borders the dorsal median sulcus; it begins at the caudal end of the cord, increases in size as it ascends, gathering fibers from the successive dorsal nerve roots, and ends in the *nucleus gracilis* in the medulla oblongata. The *fasciculus cuneatus* lies lateral to the *fasciculus gracilis;* its fibers arise also from the dorsal roots, generally those of the thoracic and cervical segments, and it terminates in the *nucleus cuneatus* of the medulla oblongata. Both tracts are concerned with discriminatory sensation, sense of position of the limbs and localization on the skin, and of muscle tension and joint movement. The *tractus dorsolateralis* lies at the tip of the dorsal horn of

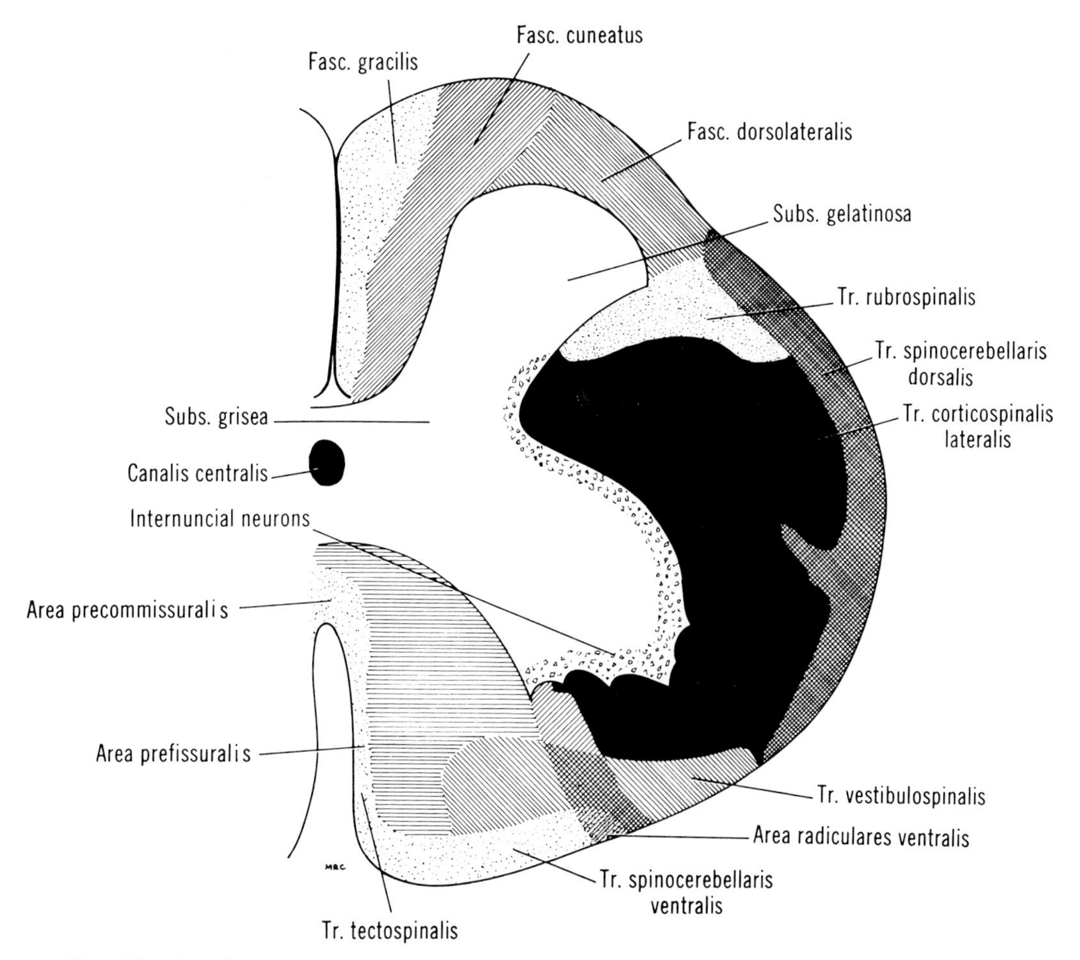

FIG. 22. Spinal cord, rabbit. Ascending and descending tracts. (Redrawn from Winkler and Potter, 1911.)

gray matter and contains myelinated and unmyelinated fibers, which probably are intersegmental; they seem to be concerned with pain and response to pain. The *tractus spinocerebellaris dorsalis* starts in the lumbar region, increases in size as it ascends, and passes to the cortex of the cerebellum through the inferior cerebellar peduncle. The *tractus spinocerebellaris ventralis* comes from the same, but mostly opposite, side of the spinal cord, and the fibers cross both in the gray and white commissures. The fibers are probably derived from the neurons in the dorsal and intermediate gray matter, ascend to the medulla and pons at the level of the posterior colliculi, and via the superior cerebellar peduncle reach the vermis of the cerebellum. Some fibers are said to continue into the dorsolateral part of the tegmentum of the midbrain to reach the thalamus. The *tractus vestibulospinalis,* situated in the marginal part of the ventral white funiculus, arises from the large-cell part of the vestibular nucleus of the same side in the medulla and can be traced to lower regions of the cord. It is probably concerned with equilibratory reflexes. It will be noted on comparison with diagrams of human spinal tracts that several ascending tracts described in the human are not present, missing, or not named in the rodent.

The descending tracts concerned with motor activity in the rabbit are different from those in the rat, and those appear to be the only ones in the latter species to which much attention has been given. In the (rabbit) diagram it will be seen that there is a *tractus rubrospinalis,* which arises in the *nucleus ruber.* It is not known whether the *tractus corticospinalis lateralis* corresponds to the human crossed pyramidal tract that arises from the motor area of the neocortex. According to Lassek (1954) there is no direct corticospinal tract in the rabbit, or in any mammal lower than primates (see also Douglas and Barr, 1950). It follows that the functional significance of the lateral corticospinal tract of the rabbit is open to speculation; yet it has been suggested that impulses from the motor cortex to the ventral horn cells of the spinal cord are mediated via the rubrospinal tracts. Obviously, this field is fertile grounds for future research. The *tractus tectospinalis* is derived from the anterior colliculus of the midbrain and crosses the median raphe to descend as the ventral longitudinal bundle in the reticular formation. Its collaterals and terminals end directly or indirectly in the motor neurons of the side in which it descends.

Just how far all these particulars apply to the rat is unknown. However, it is known that in the rat the fibers of the *tractus corticospinalis,* after the decussation of the pyramids in the ventral part of the lower medulla oblongata, almost immediately cross to the opposite side and are then localized at the ventral part of the dorsal white funiculus, i.e., occupying a part of the funiculus which also contains the *fasciculus gracilis* and *fasciculus cuneatus* in other mammals. It has been traced to the lowest region of the cord. In the rat (see Linowiecki, 1914), the fibers in this corticospinal tract can be distinguished in transverse histologic sections from the remaining fibers of the *fasciculus gracilis* and *fasciculus cuneatus* by their small size, and by the fact that many are unmyelinated. Hence, in myelin-stained preparations this area is just faintly stained, and in routine stains (such as hematoxylin-eosin) the tract is more compact and is densely stained. The only experimental paper on this murine tract is that by Barron (1934), who sectioned the pyramids above the decussation and found resultant disorders of posture, gait, and grasp, which were more pronounced in the forelimbs. He concluded that the corticospinal tract in the rat is concerned with the regulation of flexor movements of the forelimbs, especially the paws and digits.

References

ANGULO Y GONZÁLEZ, A. W. The motor nuclei in the cervical cord of the albino rat at birth. *J. Comp. Neurol.* **43**: 115-142, 1927.

ANGULO Y GONZÁLEZ, A. W. Histogenesis of monopolar neuroblast and ventral longitudinal path in albino rat. *J. Comp. Neurol.* **71**: 325-360, 1939.

ANGULO Y GONZÁLEZ, A. W. The differentiation of the motor cell columns in the cervical cord of albino rat fetuses. *J. Comp. Neurol.* **73**: 469-488, 1940.

ARIËNS KAPPERS, C. U., G. C. HUBER & ELIZABETH C. CROSBY. The Comparative Anatomy of the Nervous System of Vertebrates, Including Man. 2 Volumes. New York: Macmillan, 1936.

BARNARD, J. W. & C. N. WOOLSEY. A study of localization in the corticospinal tracts of monkey and rat. *J. Comp. Neurol.* **105**: 25-50, 1956.

BARRON, D. H. The results of unilateral pyramidal section in rat. *J. Comp. Neurol.* **60**: 45-56, 1934.

BREGMANN, L. E. Neue Untersuchungen zur Kenntnis der Pyramidenbahn. 1. Der Anteil der Pyramide am Rückenmarksquerschnitt bei verschiedenen Tieren und seine Entwicklung beim Menschen. *Anat. Anz.* **48**: 75-80, 1915.

BULLARD, PEARL B. A comparative study of the three principal regions of the spinal cord in a series of mammals. *Amer. J. Anat.* **14**: 73-105, 1912–1913.

CAJAL, S. RAMÓN Y. Histologie du système nerveux de l'homme et des vertébrés. Paris: Maloine, 1909-1911. (Reprinted by C.S.I.S., Madrid, 1952.)

CROSBY, ELIZABETH C. & R. T. WOODBURNE. Certain major trends in the development of the efferent systems of the brain and spinal cord. *Ann Arbor Univ. Hosp. Bull.* **4**: 125-128, 1938.

CROSBY, ELIZABETH C., T. HUMPHREY & E. W. LAUER. Correlative Anatomy of the Nervous System. New York: Macmillan, 1962.

DOUGLAS, A. & M. L. BARR. The course of the pyramidal tract in rodents. *Rev. canad. biol.* **9**: 118-122, 1950.

DUNCAN, D. A determination of the number of unmyelinated fibers in the ventral roots of the rat, cat and rabbit. *J. Comp. Neurol.* **55**: 459-471, 1932.

DUNCAN, D. A. A determination of the number of nerve fibers in the eighth thoracic and the largest lumbar ventral roots of the albino rat. *J. Comp. Neurol.* **59**: 47-60, 1934.

FOLEY, J. O. & F. S. DUBOIS. A quantitative and experimental study of the cervical sympathetic trunk. *J. Comp. Neurol.* **72**: 587-603, 1940.

GREENE, EUNICE C. Anatomy of the Rat. New York: Hafner, 1955.

HOOKER, D. & J. S. NICHOLAS. The effect of injury to the spinal cord of rats in prenatal stages. *Amer. J. Physiol.* **81**: 503, 1927.

HOOKER, D. & J. S. NICHOLAS. Spinal cord section in rat fetuses. *J. Comp. Neurol.* **50**: 413-467, 1930.

KING, J. L. The cortico-spinal tract of the rat. *Anat. Rec.* **4**: 245-252, 1910.

LASSEK, A. M. The Pyramidal Tract: Its Status in Medicine, 166 pp. Springfield, Illinois: C. C Thomas, 1954.

LASSEK, A. M. & W. L. HARD. The pyramidal tract. A study of the sensitivity of neurons to trauma in the rat with a comparison of methods. *J. Neuropath.* **7**: 457-461, 1948.

LASSEK, A. M. & E. L. RASMUSSEN. A comparative fiber and numerical analysis of the pyramidal tract. *J. Comp. Neurol.* **72**: 417-428, 1940.

LINOWIECKI, A. J. The comparative anatomy of the pyramidal tract. *J. Comp. Neurol.* **24**: 509-530, 1914.

MCALPINE, R. J. Selected observations on the early development of the motor neurons in the brain stem and spinal cord of the white rat as revealed by the alkaline phosphatase technique. *J. Comp. Neurol.* **113**: 211-243, 1959.

PAPEZ, J. W. Comparative Neurology. 518 pp. New York: Crowell, 1929. (Reprinted by Hafner Co., New York, 1961.)

RANSON, S. W. The fasciculus cerebro-spinalis in the albino rat. *Amer. J. Anat.* **14**: 411-424, 1913–1914.

RANSON, S. W. The tract of Lissauer and the substantia gelatinosa rolandi. *Amer. J. Anat.* **16**: 97-126, 1914a.

RANSON, S. W. A note on the degeneration of the fasciculus cerebro-spinalis in the albino rat. *J. Comp. Neurol.* **24**: 503-507, 1914b.

RANSON, S. W. Transplantation of the spinal ganglion with observations on the significance of the complex types of spinal ganglion cells. *J. Comp. Neurol.* **24**: 547-558, 1914c.

ROBINSON, A. Observations upon the development of the spinal cord in Mus musculus and Mus decumanus. *Rep. Brit. Ass. 61st Meeting, Cardiff*, pp. 691-692, 1892.

WINKLER, C. & A. POTTER. An Anatomical Guide to Experimental Researches on the Rabbit's Brain. Amsterdam: W. Versluys, 1911.

CHAPTER IV

The Cranial Nerves and Their Nuclei

A. CRANIAL NERVES

One of the most fruitful conceptions which has been brought to bear upon the study of nervous structures is that of functional components. According to this principle, the functional components of the cerebrospinal nerves may be divided as follows: Afferent fibers conduct impulses toward and efferent fibers away from the central nervous system. Each of these two may connect at the periphery with somatic structures, i.e., the somitic musculoskeletal system and skin, or they may innervate visceral structures. In regard to the cranial nerves, however, a further subdivision is made because they are also concerned with special senses and with highly specialized visceral functions. Therefore, in addition to the four previously mentioned groups of general afferent or efferent somatic or visceral fibers, we find among the cranial nerves special somatic afferent and special visceral efferent and afferent fibers. Somatic efferent fibers innervate voluntary muscles and are not divided between general and special. These facts are expressed in the accompanying diagram.

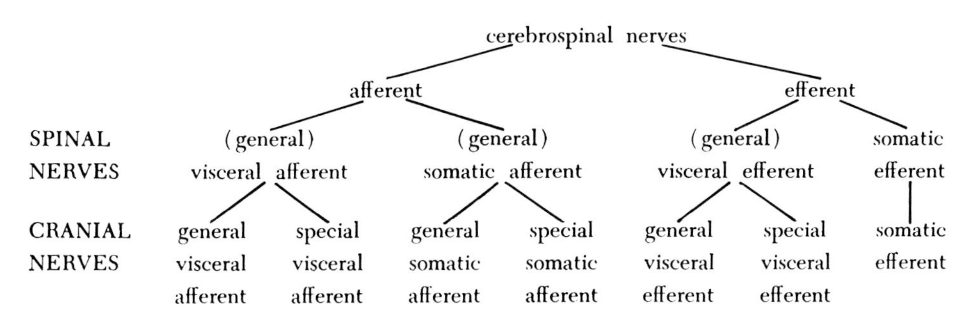

The following statements can be taken to apply to mammals in general. Details of the finer distribution of all the branches of the cranial nerves, third to twelfth, in the rat can be obtained from Greene (Chapter VI). The location of the roots of emergence from the brain are illustrated in Fig. 8 (p. 23). The nuclei of origin can be found in Figs. 23, 24, A3–A12.

I. *N. olfactorius.* Concerned with the sensation of smell, it is composed of special visceral afferent fibers which originate from the olfactory cells of the nasal mucosa. In the form of fine fibers, the *fila olfactoria,* which are not aggregated to form a nerve trunk, they pass through the foramina of the cribriform plates of the ethmoid bone (Fig. 4, p. 15) to terminate in the glomeruli of the olfactory bulbs. (For the structure of the latter see Fig. 33, p. 140).

II. *N. opticus.* This is not a true nerve, but rather a fiber tract of the brain (Figs. A21–A29). The component fibers are special somatic afferent—exteroceptive—which originate from the ganglion cells of the retina. The fibers converge within the eyeball to form the optic papilla, where they are then collected into round trunks as the optic nerves. The latter pierce the chorioid and sclera, and pass into the cranial cavity through the optic foramina (Fig. 4). Each nerve then decussates with its fellow to form the optic chiasma, the continuations of which comprise the optic tracts. These run to the lateral geniculate bodies, the pretectal areas, and the anterior colliculi (Figs. A12–A20).

The presence of efferent fibers in the optic nerves with terminal arborization in the retina has been fairly well established for birds and fish. According to Polyak, such fibers, presumably concerned with altering the sensitivity threshold of retinal nerve cells, may also exist in chimpanzees and other mammals (for reference see page 135).

III. *N. oculomotorius.* Several radicles emerge from the base of the cerebral peduncles, lateral to the interpeduncular nucleus (Fig. A12), where they form a solid nerve trunk which passes through the superior orbital fissure into the orbita. Somatic efferent fibers originate in the oculomotor nuclei situated in the floor of the cerebral aqueduct (Fig. A12). General visceral efferent fibers come from the nucleus of Edinger-Westphal, and terminate in the ciliary ganglion, from the cells of which postganglionic fibers go to the intrinsic muscles of the eyeball. General somatic afferent fibers are proprioceptive for the eye muscles. Functionally, the nerve is concerned with eye movements and pupillary control.

IV. *N. trochlearis.* The nucleus lies under the floor of the cerebral aqueduct (Figs. A10, A11). The roots emerge dorsally from the anterior medullary velum between the tectum and the cerebellum. The nerve swings around the cerebral peduncle and then runs rostrad close to the *nervus oculomotorius* on its way to the orbita. It is connected with eye movements. Somatic efferent fibers decussate in the anterior medullary velum and supply the superior oblique muscle, while general somatic afferent fibers are proprioceptive for the same muscle.

V. *N. trigeminus.* It emerges from the lateral region of the pons in the form of two roots which together make it the thickest of the cranial nerves

(Fig. A9). The much larger sensory root contains general somatic afferent fibers concerned (1) with exteroceptive sensation which fibers originate in the nerve cells of the Gasserian ganglion, and (2) with proprioceptive sensation, these fibers probably originating from the cells of the mesencephalic nucleus (Figs. A9–A12) and innervating the muscles of mastication. Most fibers from the Gasserian ganglion terminate in the main sensory nucleus and the spinal nucleus of the Vth nerve (Figs A4–A8) and are concerned with general sensation of the head, nose, teeth, and mouth. Fibers mediating painful stimuli apparently terminate in the reticular formation of the medulla oblongata (Clarke and Bowsher, 1962).

The smaller motor root is made up of special visceral efferent fibers originating in the motor nucleus of the Vth nerve (Fig. 24). It innervates the muscles of mastication.

The term trigeminus, meaning "triplet," is derived from the fact that the nerve forms three major divisions peripherally—ophthalmic, maxillary, and mandibular, each of which splits up into several smaller branches.

VI. *N. abducens.* The superficial origin is near the midline in the caudal part of the pons at its junction with medulla oblongata just lateral to the ventral median fissure. The nerve runs in the same general direction as III and IV to the orbita, where it supplies the lateral rectus muscle, which is concerned with eye movements. Its fibers are therefore largely somatic efferent, but it also carries general somatic afferent fibers for proprioceptive impulses originating in the same muscle.

VII. *N. facialis.* Its superficial origin is from the lateral part of the pons, where the nerve is separated from the *flocculus cerebelli* by the VIIIth cranial nerve (Fig. A7). Its general visceral afferent fibers originate in the *ganglion geniculi.* The peripheral branches of these axons supply deep sensibility to the face whereas the central branches enter the *tractus solitarius* and end in the nucleus of this tract (Figs. 23, A7, A8). The special visceral afferent fibers also originate in the *ganglion geniculi.* Their peripheral branches supply the taste buds of the anterior two-thirds of the tongue, whereas their central branches form part of the *tractus solitarius* and end in the *nucleus intercalatus.* General visceral efferent fibers originate from the cells of the *nucleus salivatorius superior* (Fig. 23) and supply the innervation of the submaxillary and sublingual salivary glands by way of postganglionic fibers from the submaxillary ganglion. Special visceral efferent fibers originate in the cells of the motor facial nucleus (Fig. A6) and supply the superficial musculature of face and scalp.

VIII. *N. octavus.* This nerve has its superficial origin at the lateral border of the pons near the *flocculus* and *paraflocculus cerebelli.* It consists of two major divisions, the vestibular and the cochlear nerves. The vestibular

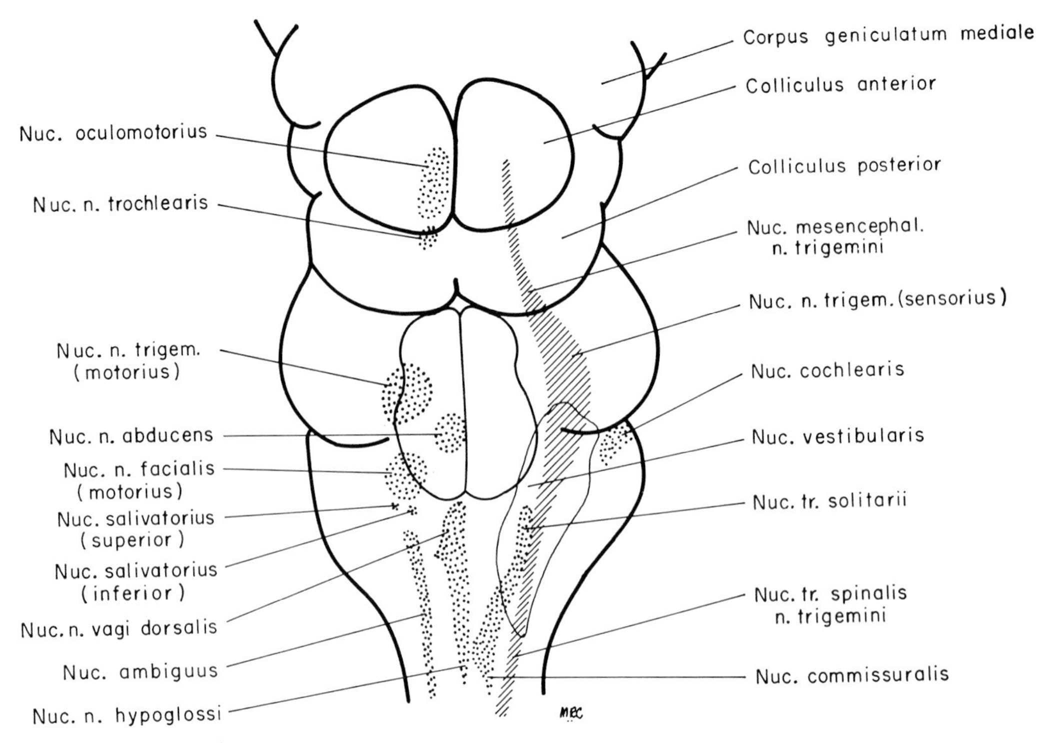

FIG. 23. Dorsal view of brainstem, schematic, with positions of cranial nerve nuclei projected on surface. Sensory nuclei on the right, motor nuclei on the left (modeled on Herrick).

nerve carries special somatic afferent fibers which are proprioceptive and originate in the vestibular ganglion. Their peripheral branches run to the semicircular canals, utricle, and saccule of the inner ear. Their central branches terminate in the medial, lateral, superior, and spinal vestibular nuclei (Figs. A5–A7). Some fibers run to the flocculonodular lobe of the cerebellum. The component fibers of the cochlear nerve are also special somatic afferent, but they are exteroceptive. The cells of origin lie in the spiral ganglion of the cochlea, their peripheral branches end in the spiral organ of Corti and the central branches terminate in the dorsal and ventral cochlear nuclei (Figs. A6–A8).

IX. *N. glossopharyngeus.* This nerve originates superficially from the rostral end of the posterior lateral sulcus of the medulla oblongata in line with the Xth and XIth nerves (Fig. 8). General visceral afferent fibers originate in the *ganglion petrosum.* Their peripheral branches supply general sensory fibers to the pharynx and to the posterior third of the tongue, whereas the central branches run to the solitary tract and its nucleus. Special visceral afferent fibers also originate in the cells of the *ganglion petrosum.* They supply the taste buds of the posterior third of the tongue, and their central branches run to the solitary tract and terminate in the *nucleus intercalatus.* General visceral efferent fibers originate in the cells of the inferior salivatory nucleus (Fig. 23), whence they run to the otic ganglion, and from there postganglionic fibers carry impulses to the parotid gland. Special visceral efferent fibers originate from the cells of the *nucleus ambiguus* (Fig. A5) and supply motor impulses to the stylo-pharyngeal muscle.

X. *N. vagus.* This nerve superficially originates immediately caudal to the IXth (Fig. 8). General somatic afferent fibers emerge from the cells of the *ganglion jugulare* and supply the skin of the external ear. Their central branches terminate in the spinal nucleus of the trigeminal nerve. General visceral afferent fibers spring from the cells of the *ganglion nodosum;* their peripheral branches run as sensory fibers to pharynx, larynx, trachea, esophagus, thoracic and abdominal vessels, and their central branches enter the *tractus solitarius* and terminate in the *nucleus tractus solitarii* (Fig. A4). Special visceral afferent fibers also originate in the cells of the *ganglion nodosum* and supply the taste buds of the epiglottis. Their central branches run to the solitary tract and terminate in the *nucleus intercalatus* (Fig. A5). General visceral efferent fibers originate in the cells of the dorsal motor nucleus of the vagus (*nucleus dorsalis nervi vagi*) (Figs. A4, A5) and run to the autonomic ganglia of the vagal plexus to innervate the thoracic and abdominal viscera. Special visceral efferent fibers originate in the cells of the *nucleus ambiguus* and terminate in the striated muscles of the pharynx and larynx. Whether the parasympathetic motor fibers for the heart muscle originate in the *nucleus ambiguus* or in the dorsal motor nucleus of the vagus is still a matter of dispute (Crosby *et al.,* 1962).

XI. *N. accessorius.* This nerve originates caudal to the Xth and from the lateral aspects of the first five or six cervical segments of the spinal cord. Its general visceral efferent fibers originate from the dorsal motor nucleus of the vagus (Figs. A4, A5). They join the latter nerve and end in the autonomic ganglia of the vagal plexus for the innervation of thoracic and abdominal viscera. Special visceral efferent fibers originate in the *nucleus ambiguus* (Fig. A5) and supply the striated muscles of the pharynx and larynx, and also in the lateral columns of the anterior gray matter of the upper cervical segments of the spinal cord innervating the trapezius and sternocleidomastoid muscles.

XII. *N. hypoglossus.* The superficial origin is from the ventral aspect of the medulla oblongata, whence it emerges from the skull through the hypo-glossal canal. It carries somatic afferent fibers which terminate in the musculature of the tongue.

B. CRANIAL NERVE NUCLEI AND THEIR CONNECTIONS

The various nuclei of the cranial nerves extend roughly from the upper cervical segments through the midbrain. It is important to realize that each cranial nerve, excluding I and II, is composed of fibers subserving different functions and that the nuclei are topographically arranged according to their function. This means that fibers from one cranial nerve may originate from or terminate in several different nuclei and that one particular nucleus may receive fibers from or send fibers into different cranial nerves. As outlined in the introduction, cranial nerve fibers with seven different types of functions are dis-

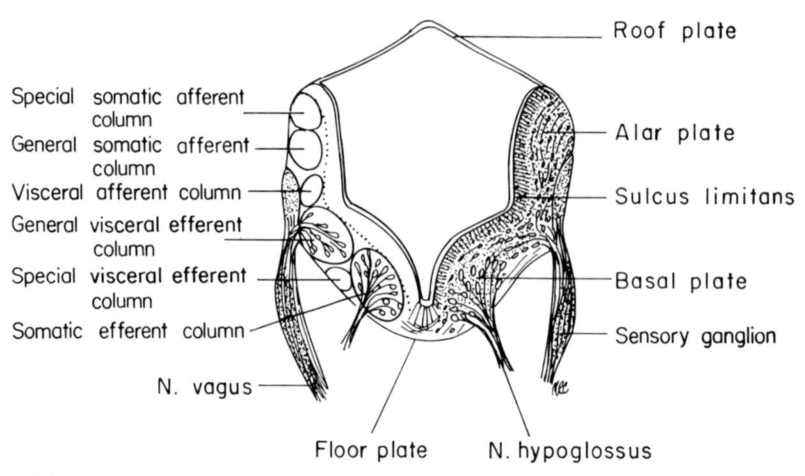

FIG. 24. Transverse section through the myelencephalon of a 10.6 mm human embryo showing the approximate location of cranial nerve nuclear columns. (Modified from His.)

tinguished. The respective nuclei are arranged in columns parallel to the longitudinal axis of the brainstem. One would expect to find seven columns of cranial nerve nuclei, but actually there are only six, because special and general visceral afferent fibers terminate in the same column (Fig. 24).

All efferent nerves originate from nuclei located in structures derived from the basal plate of the embryonal tube, whereas those of the afferent group terminate in nuclei found in the alar plate derivative. The basal plate is separated from the alar plate by the *sulcus limitans* (Fig. 24) which is still visible in the mature brain in the fourth ventricle and aqueduct.

1. Somatic Efferent Column

Going from the midline laterad and dorsad, we first encounter the somatic efferent nuclei, the cranial nerve nuclei III, IV, VI, and XII, which are the rhombencephalic and mesencephalic homologues of the anterior horn motor cells. Thus, somatic efferent nuclei of the cranial nerves are all close to the midline, where we find them in the floor of the aqueduct and the fourth ventricle.

2. Special Visceral Efferent Column

Lateral to these somatic motor centers lie the special visceral efferent nuclei concerned with the innervation of the branchial muscles for mastication, muscles for facial expression, for glutition and phonation. During phylogeny and ontogeny, these nuclei, originally in close lateral apposition to the somatic efferent group, undergo a marked change in position in a ventral and somewhat lateral direction, a change which has gone farthest in the case of the facial motor nucleus (*nucleus nervi facialis*). This large group of cells is found close to the ventral surface of the brain, midway between the spinal trigeminal root and the pyramid, and some distance dorsal to the point at which its root emerges (Fig. A6). It is composed of several separate cell masses, which Papez has found in both rat and cat to give rise to the fibers of distinct branches of the nerve. The root fibers do not run directly to the point of emergence, but pass in a dorsomedial direction toward the position whence the cells have migrated (Fig. A6). Close to the floor of the ventricle they turn forward and group themselves into a compact bundle, the genu or ascending portion of the facial motor root. After ascending a short distance to a point just in front of the *nucleus abducens,* the root turns sharply at about a right angle and runs ventrolaterally to emerge at the ventral edge of the spinal trigeminal root (Figs. A7 and A8). In the human brain, the facial motor nucleus is relatively smaller than in the rat, and is not quite so far ventral in position, while its rostral end lies dorsolateral to the superior olive instead of practically directly behind it as in the rat. This is probably due partly to the more dorsal position in man of the reduced spinal trigeminal nucleus, from which the facial motor nucleus receives impulses, and partly to the enormous development of the pons. The latter factor has pushed back the emerging facial motor root in man until it lies beside the front part of its nucleus, ventral to which the posterior portion of the pons itself extends.

The special motor cells of the glossopharyngeal and vagal nerves form a continuous column of much smaller size than the facial motor nucleus. This is the *nucleus ambiguus,* which is found in a position similar to that of the facial motor nucleus, but not so near the surface, being medial to the ventral edge of the spinal trigeminal nucleus (Fig. A5). Its rostral extremity is about on a level with that of the dorsal motor nucleus of the vagus, the general visceral motor nucleus, which has not migrated. Caudally the *nucleus ambiguus* gradually thins out until it is represented by a few isolated cells so irregularly scattered that its posterior end cannot be exactly determined. The root fibers from this nucleus run dorsomedially and join those from the dorsal motor nucleus of the vagus, passing out with them in small groups in a lateral direction. The special motor fibers of the XIth nerve arise from the *nucleus accessorius,* which may be regarded also as part of the visceral motor column that has migrated in a caudolateral direction and that is joined by visceral motor cells of those segments of the spinal cord in which it lies (Fig. A3). It extends from near the level of the caudal end of the hypoglossal nucleus through the upper cervical segments of the cord.

There remains to be considered one other special visceral efferent center, namely, the trigeminal motor nucleus (*nucleus motorius nervi trigemini; nucleus masticatorius*), which controls the movements of the jaw muscles. This nucleus consists of a rather conspicuous group of large cells which do not lie very close together (Fig. A8). It is situated medially to the chief sensory trigeminal nucleus and gives rise to the motor fibers of the trigeminal nerve. These form large fascicles which may be observed passing out in an anteroventral and somewhat lateral direction.

The various changes in position which we have just seen to have taken place in the development (both ontogenetic and phylogenetic) of the motor nuclei are prominent examples of a principle which seems to be active throughout the nervous system, and which has been called by Kappers *neurobiotaxis.* The most essential part of this principle may be summed up by saying that two nerve cells, which are simultaneously or immediately consecutively excited, exert an attractive influence on each other, as a result of which the cell body tends to migrate during development toward any other neuron from which it receives stimuli.

3. General Visceral Efferent Column

In the embryonic neural tube, the general visceral efferent nuclei have their "anlagen" lateral to the special visceral efferent nuclei and immediately medial to the sulcus limitans. While, in the mature central nervous system, this latter relationship is retained, the general visceral efferent nuclei are now directly lateral to the somatic efferent group due to the ventral displacement of the special visceral afferent nuclei, discussed above.

General visceral efferent fibers occur in the roots of nerves III, VII, IX, X, XI, whence they run as parasympathetic preganglionic fibers to autonomic ganglia. Those of the Xth and XIth nerves arise in a single column of cells which has a dorsal situation near the floor of the fourth ventricle. This nucleus—the dorsal motor nucleus of the vagus (*nucleus motorius dorsalis nervi vagi*) A4, A5—ends rostrally a short distance in front of the rostral extremity of the *nucleus hypoglossus,* where it is separated from the fourth ventricle by the large *nucleus intercalatus* and the chief vestibular nucleus and lies just medial to the corresponding sensory center (*nucleus fasciculi solitarii*). Passing backward, the *nucleus intercalatus* rapidly decreases until the dorsal vagus nucleus, which grows somewhat larger, comes to lie lateral to it and immediately under the floor of the ventricle. From here, it can be traced down into the closed part of the medulla oblongata, where it ends near the posterior extremity of the hypoglossal nucleus. All fibers from the dorsal motor nucleus of the nervus vagus are distributed to the vagal autonomic plexuses for the innervation of the thoracic and abdominal viscera.

The nucleus of Edinger-Westphal is a group of small nerve cells located in the rostral part of the oculomotor nucleus. It is said to give rise to fibers which terminate in the ciliary ganglion of the *orbita* and which influence light reflexes and accommodation.

The general visceral efferent components of the facial and the glossopharyngeal nerves are connected with the salivary glands, and their nuclei are the superior and the inferior salivatory nuclei, respectively (Fig. 24). These are small groups of scattered cells. They are practically continuous with each other and occupy a more lateral and deeper position than the dorsal motor vagal nucleus, a short distance in front of its anterior extremity.

4. Visceral Afferent Column

The nuclear columns for afferent systems (Fig. 24) are located in the alar plate derivatives. The visceral afferent nuclei are next to *sulcus limitans,* dorsolateral to the general visceral efferent group. Dorsal to the former are the general somatic afferent centers, dorsolaterally bordered by the special somatic afferent group.

Although we distinguish between a general visceral afferent system supplying deep sensibility to the face and the internal head structures, such as pharynx, larynx and tongue, and special visceral afferents concerned with taste, the respective terminals of these fibers form only one cell column composed of the *nucleus tractus solitarius,* the *nucleus parasolitarius* and *nucleus commissuralis.* Smell may also be included in this category on physiological grounds, but its structural representatives are independent and located in the telencephalon (see Chapter VII).

The sensory fibers of the glossopharyngeal and vagal nerves, upon entering the substance of the brain, run in small fascicles to a position between the dorsal end of the spinal trigeminal nucleus and the ventrolateral angle of the chief vestibular nucleus. Here they take up a longitudinal, descending direction, forming the *tractus solitarius,* which runs down to the first cervical segment of the spinal cord (Figs. A3–A6). The afferent facial fibers, which enter the brain farther rostrad, also run caudad and slightly mediad near the dorsal edge of the spinal trigeminal root and join the descending fibers of glossopharyngeal nerve in the solitary tract. This tract is accompanied by two columns of gray matter, of which the large one medial to it is the nucleus of the solitary bundle (*nucleus tracti solitarii*), while the one which lies ventrolateral to it is the *nucleus parasolitarius.* The former of these has a very clear appearance and is a conspicuous object in histologic sections. Its anterior end is bordered dorsally by the chief vestibular nucleus, but it soon emerges and occupies a position medial to this and directly under the floor of the fourth ventricle. Some of the fibers of the solitary tract end in these nuclei, but many of them descend to about the level of the decussation of the pyramids, where they decussate in a mass of gray matter dorsal to the central canal and continuous with the nuclei of the solitary tract of the two sides. This mass is the commissural nucleus of Cajal (*nucleus commissuralis*) (Fig. A3), in which the fibers terminate after decussating within it, forming the *commissura infima* or *inferior*. This commissure is not ordinarily seen in Weigert preparations as it contains very few myelinated fibers. A few of the fibers do not decussate, but run right into the upper part of the spinal cord on the same side.

While the solitary tract and its gray matter are usually considered to contain both the general visceral and the gustatory connections, Ariëns Kappers, Huber and Crosby traced the latter fibers to the *nucleus intercalatus* of Staderini (Fig. A5). This nuclear mass is wedged in between the rostral end of the hypoglossal nucleus and the dorsal motor nucleus of the vagus. It extends medially, forming a cap over the anterior extremity of the hypoglossal nucleus, and becoming continuous with a small mass next to the median line, the *nucleus eminentiae teretis*. In front of the hypoglossal nucleus, the intercalated nucleus enlarges and occupies the position of the former for a short distance. It also connects laterally, dorsal to the vagal motor nucleus, with another center to which gustatory functions are attributed, a small mass which forms the ventromedial angle of the chief vestibular nucleus, and which has usually been considered as part of that center. Allen, however, could trace no visceral afferent fibers to either of these centers in the guinea pig, but found them all to enter the solitary bundle.

The secondary visceral pathways are not well known. They include descending fibers to the cervical spinal cord, concerned probably with respiratory reflexes and reflexes of the digestive organs, such as vomiting, and an ascending path probably to the hypothalamus. Allen, however, has demonstrated in the guinea pig that the ascending secondary fibers run with the medial lemniscus of the opposite side to the thalamus. This was, in part, recently confirmed by Benjamin and Akert, who demonstrated that secondary gustatory fibers terminate in the region of the *pars ventromedialis* of the ventral nucleus of the thalamus, whence tertiary fibers project to the *regio insularis* of the neocortex. General visceral afferent fibers from the body are believed to run in thinly myelinated axons from the dorsobasal cell columns of the spinal cord, probably in the field designated as internuncial neurons in Fig. 22. They form multisynaptic chains which finally end at various nuclei of the reticular formation and probably also in the nucleus of the solitary tract. The small size of these fibers together with their diffuse distribution and their multisynaptic chain formation makes, by necessity, tracing of this system a most difficult, if not impossible, task.

5. General Somatic Afferent Column

All the general somatic afferent fibers which carry exteroceptive impulses from the head region, no matter what their peripheral course may be, end centrally in a single mass of gray matter in the pons and the medulla oblongata. Since the great majority of such fibers are found in the trigeminal nerve, this center has received the name of trigeminal nucleus. Upon entering the brain, most of the afferent fibers bifurcate, forming ascending and descending branches, of which the latter are the longer. A considerable number of unmyelinated and small myelinated fibers, however, have recently been found in the rat and other mammals to descend without bifurcating. They are believed to be pain fibers and to terminate in the reticular formation of the medulla oblongata. The descending fibers are grouped together in a compact bundle running along the dorsolateral aspect of the medulla oblongata in a superficial position. This spinal trigeminal root (*radix spinalis nervi trigemini*) extends downward from the place of entry of the trigeminal nerve to the beginning of the spinal cord, where it becomes continuous with the Lissauer tract (*fasciculus dorsolateralis medullae spinalis*). Some of the ascending branches of the sensory fibers pass upward beyond the level of the entry of the fifth nerve before ending, forming an ascending extension of the bundle for a short distance. The number of fibers in this root and, consequently, the size of the fascicle as a whole vary directly with the degree of development of general somatic sensibility in the head region. In man, where such sensibility is not especially well developed, the root is relatively small as compared with its size in the rat, which has great general sensibility in the snout region, particularly in connection with the *vibrissae,* or "whiskers." In transverse sections, the spinal trigeminal root appears as a large, crescentic area covering most of the lateral aspect of the medulla oblongata, in which position it may be followed from the beginning of the spinal cord up to the level of the fifth nerve. Traced up in this way, it will be seen to increase in size, being much smaller in the lower part of its course, a series of the descending fibers leaving it all the way along to end in the adjacent gray matter.

The gray matter in which the afferent fibers of the general somatic system end, the trigeminal nucleus, is made up of two parts which are, however, continuous with each other. The rostral segment is the chief sensory nucleus of the trigeminal nerve (*nucleus principalis trigemini*). It consists of a large mass of gray matter in the region of the entry of the nerve, lying in the lateral part of the medulla oblongata in close contact with the mass of descending sensory fibers (Figs. A4–A6), and extending rostrad a short distance along with the ascending branches of these fibers, so as to receive their terminations (Figs. A7, A8). At this level, the dorsal part of the principal trigeminal nucleus is also known as the nucleus of Lorente de Nó, which is caudally bordered by the nucleus of Åström. Bost may be considered to represent subdivisions of the principal trigeminal nucleus, which are readily recognized in the rat and mouse brain (Åström, 1953).

The trigeminal elements are covered superficially by other structures at this level, but a short distance posteriorly they emerge to the surface. Continuous with the chief nucleus is a column of gray matter situated immediately medial to the descending root and partly surrounded by it. This is the spinal trigeminal nucleus (*nucleus trigeminospinalis; nucleus tractus spinalis nervi trigemini*), which in the rat is as large as the chief nucleus (Figs. A4–A6). No precise line of demarcation can be drawn between them, though it is claimed that they differ in function. The spinal or descending trigeminal nucleus is often subdivided into a *pars interpolaris,* wedged between the nucleus of Åström and the spinal trigeminal root, caudally followed by the *pars magnocellularis.* In man, the chief nucleus appears as an enlargement at the anterior end of the column formed by the spinal nucleus. Many fibers run through the nuclei, the lower part of the spinal nucleus enclosing conspicuous bundles.

The secondary fiber tracts arising from the chief sensory and the spinal nuclei of the trigeminus cannot be followed in normal material, coursing through the reticular substance in a diffuse distribution. They comprise both short reflex connections, largely, if not entirely crossed, and ascending fibers to the midbrain and to the thalamus (trigeminal lemniscus), of which the majority are crossed. It appears that the fibers arising in the chief and spinal nuclei follow separate routes, and that the trigeminal lemniscus arises only from the chief nucleus. It comprises two portions, one in the dorsal part of the reticular formation, the other, which decussates slightly more posteriorly in the rat, running close to the dorsal portion of the medial lemniscus and to the raphe. Fuse (1919a,b) states that in the rat the ventral trigeminal lemniscus ends largely (he believes entirely) in the ventral reticular nucleus of the tegmentum, from which, apparently, new fibers continue the pathway forward with the medial lemniscus to the thalamus.

Dorsomedial to the chief sensory nucleus, and continuing rostrad, lies a conspicuous group of large unipolar cells mingled with several small bundles of stout myelinated fibers, the mesencephalic trigeminal nucleus (*nucleus mesencephalicus nervi trigemini*). Its cells give off similar fibers, which join those in the small bundles and run with them into the fifth nerve. Each fiber bifurcates, however, before passing out of the brain, one branch remaining within and ending either in the motor trigeminal nucleus or in a small group of cells dorsomedial to the sensory trigeminal nucleus. If the small bundles are now followed up the brain, they are found to be associated with a continually decreasing number of the unipolar cells, each of which gives rise to one of the fibers in the bundles, scattered along the lateral aspect of the central gray matter up to nearly the anterior end of the midbrain. These fibers form the mesencephalic root of the trigeminus (*radix mesencephalica nervi trigemini*), the unipolar cells making up its nucleus (Figs A9–A20). They are sensory in function, probably concerned with proprioceptive muscle sensibility, the unipolar cells being apparently equivalent to peripheral ganglion cells which have developed within the brain instead of outside it. However, some of the fibers of the mesencephalic root do arise from nerve cells in the semilunar ganglion of Gasser.

6. Special Somatic Afferent Column

The special somatic afferent division comprises the auditory and vestibular elements and also the visual neurons. It really includes the olfactory neurons in addition to these, though the olfactory functions combine exteroceptive with interoceptive components, and it is usual to consider the olfactory structures with the visceral afferent group. Some authors object to this usage, however. Only the auditory and vestibular systems, which occur in the hindbrain, will be considered in the present chapter.

The fibers which convey auditory impulses to the brain form the cochlear branch of the VIIIth nerve; this branch ends in two large nuclei situated superficially on the dorsolateral aspect of the medulla oblongata in its more anterior part. The dorsal cochlear nucleus (*nucleus cochlearis dorsalis,* or *tuberculum acusticum*) extends from the dorsal part of the lateral surface round on to the dorsal surface, where it runs medially as far as the edge of the ventricle. It is thus situated dorsal and caudal to the inferior cerebellar peduncle (Fig. 28). Its ventral end extends along the lateral aspect of the medulla oblongata, covered by the cerebellum, from which it is separated by the *recessus lateralis,* which forms a communicating channel between the fourth ventricle and the subarachnoid space. In the angle between the ventral extremity of this nucleus and the side of the medulla oblongata lies another mass of gray matter of a more rounded shape, the ventral cochlear nucleus (*nucleus cochlearis ventralis*) (Figs. A6–A8). This does not extend so far dorsad as the *tuberculum acusticum,* but reaches considerably farther ventrad. It is quite distinct from the latter nucleus in sections, owing to the arrangement of the nerve fibers, and the character of the cells in the two centers differs. Recently, it has been found, that in addition to these two centers, the acoustic nerve proper contains another nucleus, termed *nucleus nervi acustici* which receives collaterals from the cochlear fibers (Harrison *et al.,* 1962).

Some of the secondary fibers from the dorsal nucleus pass ventrally along the medial aspect of the ventral nucleus, where they join those arising in the latter. These fibers form a large tract, the trapezoid body (*corpus trapezoideum*) which passes ventrally and a little anteriorly over the surface of the medulla oblongata until it gets near the median line, where many of the fibers become deeper in position, breaking up into smaller fascicles and leaving only a thin layer superficial to the pyramids (Figs. A7, A8). They decussate and pass toward the lateral part of the other side of the medulla oblongata in a somewhat more diffuse distribution than in the earlier part of their course. Then the fibers change their direction, running rostrad in a compact bundle, the lateral lemniscus (*lemniscus lateralis,* lateral fillet) (Figs. A9, A10). In the human brain the trapezoid body is completely covered ventrally by the greatly enlarged pons.

Other secondary fibers arising in the dorsal cochlear nucleus pass medially in the floor of the fourth ventricle not in but underneath the *striae medullares,* dipping some distance below the floor of the fourth ventricle in the form of small scattered groups of arcuate fibers. About two-thirds of these decussate in the *decussatio cochlearis dorsalis* and, passing dorsal to the superior olive, join the lateral lemniscus.

The trapezoid body comes into relation with certain masses of gray matter in the transverse part of its course, of which the most conspicuous are the superior olivary nuclei (*nucleus olivaris superior*) (Fig. A7). These are more largely developed in the rat than in man—as are also the cochlear nuclei—and have the form in this and many other mammals of a lamina folded twice, so as to appear S-shaped in cross section. Immediately medial to each is a smaller lamina, the accessory superior olivary nucleus (*nucleus accessorius olivaris superior*), and some little distance medial to this again is a much less definitely circumscribed group of cells, the nucleus of the trapezoid body (*nucleus corporis trapezoidei*). Some of the trapezoid fibers end in these nuclei, either before or after crossing the median plane, and fibers arising from them pass into the lateral lemniscus. Many of the fibers arising in the superior olivary nucleus, however, run in a rather diffuse tract, the superior olivary peduncle, to the *nucleus abducens*. These fibers mediate impulses which elicit direct reflex movements of the eyes in response to auditory stimuli. In addition there are rich, but uncharted fiber connections between the superior olivary complex, the reticular formation and the nuclei of the eye muscle nerves.

The superior olivary complex of the rat, which has been analyzed by Fuse, contains more elements than are enumerated above. Besides the principal superior olivary nucleus, there are (1) the accessory superior olivary nucleus, consisting of a small, dorsoventrally elongated gray mass and a largely developed dorsomedial accessory group of cells; (2) the nucleus of the trapezoid body; (3) the *nucleus praeolivaris internus;* (4) the dorsal accessory nucleus of the superior olive; and (5) the *nucleus praeolivaris externus* (poorly developed in the rat).

The accessory superior olivary nucleus receives trapezoid fibers (mostly heterolateral) and gives off axons to the medial lemniscus and to the homolateral nucleus of the trapezoid body. It also has connections with its own mediodorsal accessory cell group, and with the internal praeolivary nucleus of the same side. The mediodorsal cell group is larger than the rest of the nucleus and is separated from the nucleus of the trapezoid body by thick bundles of trapezoid fibers. Its connections are similar to those of the other part of the nucleus.

The nucleus of the trapezoid body lies medioventral to the last-mentioned group and is differentiated from the more ventrolaterally placed internal preolivary nucleus by its larger cells. It is traversed by many longitudinal fiber bundles. There are extensive fiber connections with the lateral parts of the medial lemniscus and the pyramidal tract as well as with the accessory superior olivary nucleus, but none with the lateral lemniscus of the same side. There are considerable heterolateral connections also.

The *nucleus praeolivaris internus* receives fibers from the *corpus trapezoides*, mostly of heterolateral origin. The lateral part of the nucleus sends most of its axons across the raphe, while the majority of those from the medial part enter the homolateral medial lemniscus and pyramidal tract.

The trapezoid fibers ending in the principal superior olivary nucleus are partly hetero- but chiefly homolateral in origin, and only about one-quarter to one-third of the fibers coming directly from the cochlear nuclei decussate. These apparently originate chiefly in the ventral cochlear nucleus. The crossed fibers of the trapezoid body originating in the nucleus of the trapezoid body, superior accessory olivary nucleus, internal preolivary nucleus, ventral cochlear nucleus, dorsal cochlear nucleus, and chief superior olivary nucleus are of decreasing numerical importance in the order named, and are accompanied by a few fibers from the spinal trigeminal nucleus and from the reticular formation. Most of these fibers are distributed more caudally after decussating, while the majority of those from the cochlear nucleus end in the superior olivary complex.

The functional significance of the superior olivary complex and its connections is poorly understood. It can be assumed that it represents a relay center for auditory signals to elicit motor responses. In addition, there is some evidence that it serves as a feedback mechanism controlling the sensitivity threshold of the organ of Corti by way of olivo-efferent fibers to the cochlea.

The lateral lemniscus, primarily conducting auditory impulses, passes directly forward into the midbrain, where many of its fibers may be followed into the posterior colliculus. Others pass on with the fibers arising in that region to the medial geniculate body. In the lower part of its course, the fibers of the lateral lemniscus enclose a group of cells (Fig. A9), the ventral nucleus of the lateral lemniscus (*nucleus ventralis lemnisci lateralis*), in connection with which a number of them end. The lemniscus then follows a somewhat rostrodorsal course and breaks up into small fiber bundles as it approaches the midbrain. Between the bundles is a large amount of gray matter, constituting the dorsal nucleus of the lateral lemniscus (*nucleus dorsalis lemnisci lateralis*). At this point the lemniscal fibers are not very easily distinguished from those of the ventral spinocerebellar tract, which have a similar arrangement and general direction, and which lie immediately lateral and dorsal to the lemniscus.

The vestibular nerve, which conveys proprioceptive impulses, chiefly of an equilibratory nature, ends in relation with an extensive group of nuclei placed dorsolaterally. These consist of a more or less continuous column of gray matter which is divisible into four parts (Figs. A5–A7). At the level of entry of the root is a large-celled mass in a lateral position close to the ventricle, the lateral vestibular nucleus (*nucleus vestibularis lateralis*; nucleus of Deiters). Extending posteriorly from this, just as the spinal trigeminal nucleus extends posteriorly from the chief sensory nucleus, is the descending or spinal vestibular nucleus (*nucleus vestibularis inferior*), which is accompanied by bundles of the root fibers, the descending vestibular root. This root can be traced down as far as the beginning of the spinal cord, where it ends between the cuneate nucleus and the *substantia gelatinosa.*

There are also ascending branches of the root fibers forming an ascending root, each fiber bifurcating on entering the brain. Many of these ascending branches end in an anterior vestibular nucleus or nucleus of Bechterew (*nucleus vestibularis superior*), which extends from the nucleus of Deiters anterodorsally, projecting into the cerebellar peduncles.

Medial to the nucleus of Deiters and the descending nucleus, and immediately under the floor of the fourth ventricle, lies a small-celled nucleus of roughly triangular form in cross section, the chief or dorsal vestibular nucleus (*nucleus vestibularis medialis*). This large nucleus extends all the way from the level of the entrance of the trigeminal nerve root to the level of the anterior part of the hypoglossal nucleus.

Some of the ascending vestibular fibers do not end in any of these nuclei, but run directly into the cerebellum, where they end in the roof nuclei and in certain parts of the cortex. Secondary fibers from the nuclei of Deiters and Bechterew join the direct fibers to the cerebellum and end with them in that structure.

Droogleever-Fortuyn (1918) also saw vestibular fibers entering the ventral cochlear nucleus in the rat.

Other fibers arising from the vestibular nuclei pass medially to enter the medial longitudinal tract on either the same or the opposite side. This bundle lies in the angle between the raphe and the gray matter of the ventricular floor. The vestibular impulses are conveyed to various motor centers, particularly the eye-muscle nuclei, the ascending tract of Deiters (*tractus Deiters ascendens*) forming a definite group of fibers in the lateral part of the medial longitudinal bundle in the midbrain.

Yet other fibers from Deiters' nucleus form a diffuse tract in the reticular formation, which runs down to the spinal cord, conveying impulses to the spinal motor neurons. This is the vestibulospinal tract (*tractus vestibulospinalis*; descending tract of Deiters) (Fig. 22). Its fibers pass obliquely between the more lateral fascicles of the ascending limb of the facial root, and appear to be partly of heterolateral origin. Fibers arising from the dorsal funicular gray of the spinal cord and concerned with proprioceptive impulses from muscles, joints, and tendons ascend in the ventral funiculus and terminate in the inferior vestibular nucleus. This spinovestibular tract is diffusely intermingled with the fibers of the vestibulospinal tract (Fig. 22).

The fibers arising in the chief vestibular nucleus cross to the opposite side where they course through the reticular formation to make various reflex connections. Fuse (1920) states that many of these fibers are uncrossed in the rat.

The complexity of the cochlear and vestibular systems is probably considerably greater than is indicated by the foregoing account, as has been shown by Winkler and Potter (1911) to be the case in the rabbit.

References

ARIËNS KAPPERS, C. U., G. C. HUBER & ELIZABETH C. CROSBY. The Comparative Anatomy of the Nervous System of Vertebrates, Including Man. 2 Volumes. New York: Macmillan, 1936.

ÅSTRÖM, K. E. On the central course of afferent fibers in the trigeminal, facial, glossopharyngeal, and vagal nerves and their nuclei in the mouse. *Acta Physiol. Scand.* 29 *Suppl.* **106**: 209-330, 1953.

BARNARD, J. W. The hypoglossal complex of vertebrates. *J. Comp. Neurol.* **72**, 489-524, 1940.

BENJAMIN, R. M. & K. AKERT. Cortical and thalamic areas in taste discrimination in the albino rat. *J. Comp. Neurol.* **111**: 231-259, 1959.

BOUGHTON, T. H. The increase in the number and size of the medullated fibers in the oculomotor nerve of the white rat and of the cat at different ages. *J. Comp. Neurol.* **16**: 153-165, 1906.

CAJAL, S. RAMÓN Y. Histologie du système nerveux de l'homme et des vertébrés. Paris: Maloine, 1909-1911. (Reprinted by C.S.I.S., Madrid, 1952.)

CLARKE, W. B. & D. BOWSHER. Terminal distribution of primary afferent trigeminal fibers in the rat. *Exptl. Neurol.* **6**: 372-383, 1962.

CROSBY, ELIZABETH C., T. HUMPHREY & E. W. LAUER. Correlative Anatomy of the Nervous System. New York: Macmillan, 1962.

DROOGLEEVER-FORTUYN, A. B. Some remarks about the nervus octavus in three tame rats with inflammation of the internal ear. *Psych. en Neurol. Bladen* (Feestbundel Winkler), 211-257, 1918.

FUSE, G. Experimentelle Beiträge zur Anatomie des Corpus trapezoides—Pararapheale Durchschneidung des letzteren (Guddensche Methode) an einem Meerschweinchen und rapheale Durchschneidung desselben an einer Ratte (Guddensche Methode). *Arb. Anat. Inst. K. Japanischen Univ. Sendai* **2**: 191-250, 1919a.

FUSE, G. Innerer Aufbau der zentralen akustischen Bahnen. *Arb. Anat. Inst. K. Japanischen Univ. Sendai* **2**: 275-384, 1919b.

FUSE, G. Beiträge zur mikroskopischen Anatomie des Truncus cerebri: einiges vergleichendanatomisches über das bislang unbekannte resp. nicht genügend berücksichtigte Grau in der Zone zwischen der oberen Olive und der spinalen Quintuswurzel, u. s. w. *Arb. Anat. Inst. K. Japanischen Univ. Sendai* **4**: 1-107, 1920.

HARRISON, J. M., W. B. WARR & R. E. IRVING. Second order neurons in the acoustic nerve of rat. *Science* **138**: 893-895, 1962.

HOGG, I. D. The motor nuclei of the cranial nerves of Mus norvegicus albinus at birth. *J. Comp. Neurol.* **44**: 449-495, 1928.

KRIEG, W. J. S. Subdivisions of the nuclei of spinal trigeminal tract in rat. *Anat. Rec.* **106**: 279, 1950.

ONDINA, D. M., W. S. YAMAMOTO & W. S. MASLAND. Respiratory centres in the albino rat. *Amer. J. Physiol.* **198**: 389-392, 1960.

PAPEZ, J. W. Comparative Neurology. 518 pp. New York: Crowell, 1929. (Reprinted by Hafner, New York, 1961.)

RILEY, H. A. An Atlas of the Basal Ganglia, Brain Stem and Spinal Cord. New York: Hafner, 1960.

SHUTE, C. C. & P. R. LEWIS. The salivatory centre in the rat. *J. Anat. (London)* **94**: 59-73, 1960.

TORVIK, A. Afferent connections to the sensory trigeminal nuclei, the nucleus of the solitary tract and adjacent structures. An experimental study in the rat. *J. Comp. Neurol.* **106**: 51-141, 1956.

WILSON, E. E., W. F. WINDLE & J. E. FITZGERALD. Development of the tractus solitarius *J. Comp. Neurol.* **74**: 287-207, 1941.

WINCKLER, G. Les nerfs de l'orbite et le ganglion ophthalmique dans la série des mammifères et chez l'homme. *Arch. Anat. Histol. Embryol. (Strasbourg)* **14**: 303-386, 1931–1932.

WINKLER, C. & A. POTTER. An Anatomical Guide to Experimental Researches on the Rabbit's Brain. Amsterdam: W. Versluys, 1911.

CHAPTER V

Rhombencephalon (Hindbrain)

Embryologically the brain develops from the rostral end of the neural tube. This part grows more rapidly than the remainder of the tube and develops three enlargements, the primitive brain vesicles. These are characteristic of any vertebrate embryo and are named from rostral to caudal, *prosencephalon* (forebrain), *mesencephalon* (midbrain), and *rhombencephalon* (hindbrain). The latter becomes subdivided into a caudal part, the *myelencephalon* (medulla oblongata) and a rostral part, the *metencephalon* which gives rise to the ventrally located *pons* and the dorsally positioned *cerebellum.* Thus the metencephalon occupies in the *neuraxis* a position between the medulla oblongata and the mesencephalon on its rostral boundary.

Figure 24 is particularly helpful for an understanding of the ontogenesis of the hindbrain, although it applies to mid- and forebrain as well. The floor plate provides the "anlage" or precursor for decussations and commissures, i.e., its rhombencephalic derivative is the *raphe.* From the basal and alar plates develop all other structures of the brain, in particular those containing gray matter which is populated by neuronal perikarya. Finally, the roof plate develops into the lining of the chorioid plexuses and their supporting structures, the *telae chorioideae.* In the rhombencephalon, the dorsal edges of the alar plates become greatly enlarged and fused across the midline, and it is from this structure that the cerebellum develops. It is now easy to understand that cerebellum and pons together form the extremely thickened walls which completely surround the anterior part of the fourth ventricle (Fig. A7), the original lumen of the neural tube. This is quite in contrast to the situation in the medulla oblongata, where the roof plate derivative in the form of the tela chorioidea constitutes the dorsal wall of the *neuraxis* (Figs. A5, A6). The part of the cerebellum which is seen on these cross sections is only a caudal projection, which is completely separated from the medulla oblongata by extraneuraxial, that is subarachnoid, space.

A. MYELENCEPHALON (MEDULLA OBLONGATA)

At the rostral end of the spinal cord is a cone-shaped enlargement, the *medulla oblongata,* which appears as a direct continuation of the cord (Figs.

7–9). On account of its shape, the medulla oblongata is sometimes referred to as the bulb. It is not sharply demarcated from the spinal cord, but, by definition, is said to begin just rostral to the highest rootlet of the first cervical nerve, at about the level of the *foramen magnum.* Rostrally, the medulla oblongata is bordered by the pons, ventrally it rests upon the basilar part of the occipital bone (Fig. 3), dorsally it is partially covered by the cerebellum and caudad to that structure is in close approximation to the dorsal rim of the foramen magnum. At this level the medulla oblongata bends ventrally to continue as the spinal cord.

In the rat, little of the structures of the medulla oblongata can be discerned with the naked eye. It is roughly quadrilateral in shape, being wider rostrally, and is slightly flattened in a dorsoventral plane. It extends over a distance of about 3 mm between the cord and the pons, and its average width is about the same. Its ventral surface (Fig. 8) is convex from side to side with a median fissure (*fissura mediana ventralis*) which continues caudad as the ventral spinal fissure and rostrad as the median sulcus of the pons which accommodates the basilar artery. The rostral part of the ventral surface of the medulla oblongata is formed by a distinct transverse band, the *corpus trapezoideum,* in which afferent fibers from the cochlear nuclei to the medial geniculate bodies, subserving auditory function (see page 74) decussate. Caudal to this band, on each side of the median fissure, is an elongated eminence, the pyramid, formed by the corticospinal tract. Caudad, these eminences become flatter owing to the motor decussation (*decussatio pyramidum*) where the corticospinal tracts cross over. The caudal continuation of this motor tract into the spinal cord was followed in the description of the latter. In Fig. A3, it is seen how these fibers bend sharply dorsad to occupy a position in the dorsal white columns. The dorsal surface of the medulla oblongata (Fig. 9) forms the greater part of the floor of the fourth ventricle, which is partly concealed by the cerebellum. The medulla oblongata is here connected with the cerebellum by the inferior cerebellar peduncle (*pedunculus cerebellaris inferior; corpus restiforme*) (Fig. 9).

The lateral walls of the fourth ventricle converge caudad to form the *calamus scriptorius* (meaning a writing pen). The bounding ridges of this structure harbor a highly specialized tissue covered by atypical ependyma and known as *area postrema.* This organelle contains capillaries which are highly permeable for many compounds which cannot penetrate the walls of other vessels in the central nervous system, except those of the hypothalamus. It is assumed that the *area postrema* represents a chemoreceptive mechanism, involved in vomiting, among other functions.

The medulla oblongata contains a number of cranial nerve nuclei (Fig. 24) with their fiber tracts, and ascending and descending neuronal systems which connect the spinal cord with other parts of the central nervous system. In this respect, the medulla oblongata is similar to the spinal cord and also to pons and midbrain. In order to avoid unnecessary repetition, these connecting systems are mostly discussed in the present chapter. The respective levels at which the transverse sections (Figs. A3–A7) were cut are depicted in Fig. A2. A glance at the caudal levels reveals a topographical pattern which is similar to that of the spinal cord (Fig. A3). Here, the peripheral rim of the medulla is occupied by long fiber systems, whereas the inner core contains various nuclear masses together with their fiber systems. As one proceeds rostrad, this general pattern changes. With the appearance of the fourth ventricle some cranial nerve nuclei assume a superficial position. It will be noted, however, that these nuclei have the same topographical relationship to the ventricle as have the ventral horn cell groups of the spinal cord to the central canal. The ontogenetic principle of this arrangement has been discussed earlier together with the cranial nerve nuclei. Many systems of the long connecting fibers assume now a position near the sagittal plane or midline. The same general pattern prevails throughout the pons, but, as will be seen later, in the midbrain these long fiber tracts diverge to assume a lateral position. Throughout medulla, pons, and midbrain almost the entire sagittal plane is occupied by crossing fibers (Figs. A3–A12). They are diffusely arranged, rather than forming well-defined decussational or commissural tracts. This peculiar fiber architecture gives the midline of the brainstem a very distinctive appearance in myelin-stained sections, well characterized by the term *raphe* which in a literal translation means "seam."

Interconnecting Fiber Systems of Brainstem and Correlation Centers of Medulla Oblongata

The interconnecting fiber systems are of two types, afferent and efferent. The afferent systems conduct sensory impulses from the periphery to cerebrum and cerebellum. In a dorsomedial location, we find the *fasciculus gracilis* as it ascends from the spinal cord, and lateral to it the *fasciculus cuneatus.* Both together form part of the dorsal columns of the spinal cord and both belong to the same functional and anatomical system. This system is concerned with proprioception, i.e., it conveys the impulses arising in muscles, tendons, and joints, and also with highly specific tactile, i.e., exteroceptive impulses, which originate in Meissner's corpuscles in the skin. The perikarya of these neurons all lie in the dorsal root ganglia of the spinal nerves and their axons terminate in the *nucleus gracilis* and *cuneatus* (Figs. A3–A5), respectively. Passing up the spinal cord, the dorsal gray columns are seen to spread apart somewhat, and a little below the decussation of the pyramids, a small mass of gray matter appears projecting dorsally from the central gray among the fibers of the fasciculus cuneatus. This is the beginning of the *nucleus cuneatus.* A little more cranial than the pyramidal decussation, a broad median eminence also appears on the dorsal surface of the central gray matter, the *nucleus gracilis.* Still farther rostrad, another small part of the nucleus gracilis is seen on each side among the fibers of its fasciculus, and this becomes continuous with the projection from the central gray matter. These nuclei (*nucleus gracilis* and *cuneatus*) divide into a small median part and much more prominent lateral portions (Figs. A4, A5). The cuneate and gracile nuclei increase rapidly in size, and as the fibers of the fasciculi end within them, the latter are correspondingly reduced and finally disappear. The *fasciculus gracilis* conducts the fibers projecting from thoracic, lumbar, and sacral dermatomes, the *fasciculus cuneatus,* those of the upper thoracic and all cervical ganglia. Ventrolateral to the cuneate fascicle is the spinal tract of the trigeminal nerve, which supplies proprioceptive and special tactile sensibility to the face. The trigeminal nucleus thus corresponds to the gracile and cuneate nuclei. Secondary fibers, originating in the cells of these three nuclei, emerge ventrally in a medially directed curve as internal arcuate fibers (*fibrae arcuatae internae*), cross the midline rostral to the motor decussation in the *decussatio lemniscorum* (Fig. A4) and turn caudad to ascend through brainstem to the thalamus as the medial lemniscus or medial fillet (*lemniscus medialis*). In its dorsal segments, the medial lemniscus probably contains fibers which have ascended the spinal cord in the so-called spinothalamic tract (*tractus spinothalamicus*; spinal lemniscus or fillet), an exteroceptive system concerned with the mediation of fine tactile, painful, and thermal stimuli. The component fibers of this tract originate from the nerve cells of the dorsal column of the spinal cord. The precise position of this tract in the rat's central nervous system is not known. In primates, the spinothalamic system is rather conspicuous and forms two tracts, the lateral and the ventral spinothalamic tract of which the former is concerned with the conduction of painful and thermal stimuli. Its topographical position is very well traced, and it is this tract which is sometimes purposely destroyed in man in order to alleviate intractable pain.

In summary, the medial lemniscus, which throughout the brainstem maintains a midline position dorsal to the corticospinal tracts, consists of four components, the gracilo- and the cuneothalamic, and the trigeminal and the spinal lemnisci. All these fibers terminate in the ventral nucleus of the thalamus (Figs. A10–A20, Chapter VII). It should be noted that the exteroceptive and proprioceptive fibers which terminate in the gracile, cuneate, and trigeminal nuclei originate from perikarya located in the spinal and Gasserian ganglia, respectively, whereas the fibers of the spinothalamic system originate in the nerve cells of the dorsal horn of the spinal cord and may synapse once or several times before they join the medial lemniscus.

A second afferent system concerned with the mediation of proprioceptive and tactile impulses is represented by the dorsal and ventral spinocerebellar tracts (*tractus spinocerebellaris dorsalis et ventralis*). The dorsal spinocerebellar tract originates in the cells of the dorsal nucleus of Clarke in the spinal cord and mediates impulses from the sacral, lumbar, thoracic, and lower cervical segments. It forms a compact bundle at the level of the cuneate nucleus which is joined by olivocerebellar and cerebello-olivary fibers to form the inferior cerebellar peduncle (Figs. A6–A8). The ventral spinocerebellar tract originates from nerve cells of the dorsal gray matter of the spinal cord and receives impulses from the sacral, lumbar, and thoracic segments. Throughout its course in the spinal cord and in the caudal medulla oblongata, it also has a superficial position. At the level of the trapezoid body, its fibers are seen to dip into the medulla oblongata (Fig. A8) in a dorsal direction on their way to the superior cerebellar peduncle.

A number of afferent ascending systems are known from physiologic evidence or from anatomical studies in primates. They have not been studied in the murine central nervous system and are therefore only mentioned in passing. The spinotectal tract originates from the dorsal funicular gray and possibly the *substantia gelatinosa* of the upper cervical cord levels. It probably mediates cutaneous pain signals. Its fibers accumulate in the lateral white column and gain a dorsal position in the medial lemniscus to terminate in the anterior colliculus of the midbrain. Also from the cervical levels of the spinal cord originates the spino-olivary tract. Its axons cross in the anterior commissure and ascend in the cord immediately ventral to the ventral spinocerebellar tract and terminate in the caudal end of the inferior olivary body. The spinovestibular tract fibers originate from the cervical segments of the dorsal funicular gray. They are, for the most part, intermingled with the fibers of the vestibulospinal tracts, the course of which has already been described in Chapter IV. The secondary ascending visceral system is concerned with general visceral afferent impulses. It is a multisynaptic pathway, the termination of which is obscure, but it has been suggested that some fibers have terminal arborizations in the gray matter associated with the solitary tract.

The most conspicuous efferent fiber path, which runs through pons and medulla oblongata is the pyramidal tract (*tractus corticospinalis*) occupying a ventral position on both sides of the midline. As it enters the pons from the midbrain, numerous fibers, the so-called corticopontine fibers, split off to end in the pontine nuclei, and a similar pattern is repeated in the medulla oblongata, where the corticobulbar fibers pass to the efferent nuclei on the floor of the fourth ventricle. The remainder of the fibers, the corticospinal tracts, have already been traced to the caudal end of the medulla oblongata where they decussate and turn dorsad to assume a dorsolateral position in the spinal cord.

Related functionally to the pyramidal tract is the rubrospinal tract (*tractus rubrospinalis*). It originates, as the term implies, in the *nucleus ruber* of the midbrain and conveys impulses which influence the tone of the body muscles. As this bundle runs through the midbrain it is not very distinct from its surroundings, but upon entering the pons, it forms a solid tract which lies medial and slightly lateral to the lateral lemniscus. Upon reaching the level of the superior olivary body, which forms its medial border, it can be seen wedged between the latter and the penetrating root of the VIIth nerve (Figs. A8, A9). Here it is in close relationship to the ventral spinocerebellar tract.

Dorsal to the medial lemniscus, also in a paramedian position, is another efferent tract, the tectospinal tract (*tractus tectospinalis*) (Figs. A5, A6, A10-A12).

The fibers of this tract originate in the tectum, i.e., the anterior and posterior colliculi, and are concerned with turning the head and moving the upper extremity in response to various kinds of sensory stimuli, in particular visual and acoustic signals. This tract is very conspicuous in the cat; in the rat, it is somewhat diffuse but contains a considerable number of fibers.

In a position dorsal to the latter tract and ventral to the column of cranial nerve motor nuclei is the *fasciculus longitudinalis medialis,* the medial longitudinal bundle (Figs. A6–A8). This tract is the most important coordinating system of the brainstem and contains both afferent and efferent fibers concerned with coordinated movements. Thus, it is made up of ascending and descending fibers. Its bed nucleus is the *nucleus interstitialis* of Cajal (Fig. A14). Fibers originating in the various vestibular nuclei and terminating at the cranial nerve nuclei III, IV, and VI provide for a coordination of eye movements and equilibrium. Some vestibular fibers also connect with the interstitial nucleus of the longitudinal bundle, others with the nucleus of posterior commissure (Figs. A15, A16). The latter consists of two parts in the rat brain, the *nucleus proprius commissurae posterioris* (Fig. A17) and the nucleus of Darkschevitch (Fig. A14). These fibers terminate either ipsilaterally or, after crossing in the posterior commissure, in the contralateral nuclei. Another component provides interconnections between the oculomotor and facial motor nuclei, which coordinate opening and closing of the eyes. Also, there are interconnections between the motor nuclei of the Vth and VIIth cranial nerves, the contralateral *nucleus ambiguus* and the motor nucleus XII, which are essential for phonation, mastication, and glutition. The nucleus of the posterior commissure and the interstitial nucleus of Cajal receive impulses from the *globus pallidus,* and may be from corticomotor areas, in addition to fibers from contralateral portions of the cerebellum through the superior cerebellar peduncle. All these fibers are concerned with extrapyramidal motor functions.

The central tegmental bundle (*tractus tegmentalis centralis*) (Figs. A10, A11) is a similarly complex fiber system as the preceding one. In addition to fibers from the red nucleus and the periaqueductal gray, it receives impulses from the *zona incerta* and the basal ganglia; it terminates massively in the inferior olivary complex and to a much lesser extent in the nucleus ambiguus and the upper spinal cord. The fibers of this tract are also concerned with extrapyramidal motor mechanisms. The dorsal longitudinal fasciculus (*fasciculus longitudinalis dorsalis;* bundle of Schütz), or the periventricular fiber system, sends many mostly thin myelinated fibers through pons and medulla oblongata. It gives off fibers to various visceral efferent nuclei. Its ascending components originate from the dorsal visceral gray and are largely concerned with visceral afference.

Between the raphe and the spinal root of the trigeminal nerve is a region of more or less well-defined nuclear masses, connected by a rich feltwork of nerve fibers. This reticular formation (*substantia reticularis*) (Figs. A3–A6, A7) is a most important interconnecting region. It receives impulses from all afferent systems by collaterals and gives rise to ascending (*reticulothalamic*) and descending (*reticulospinal*) pathways. It stretches, always in a paramedian position, from the upper cervical spinal cord to the thalamus. In a zone extending dorsoventrally along each side of the raphe, the white fibers predominate, and hence this area is called the *substantia reticularis alba,* while the remainder of the formation, in which there is a larger proportion of gray matter, is the *substantia reticularis grisea.* The functions of the reticular formation have been elucidated only recently and are discussed in Chapter VIII.

Neuroanatomical studies on secondary degeneration have shown that the reticular formation harbors a number of interconnecting tracts which are apparently related to the latter structure via axon collaterals, though the main fibers of these tracts reach down into the spinal cord. The rubrospinal tract has already been mentioned. It lies medial to the lateral lemniscus and then on its way through the medulla finally reaches a superficial position in the form of a compact fiber bundle. Likewise, the fibers of the central tegmental tract traverse the reticular formation on their way to the inferior olivary complex. Bundles of the spinothalamic, the spinotectal, the vestibulospinal, and the spino-vestibular tracts are found in the territory occupied by the reticular formation.

The inferior olivary complex represents an important correlation center in the medulla oblongata relaying impulses from and to the periaqueductal gray, the zona incerta and the basal ganglia on the one hand, and the cerebellum and the spinal cord on the other, probably instrumental in motor control. In primates, the inferior olivary complex is a very conspicuous structure, but it is not nearly as well developed in the rodent. Nevertheless, this accumulation of nerve cell nuclei is readily discerned by its characteristic appearance in histological sections (Figs. A4, A5). The mass is divisible into three distinct nuclei, the medial olive (*nucleus olivaris accessorius medialis*), the dorsal olive (*nucleus olivaris accessorius dorsalis*), and the ventrolateral or principal olive (*nucleus olivaris inferior; oliva inferior*), which are continuous with each other at certain points. Each of these is an elongated lamella of rather irregular outline, so that its exact form and position vary in sections at different levels. The medial nucleus extends considerably farther posteriorly than do the other two, which are nearly coextensive. The principal nucleus differs from the others in being folded lengthwise so as to form a sort of pocket with an opening, the hilus, directed medially. Thus a section through the middle part of the nucleus is U-shaped, but as the pocket is somewhat narrowed round the opening, this form does not appear in sections near either end of the nucleus. In higher mammals, including man, the accessory nuclei are similar to those of the rat, but the principal nucleus is very greatly enlarged and folded, though still retaining the pocketlike form. Streaming through the hilus and around and through the nuclei are many fibers which form reciprocal connections with the cerebellum. They form part of the internal arcuate system and reach the cerebellum by way of the inferior cerebellar peduncle. Afferent systems, in the form of the central tegmental tract and the spino-olivary bundle have been mentioned above.

B. METENCEPHALON

According to ontogenetic principles of classification, the metencephalon consisting of cerebellum and pons is considered a subdivision of the rhombencephalon, having the same order as the medulla oblongata. The close relationship of the two derivatives of the metencephalon, pons and cerebellum, will become abundantly clear when their intrinsic neuronal systems are discussed. It is desirable that this useful classification is retained, although this practice has been abandoned in most modern texts.

1. Pons

Pons literally means, and is, a "bridge" which as part of the hindbrain has been developed for communication between the cerebellum and cerebrum. Since the latter two structures are relatively small in the rat, the pons is not nearly so well developed in this animal as it is in primates. In Fig. 8 the pons appears as a transverse band rostral to and parallel with the trapezoid body. It is marked off from the cerebral peduncles rostrally and from the medulla oblongata caudally by shallow anterior and posterior transverse grooves. Its lateral limits coincide with the superficial points of exit of roots of the trigeminal nerves where the pons disappears from view as it turns dorsad at each side to pass into the cerebellum as the middle cerebellar peduncle (*pedunculus cerebellaris medius; brachium pontis*). In the ventral midline, there is a longitudinal fissure (*sulcus basilaris*) which accommodates the basilar artery (Fig. 14). On either side of this is a slight longitudinal swelling which marks the position of the pyramidal tracts of the motor system covered by the superficial transverse fibers of the pons. The dorsal surface is hidden by the cerebellum, and when the latter is removed (Fig. 9) the dorsal surface of the pons is seen to form the anterior part of the floor of the fourth ventricle, the rhomboid fossa, discussed on page 27 in connection with the ventricular system.

Transverse sections of the pons are illustrated in Figs. A8 and A9, but rostroventral parts of the pons are still visible in Figs. A10 and A11, which represent the metencephalic-mesencephalic junction. In this connection, reference should be made to Figs. 6 and A1, which indicate the obliquity of the plane of cutting.

The transverse sections demonstrate that the pons is composed of two parts differing in structure. The ventral or basilar part (*basis pontis*) harbors predominantly fiber tracts. Those forming the ventral surface traverse from side to side and are composed of pontocerebellar fibers. They are spread out into bundles allowing the massive collections of descending fibers to pass between, namely, the corticobulbar, corticopontine, and pyramidal tracts. The gray matter in this area is scattered and broken up into small masses to form the *nuclei pontis*. The pontocerebellar fibers after having crossed over in the midline of the pons gather into a compact mass forming the middle cerebellar peduncle (*brachium pontis*), which turns dorsally and caudally into the cerebellum.

The dorsal, or tegmental, part (*tegmentum pontis*) is covered by the ependyma of the fourth ventricle, and is in essence a contiguous extension of the dorsal parts of the medulla oblongata. In turn it continues rostrally as the tegmentum of the midbrain (Chapter VI; Figs. A11–A13). Cranial nerve nuclei and their connecting fiber systems are located in the *tegmentum pontis*. The raphe of the medulla oblongata extends into the pons, dividing it into two bilaterally symmetrical halves, although if comparison is made among Figs. A7–A9, it will be noted that the raphe does not extend as far dorsad in the pons.

The longitudinal fiber tracts of the pons have already been dealt with in the description of the medulla oblongata. Likewise, the cranial nerve nuclei, their roots and secondary fiber systems have been described previously. There remain to be discussed a number of anatomical facts which were not considered in the preceding chapters because they are inherent to the pons only.

As the descending fibers from the forebrain, which have accumulated in the *pes pedunculi*, enter the pons, they are split up into smaller bundles. The bundles forming the corticospinal or pyramidal tracts remain in a central position and continue through the pons. Other bundles running in the same direction split off successively to terminate in the pons and are called corticopontine tracts. They synapse with the nerve cells of the pontine nuclei. Some of the corticopontine fibers descend to the medulla oblongata, where they terminate in the arcuate nuclei. These are located in the form of a cap over the ventromedial aspects of the pyramids but are considered to be functionally and developmentally related to the pontine nuclei. Other fibers of the pyramidal tract, usually referred to as the corticobulbar component, connect with the various efferent cranial nerve nuclei. This terminology is somewhat inconsistent, as the term "bulbar" is here used as pertaining to the brainstem, including midbrain, pons and medulla oblongata, rather than being restricted to the latter alone. Some of these pyramidal fibers run straight dorsad to their respective cranial nerve nuclei, whereas others split off dorsad from the pyramidal tract parallel to the latter, and then run caudad in separate bundles in the area of the medial lemniscus as aberrant pyramidal tracts, before they swing again dorsad to connect with their respective efferent nuclei.

The corticopontocerebellar system represents the most important correlation mechanism for the forebrain with the cerebellum. The corticopontine fibers originate in various parts of the cerebral neocortex and synapse with the nerve cells of the pontine nuclei. The axons of the latter fibers cross the midline and then collect to make up the massive brachium pontis (*pedunculus cerebellaris medius*). There is evidence that the nerve cells of the pontine nuclei receive also impulses from collaterals of the pyramidal tract fibers. The axons from the arcuate nuclei to the cerebellum take an entirely different course. These so-called arcuatocerebellar fibers run dorsad, close to the midline of the upper medulla oblongata, and as they reach the floor of the ventricle they bend laterad along the floor to enter the cerebellum through the inferior cerebellar peduncle. In crossing the floor of the fourth ventricle these fibers form prominent white stripes known as *striae medullares,* often erroneously called "striae medullares acousticae." This tract is supplemented by fibers arising from the pontine nuclei which pass over the ventrolateral surface of the medulla as external arcuate fibers to join the arcuatocerebellar fascicles and proceed toward the midline as part of the striae medullares; they decussate and continue, still on the floor of the fourth ventricle, to the contralateral inferior cerebellar peduncle.

As we proceed rostrad in the pons we note a gradual transition in the shape of the medial lemniscus (Fig. A8), which in a dorsoventral direction becomes flattened. At this level, a well-defined tract in the dorsal aspect of the pons makes its first appearance, the *brachium conjunctivum* (*pedunculus cerebellaris superior*). This tract is approached from ventrad by the fascicles of the ventral spinocerebellar tract which join the superior cerebellar peduncle on their way to the cerebellum. The superior peduncle is separated by transverse, probably vestibuloreticular fibers, from the motor and sensory trigeminal nuclei (Fig. A8). Between this nuclear group and the raphe extends the pontine part of the reticular formation, which contains a number of fiber tracts in a diffuse distribution.

Medial to the superior cerebellar peduncle in Fig. A8 is a lightly stained area containing very few myelinated fibers. This general area constitutes part of the *substantia grisea periventricularis* and harbors a number of nuclei and tracts concerned with visceral functions. The most conspicuous nucleus is known as *locus coeruleus,* the "blue spot" so named on account of its bluish-gray appearance upon inspection of the floor of the fourth ventricle in human brains. This bluish color is due to pigment granules within the nerve cells considered to be melanin, which is also present in the cells of the *substantia nigra.* It is conspicuous only in primates, but allegedly present in subprimate species. The present authors, however, have never seen pigment in the *locus coeruleus* nor in the *substantia nigra* of laboratory rats, which may in part be due to the fact that most laboratory rats are albinos. On account of its large, densely packed perikarya, the *locus coeruleus* forms a very conspicuous nucleus in the rat. Medial to this center is the dorsal tegmental nucleus, and both centers together are believed to be concerned with the regulation of respiration. Dorsal to these nuclei at the lateral angle of the fourth ventricle is located the dorsal longitudinal fascicle of Schütz (*fasciculus longitudinalis dorsalis*), which constitutes a correlation tract between the hypothalamus and the various nuclei and nerve cells in the periaqueductal and periventricular gray concerned with the control of visceral mechanisms.

2. Cerebellum

Before the anatomy of the cerebellum is discussed, a few remarks about the functional significance of this part of the central nervous system are offered which, it is hoped, will facilitate the understanding of some anatomical features. In the late 19th century, a surge of studies on the cerebellum erupted which has continued ever since and produced a voluminous amount of literature.

Obviously, only a few authors who have substantially contributed to our knowledge of the cerebellum can be mentioned here, and in this context it should be pointed out that only a combined physiologic, morphologic, and clinical approach provided insight into the highly complex functions of the cerebellum. In regard to the scientific works which contributed much to the elucidation of the mechanisms vested in the cerebellum, we mention those of Elliot Smith (1902), Bradley (1903 and 1904), Bolk (1906), Ingvar (1918 and 1928), Riley (1929), Holmes (1922, 1927, and 1939), Larsell (since 1923), Fulton and Dow (1937), and Snider (since 1940). All these references can be found in Dow and Moruzzi (1958), who have produced a classical treatise on the physiology and pathology of the cerebellum in which all aspects of cerebellar function related to structure are covered and discussed in the light of experimental work with laboratory animals and of clinicopathologic observations in man. A companion volume to this work on the comparative anatomy of the cerebellum by O. Larsell is still in preparation. Any attempt to summarize with concise clarity the highly complex data now available on the cerebellum must by necessity be incomplete and oversimplified. Nevertheless, the following statements by outstanding students in the field may be helpful. Fulton and Dow (1937) refers to the cerebellum as "a vast organ of the motor system lying downstream in the reflex arc from the major projection systems of the cerebellar cortex." Crosby and co-workers (1962) define the cerebellum as a "suprasegmental portion of the brain concerned with coordinating motor responses at reflex, automatic and conscious levels." Bowsher (1961) states that "the cerebellum represents a feedback mechanism, the purpose of which is to control movement while it is taking place, which concerns both the pyramidal and extrapyramidal systems." In other words, the cerebellum is chiefly concerned with maintenance of muscle tone and with the steadiness of the latter during movements. These mechanisms require a continuous inflow of proprioceptive and exteroceptive general and special somatic afferent signals. The respective afferent systems relay their signals to the cerebellum where they are encoded and "computed" in analog fashion to modify efferent impulses concerned with motor function. If this system is interfered with, either at the level of the cerebellum proper or in the afferent or efferent arc of its reflex pattern, motor disturbances concerning the maintenance of steadiness and the smoothness of movement occur, a condition which is clinically known as *ataxia,* and which summarily designates a great variety of motor disturbances. How the various structural elements of the cerebellum have to cooperate in order to perform this motor control is still unknown and "the time is not ripe for attempting formulation of new concepts" (Dow and Moruzzi). In this respect, the situation as it pertains to the cerebellum is certainly no different from that of other parts of the central nervous system. It should be made clear that studies on the physiology of the rat cerebellum are few and inconclusive; most of our present knowledge of cerebellar physiology has been obtained from the study of human and simian primates and cats.

The cerebellum of all four-legged animals lies immediately caudal to, i.e., behind the cerebral hemispheres from which it is separated by the *tentorium cerebelli* (see page 18). Furthermore, the cerebellum is dorsal, i.e., above pons and medulla oblongata. This topographical relationship results from the fact that brainstem and forebrain are oriented along the same longitudinal axis (Fig. 6). In primates, because of their upright position, the brainstem emerges from the forebrain at an angle in a downward direction. Thus, the cerebellum comes to lie caudal, i.e., below the cerebral hemispheres and dorsal to, i.e., behind pons and medulla oblongata.

In larger mammals much of the cerebellar morphology can be discerned by the naked eye. The small size of the rat brain makes it a different problem of study. Except for a few superficial anatomical landmarks little can be distinguished macroscopically and it is necessary to have available histologic preparations as well as anatomic specimens cut sagittally, transversely, and horizontally which can be examined at low magnifications. Figures 7, 25, 29, A6–A8, and A35 provide the necessary illustrations.

In all mammals, the cerebellum presents the same general pattern. Its surface is convoluted or folded, but in quite a different fashion from that of the cerebrum. In higher mammals, the latter forms broad twisting bands, the gyri, which are separated by sulci of varying depths. The rat cerebrum, however, is lissencephalic, i.e., it does not form gyri but is smooth. The cerebellar foldings

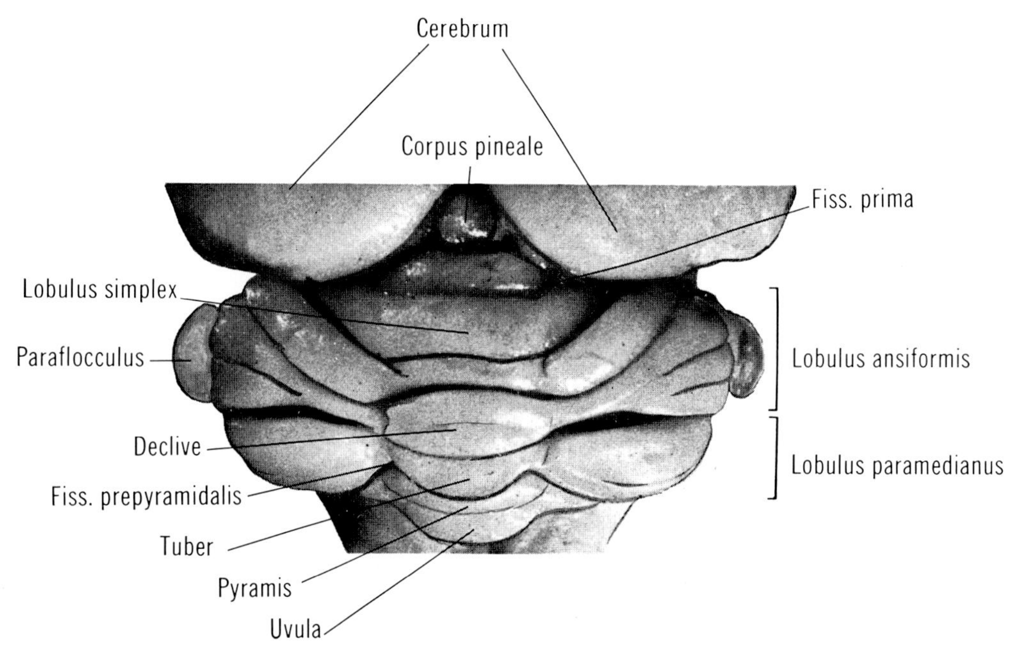

Fig. 25. Cerebellum, dorsal view, rat. × 6. The *paraflocculus* is depicted on both sides; it is not part of the *lobulus ansiformis*.

in contrast form thin, closely packed, more or less parallel laminae separated by deep somewhat curved fissures which run predominantly from side to side (Fig. 25), and this pattern is present even in the lowest mammals. The main deep fissures divide the organ into lobes which are found subdivided by shallow fissures into lobules, and, the latter in turn consist of folia, again separated by even shallower fissures. In the rat, all the lobules and fissures characteristic of the primate cerebellum are present, but some are almost vestigial while others are much more complex.

By careful dissection, the cerebellum can be removed from the brainstem. This requires first the cutting of the arachnoid membrane and then a severing of the three cerebellar peduncles by which the cerebellum is attached to pons and medulla oblongata. When this is done, the cerebellum is still connected to the brainstem by two membranes which are easily torn, the anterior and posterior medullary vela. These two membranes together with the ventral surface of the cerebellum form the roof of the rostral two-thirds of the fourth ventricle; the caudal third is covered by the *tela chorioidea.*

The cerebellum has a relatively uniform structure when studied in histologic sections at low magnification (Figs. 26 and 27). There is a superficial layer of gray matter, right underneath the pia mater, which covers a branching central white matter corresponding to the surface outline of the folia. On sagittal sections, the white matter displays a pattern reminiscent of a tree and its branches to which the name "arbor vitae" has been given by the older anatomists. The cortical gray matter consists of a superficial molecular layer with few neuronal

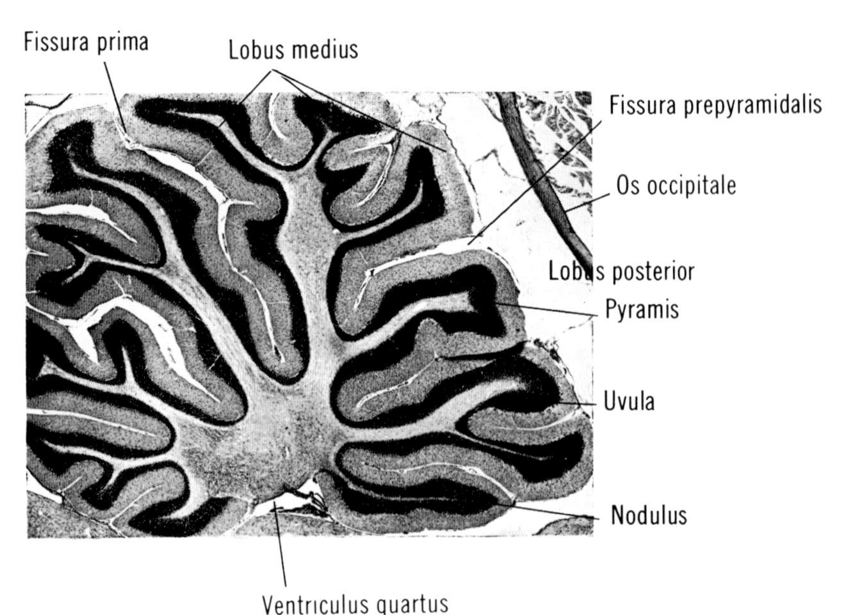

FIG. 26. Cerebellum, rat; saggittal section near midline. Hematoxylin-eosin. × about 13.

perikarya and abundant dendrites, a deep granular layer densely packed with small and rather uniform neuronal perikarya, and in between them lies the zone of Purkinje cells forming a single row embedded in astrocytes. The Purkinje cells are large pear-shaped perikarya; their axons emerge from the base and dip into the white matter after having negotiated the granular layer, whereas their dendrites spread out in prodigious fanlike ramifications arranged in parasagittal planes into the molecular layer. The fine histologic organization of the cortex, as revealed by silver impregnations, is infinitely more complex than it appears from the above description.

The anatomic terminology which has developed around the various parts and structures of the cerebellum has been characterized as "appalling" by Crosby *et al.* In order not to confuse the issue further, we have simply followed Larsell's terminology as presented in his very extensive studies on the comparative anatomy of the cerebellum. A combined phylogenetic and ontogenetic approach is probably most expedient for gaining insight into the functional anatomy of this part of the central nervous system. This approach is represented in the diagrams of Figs. 28 and 29.

The cerebellum arises as an outgrowth of the dorsal lips of the alar plates of the rhombencephalon, more specifically from the somatic afferent segments. A primitive cerebellum is present in the lowest species of fishes in the form of two lateral protuberances fused medially and anteriorly. With ascending phylogeny this hindbrain structure becomes greater in size and more complicated in development.

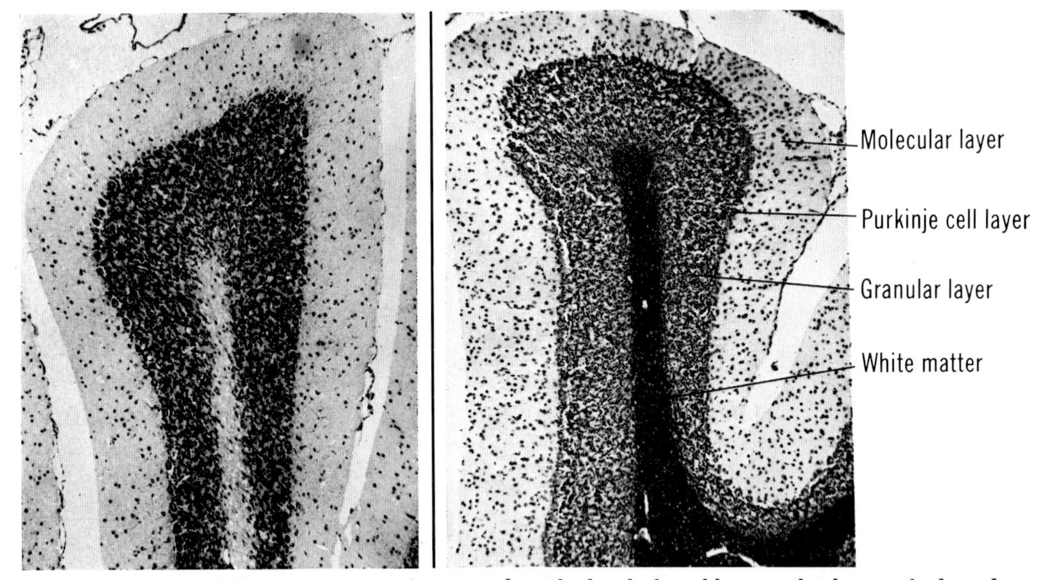

FIG. 27. Cerebellum, rat; at right stained with luxol fast blue-cresylviolet method and at left with toluidene blue. × about 45.

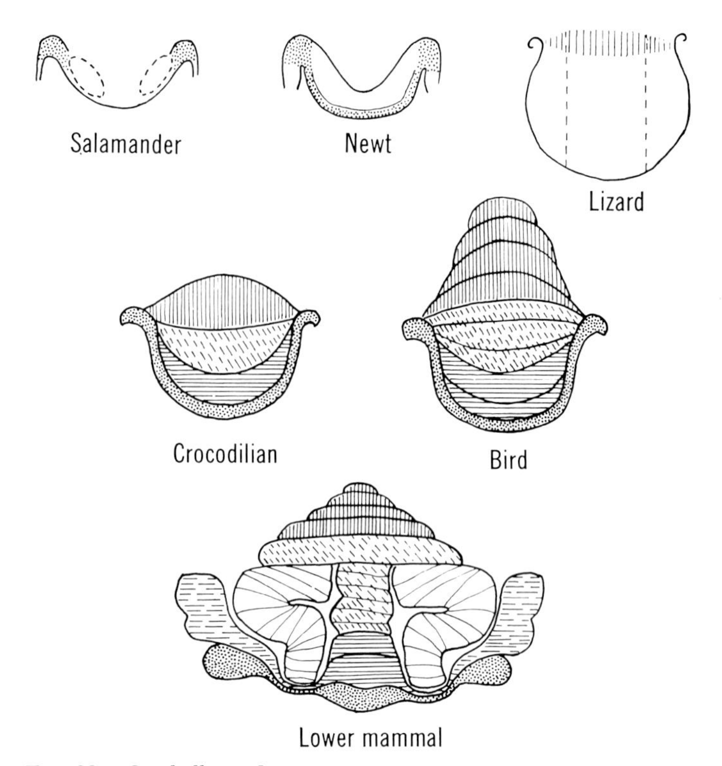

FIG. 28. Cerebellum, diagram showing phylogenetic development.

In the salamander, the vestibular projection area of the cerebellum is still continuous with the medulla oblongata. These primitive parts of the cerebellum do not unite, but protrude laterally as two distinct lobes, the so-called "auricles," from the region of the vestibular nuclei. Spinal and trigeminal somatic afferent fibers end in the paired ventral *eminentia cerebelli,* outlined with dashes in Fig. 28. In the newt, the stippled vestibular projection areas have become continuous by fusion due to neural biotactic migration along the vestibular commissure to form the flocculonodular lobe, separated from the *corpus cerebelli* (white) by the *fissura posterolateralis.* This is the first step of a structural organization of the cerebellum which is found throughout the entire higher vertebrate series. In the lizard, the *corpus cerebelli* forms a broad thin plate with a cerebellar commissure indicated by vertical lines and divided into a pars medialis, the precursor of the *vermis,* and two lateral parts, the precursors of the hemispheres. These divisions are indicated by dashed lines. In this animal, the vestibular portions are poorly developed and the auricles have disappeared. The body of the cerebellum (*corpus cerebelli*) appears as a simple-structured cell mass arching over the dorsal aspect of the medulla oblongata.

In reptiles a further division occurs, afforded by the *fissura prima* which

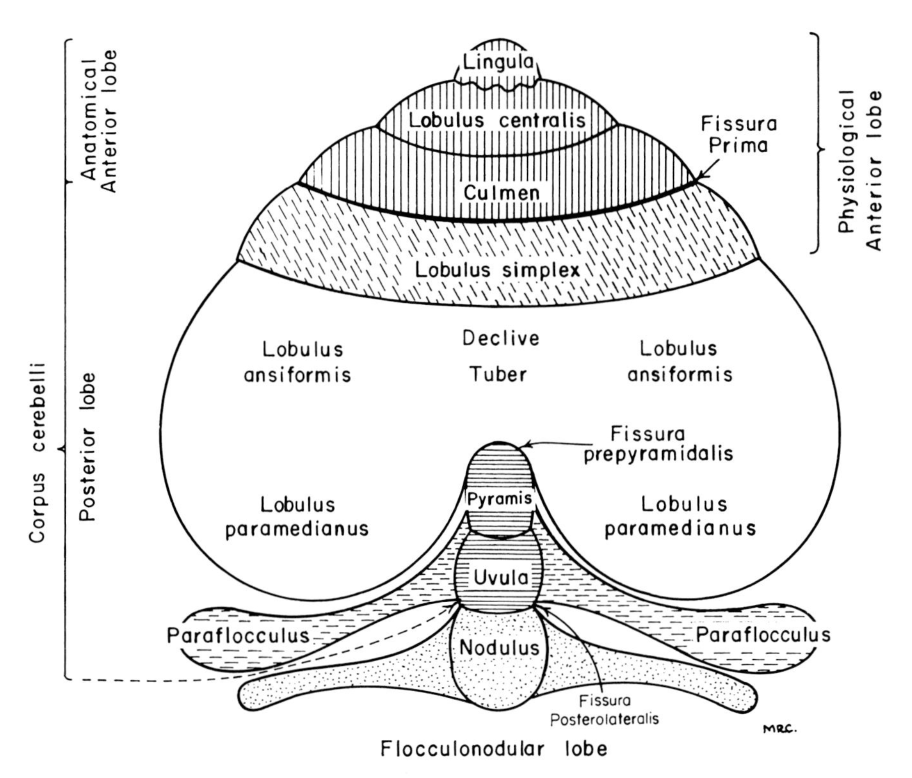

FIG. 29. Diagram of cerebellar cortex of primates with principal divisions and afferent fiber connections (after Larsell). The *fissura posterolateralis* separates the two primary divisions, flocculonodular lobe and *corpus cerebelli.* The vestibular area in all drawings of Figs. 28 and 29 is stippled; the shading for lower mammals in Fig. 28 corresponds to that used in Fig. 29. The vestibular (stippled) area plus all other shading equals paleocerebellum; the white area equals neocerebellum.

divides the corpus cerebelli into an anterior and posterior lobe. At the same time a second fold develops in the posterior lobe, the *fissura prepyramidalis,* which separates the latter into a medial part and a posteromedian lobule, represented by the *pyramis* and *uvula* of the *vermis.* This state is well exemplified in the crocodile, where the flocculonodular lobe (stippled) is similar to that of the newt. The *fissura prima* separates the anterior lobe (vertical lines) from the precursor of the medial part of the posterior lobe (diagonal dashes), which at this state is a homolog of the *lobulus simplex.* The posteromedian lobe (vertical lines) in turn is anteriorly bordered by the *fissura prepyramidalis* and is separated from the (stippled) flocculonodular lobe by the *fissura posterolateralis.* In birds these three lobes of the *corpus cerebelli* are further differentiated by new folds, but it is only in the lower mammals that there takes place a new development which occurs predominantly in the lateral regions. First, there is a lateral extension of the posteromedian lobule, consisting of pyramis and uvula, which develops into the *paraflocculus* attached to the posteromedian lobule by a slender stalk. Simultaneously, the caudal parts of the primitive posterior lobe mushroom in a lateral direction to form the *lobulus ansiformis* and the *lobulus paramedianus.* Further developments lead to the subdivision of the anterior lobe into a midline part, the *lingula,* which is rostrally continuous with the anterior medullary velum. This is followed caudally by the *lobulus centralis* and further caudad by the *culmen;* both possess lateral extensions. The most prominent changes take place in the posterior lobe, with the *lobulus simplex* now clearly separated from the remainder, and it is the remaining part which becomes so voluminous in primates that it dwarfs and almost obliterates all other parts of the cerebellum. Because of its phylogeny, this part of the posterior lobe is known as the *neocerebellum, paleocerebellum* referring to the rest of the organ. The mushrooming of the posterior lobe is commensurate to the increased volume of the musculature on the one hand and the growth of the cerebral hemispheres on the other. Likewise, the development of the cerebral and cerebellar hemispheres makes it easily understood that the corticoponto-cerebellar system, to be discussed later, terminates predominantly in the neocerebellum.

After having elucidated these phylogenetic and ontogenetic principles, we can now turn to a consideration of the rat cerebellum. Its superficial aspects as viewed from dorsal, ventral, anterior, and posterior directions are represented in Figs. 30 and 31, redrawn from Larsell (1952). From his extensive studies on the cerebellum of rats, rabbits, pigs, and man, representing any state of development, Larsell realized the necessity of introducing for fissures, lobules, and folia new terms which are based on human anatomic terminology because these structures have homologies throughout the mammalian kingdom. The midline structures in their entirety are generically referred to as *vermis cerebelli,* which is relatively large in the rat as compared to the hemispheres. Caudal to the hemispheres are *paraflocculus* and *flocculus,* medially bordered by the three cerebellar peduncles. The vermian portion of the cerebellum is divided by fissures into segments, of which those delimited by deeper fissures continue into the hemispheres. The lingula is the most rostral part of the cerebellum, probably a projection area for the tail, which has been designated by Larsell as lobule I. Turning around, caudad in an almost complete circle, the various vermian lobules are identified by Roman numerals, the last (X) designating the nodule. Subdivisions into *a, b, c,* and *d* are determined by secondary and tertiary formation of fissures. After the principles of this scheme are understood, it is relatively simple to get oriented on Figs. 30 and 31.

The gray matter of the cerebellum is represented not only in the superficially located cortex, but also in the form of nuclear masses deeply embedded in the white matter near the roof of the fourth ventricle. In the lower mammalian species, a simple nuclear mass appears in the midline of the roof, the fastigial nucleus (*nucleus fastigii*). In higher mammals further nuclear masses become differentiated laterad which from medial to lateral are the *nucleus globosus*, the *nucleus emboliformis*, and the *nucleus dentatus*. The emboliform and globose nuclei cannot be distinguished in species below the anthropoids. Therefore this complex is usually known as the *nucleus interpositus* or the *nucleus intermedius*. Phylogenetically, the fastigial nucleus is the oldest subcortical cell mass, and it accordingly receives fibers entirely from the paleocerebellar cortex, in addition to afferent fibers from the vestibular and cochlear nuclei. The *nucleus interpositus* is also phylogenetically old and consequently receives fibers from the paleocerebellum, predominantly from the anterior lobe. The most recent phylogenetic acquisition is the dentate nucleus, which develops to macroscopic proportions in primates and which receives its afferent fibers from those Purkinje cells which are predominantly located in the neocerebellar cortex. Clearly, this nucleus develops commensurately with an increase in the size of the neocerebellar cortex. The dentate nucleus of the rat is a little larger than the other nuclei of the cerebellum and stretches out into the base of the stalk of the floccular lobe. It is a compact mass slightly hollowed medially, so that it appears somewhat curved in sections. In man, the hollowing is much more prominent and the nucleus has grown as a whole into the form of a much-folded, pouch-shaped lamella, similar to the inferior olivary body. This shape accounts for the name "dentate," and also for the obsolete designation "cerebellar olive" (Figs. A6 and A7).

Cerebellar Fiber Connections. The cerebellum is endowed with different fiber systems which can be classified according to anatomical and physiological parameters. Those fibers which both originate and terminate within the cerebellum are generically called intrinsic systems. Fibers which originate in, or which terminate outside of, the cerebellum make up the extrinsic systems. As will be seen, these two groups of systems can be further divided.

The intrinsic fiber system is best understood by following an impulse which is mediated to the cerebellum by an extrinsic fiber. This has been adequately discussed by Fox in Crosby *et al.* (1962). These extrinsic afferents, with few exceptions, terminate in the cerebellar cortex. They are of two types, the climbing fibers, which run in a straight course through the cortex and terminate in the molecular layer, and the mossy fibers. The latter run parallel to the cortex, in the subcortical white matter, from where they send many terminal sprouts into the granular layer, forming curious, microscopically small, moss-like excrescences with which the granule cells synapse. The mossy fibers originate from the general and special somatic sensory nuclei and possibly from the pontine and arcuate nuclei. The origin of the climbing fibers, according to most texts, is still a matter of dispute. It appears, however, that Szentágothai and Rajkovits (1959) have conclusively shown that in the cat brain the largest part of the climbing fibers originates in the inferior olivary complex, which does

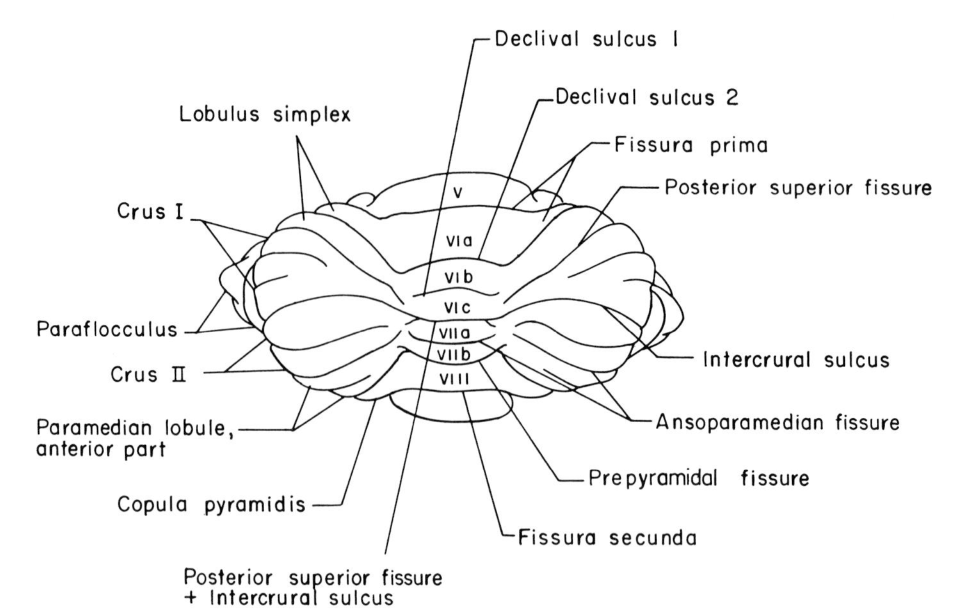

DORSAL

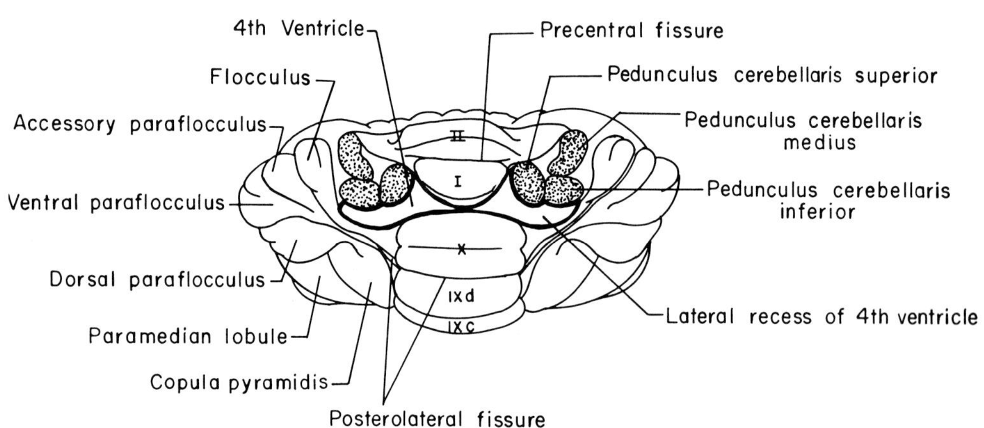

VENTRAL

FIG. 30. Cerebellum, rat (redrawn after Larsell, 1952). Dorsal and ventral views.

ABBREVIATIONS (after Larsell)

I, vermian lobule I, the lingula
II, vermian lobule II, the ventral lobule of lobulus centralis
IIa, sublobule IIa
IIb, sublobule IIb
III, vermian lobule III, the dorsal lobule of lobulus centralis
IIIa, sublobule IIIa
IIIb, sublobule IIIb
IV, vermian lobule IV, the ventral lobule of culmen
V, vermian lobule V, the dorsal lobule of culmen
VI, vermian lobule VI, the declive
VIa, sublobule VIa
VIb, sublobule VIb

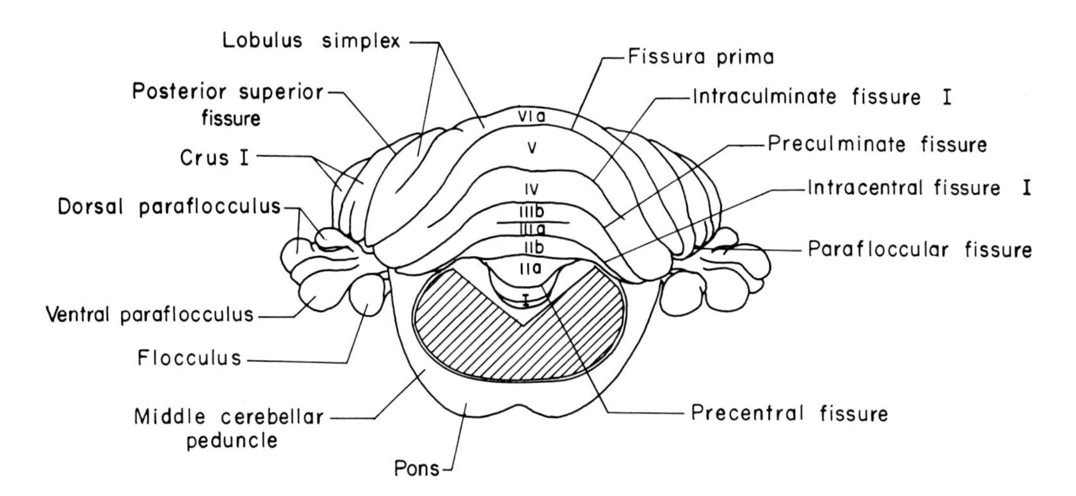

ANTERIOR

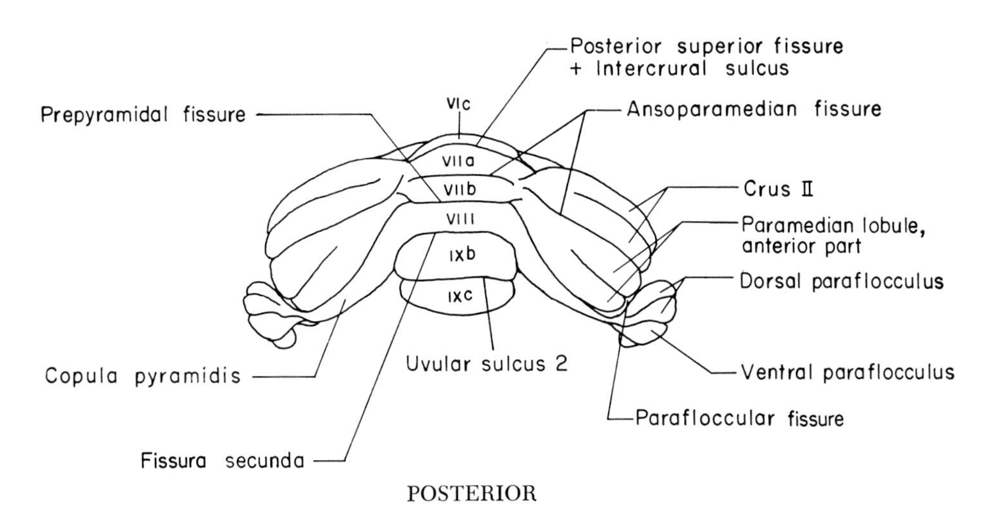

POSTERIOR

FIG. 31. Cerebellum, rat (redrawn after Larsell, 1952). Anterior and posterior views.

ABBREVIATIONS (*Cont.*)

VIc, sublobule VIc
VIc, s.p., posterior surface of sublobule VIc
VId, sublobule VId
VII, vermian lobule VII, the tuber vermis lobule
VIIa, sublobule VIIa
VIIb, sublobule VIIb, the posterior tuber vermis
VIII, vermian lobule VIII, the pyramis
VIII, s.a., anterior surface of lobule VIII
IX, vermian lobule IX, the uvula
IXa, sublobule IXa
IXb, sublobule IXb
IXc, sublobule IXc
IXd, sublobule IXd
X, vermian lobule X, the nodulus

not give rise to mossy fibers at all. The other afferent cerebellar systems carry only a small number of climbing fibers, which usually terminate outside of their respective main projection area.

In a greatly simplified version, an extrinsic or afferent impulse may travel over the following routes: The incoming mossy fiber synapses with many granule cells spread over at least two adjacent folia. The granule cells receive the impulses through their dendrites and each sends an axon towards the surface. The axon bifurcates in the molecular layer in the form of a T, the two branches running transversely and making synaptic connections with the dendrites of numerous Purkinje cells. In the molecular layer are also stellate and basket cells receiving impulses from the granule cells and discharging to the Purkinje cells. The stellate cells connect with Purkinje cell dendrites, whereas the basket cells send their axons down into the Purkinje cell layer where they form extremely rich terminal aborizations around the bodies of the latter. Thus, any single impulse reaching the cerebellum is immediately mediated to a number of neurons and its signal is thus very probably altered and modified. The resulting signal pattern has been aptly designated as "avalanche conduction" by Cajal, although it would be wrong to assume that each of the many synaptic connections would, upon stimulation, result in excitation. Whatever information is eventually impressed upon the Purkinje cell, its own signal is then transmitted by a short, stout axon to the subcortical nuclei where most of the Purkinje cell axons terminate. All subcortical nuclei are interconnected by association fibers. Furthermore, the opposite cerebellar cortices are connected by commissural fibers, which form the anterior and posterior cerebellar commissures in the roof of the fourth ventricle close to the fastigial nuclei. The discharge of the Purkinje cells to the intracerebellar nuclei is in general such that the vermis, the medial portion of the cerebellum, projects to the medially situated nuclei fastigii and the medial part of the nucleus interpositus, whereas the hemispheres discharge to the lateral parts of the interposite nucleus and to the dentate nucleus. This discharge is largely ipsilateral, although some corticonuclear fibers may decussate. From the subcortical cerebellar nuclei originate the cerebellofugal or efferent cerebellar systems.

The extrinsic fiber systems can be classified in different ways. On a functional basis we distinguish afferent systems which conduct impulses to the cerebellum and efferent systems which discharge from the cerebellum to various structures of the central nervous system. From our initial considerations of the general function of the cerebellum, it is clear that the afferent systems are predominantly concerned with proprioceptive and exteroceptive stimuli. These project to the cerebellar cortex in such a way that the anterior lobe together with the lobulus simplex receives ipsilateral fibers with the trunk located in the vermian portion and the extremities represented in the hemispheres. In the posterior lobe, however, which is so extremely well developed in higher mammals, the projection of exteroceptive stimuli is bilateral, primarily to the paramedian lobes. Thus, exteroceptive stimuli from one particular area of the body are projected to three different sites in the cerebellar cortex. Visual and auditory stimuli are projected largely to the lobulus simplex. Vestibular impulses, which as we have seen concern the phylogenetically oldest parts, project to the flocculonodular lobe.

There is a second afferent system to the cerebellum which reaches its greatest development in the human being, the function of which, however, is not so well understood; this is the pontocerebellar system. Nerve fibers originating in various areas of the telencephalic cortex descend as corticopontine fibers together with the pyramidal tracts and terminate in the pontine and arcuate nuclei of the medulla oblongata. These nuclear masses also receive collaterals from the pyramidal fibers. The second neuron in this system originates in the pontine and arcuate nuclei and enters the cerebellum to terminate in the cerebellar cortex. Most of these fibers cross before they turn into the cerebellum. This afferent system appears to place the cerebellum under the influence of the cerebral cortex and may be therefore considered to regulate the flow of voluntary and associated movements. By way of its efferent fiber systems, the cerebellum exerts its control upon muscle tone and muscle movement via several circuitous routes which terminate in various nuclear masses belonging to the extrapyramidal system.

The various afferent and efferent cerebellar fiber tracts form three bundles, known as the superior, middle, and inferior cerebellar peduncles, respectively. As a rule of thumb, the superior peduncle, or *brachium conjunctivum,* connects cerebellum and midbrain and provides the main path for cerebellofugal discharges to diencephalon and brainstem. The brachium pontis (*pedunculus cerebellaris medius*) harbors the afferent pontocerebellar path and connects pons and cerebellum. The restiforme body (*pedunculus cerebellaris inferior*) coming from the medulla oblongata contains both afferent and to a lesser degree efferent systems originating or terminating in medulla oblongata and spinal cord. The latter peduncle contains an interstitial nucleus (*nucleus peduncularis cerebellaris inferior*) (Fig. A6), the function of which is unknown. It is believed that some or all afferent fibers of the inferior peduncle synapse in this center.

The various tracts of the inferior cerebellar peduncle and their terminations can be enumerated as follows:

a. The vestibulocerebellar tract is composed of fibers which originate in the vestibular nuclei, but it also contains direct root fibers originating in the vestibular ganglion. It projects to the flocculonodular lobe and the uvula as mossy fibers. A small number of the vestibular fibers terminate in the fastigial nuclei which, in turn, give rise to cerebellovestibular fibers terminating in the lateral and inferior vestibular nuclei.

b. The olivocerebellar tract is formed by the converging internal arcuate fibers originating in the contralateral inferior olivary complex, and projects to the vermis and the cerebellar hemisphere as climbing fibers. A small number of fibers terminate in the fastigial and interposit nuclei. Cerebello-olivary fibers follow the same pathway, but their origin in the cerebellum is not known. It has been suggested that the nerve cells of the dentate nucleus give rise to such fibers, but they appear to leave the cerebellum by way of the superior cerebellar peduncle.

c. The fibers of the dorsal spinocerebellar tract terminate in the anterior lobe and the vermis as mossy fibers.

d. A small number of fibers originate in the lateral cuneate nucleus which do not accompany the majority of the efferent fibers of this nucleus to form the medial lemniscus. Instead, they bend dorsad and laterad into the restiform body as cuneocerebellar tract, where they lie in close approximation to the dorsal spinocerebellar tract fibers and terminate in the same general location.

e. Efferent axons from the arcuate nuclei form the arcuatocerebellar tract, a part of which is known as *striae medullares.* They terminate in the flocculus.

f. The cerebellospinal tract, also known as the uncinate fascicle or Russell's fascicle, originates in the fastigial nuclei. This bundle takes a peculiar course, first arching forward to join the fascicles of the superior cerebellar peduncle, where it can be seen in Fig. A8 as a relatively well-defined tract of transverse fibers immediately dorsal to the peduncle. At this point, however, the fibers turn backward and caudad to leave the cerebellum via the inferior cerebellar peduncle. The fibers of this tract terminate at the motor cells of the cervical spinal cord.

In addition to these fiber systems which can be identified with relative ease, the inferior cerebellar peduncle harbors a number of other systems which are not discernible in the normal rat brain because of the diffuse distribution of their respective fibers. They are, however, sufficiently important to be enumerated. Reciprocal connections between the fastigial nuclei and the reticular formation of the brainstem are known as reticulocerebellar and cerebelloreticular or cerebellotegmental fibers. Connections between the chief sensory nucleus of the trigeminal nerve and the cerebellum on the one hand, and the *nucleus fastigii* and the motor cranial nerve nuclei on the other, are known as nucleocerebellar and cerebellomotor tracts, respectively. These systems can be easily understood in reference to the global functions of the cerebellum, which is always interposed between somatic afferent and somatic efferent systems.

As mentioned before, the middle cerebellar peduncle, although the largest of the three in primates, contains practically only pontocerebellar fibers.

The superior cerebellar peduncle contains one important afferent system in the form of the ventral spinocerebellar tract. We have already traced its fibers as they ascend over the ventral surface of the medulla oblongata, at the upper end of which they dip into the brain to join the superior peduncle on the dorsal surface of the pons (Fig. A8). These fibers, like those of the dorsal spinocerebellar tract, terminate in the anterior lobe as mossy fibers; a few, however, end in the fastigial nuclei. The remainder of the superior peduncle is usually divided into an uncrossed part represented by fastigioparaventricular, cerebellotegmental, and cerebellomotor fibers, and into a much larger crossed fiber system. The latter is again divided into an ascending and a descending limb; both cross in the decussation of the superior cerebellar peduncle (*decussatio pedunculorum cerebellarium superiorum*) in the midbrain, after which the descending limb turns caudad. It thus comes to lie adjacent to the central tegmental bundle and discharges its fibers into the reticular gray and into the inferior olivary complex.

Of greatest importance is the ascending limb of the superior peduncle, which is made up of a massive tract which terminates in the red nucleus, the dentatorubral tract. Most of its fibers, as implicit in the term, originate in the dentate nucleus, but some come from the *nucleus interpositus*. A relatively small part of the ascending limb bypasses the red nucleus as the cerebellothalamic tract, or dentatothalamic component, to proceed rostrad to the *nucleus ventralis lateralis thalami* and the *nucleus centromedialis thalami*. It is the ascending crossed limb of the superior peduncle, through which most of the cerebellar impulses are channeled into the extrapyramidal motor system for control of muscular tone and movement.

References

Addison, W. H. F. The development of the Purkinje cells and of the cortical layers in the cerebellum of the albino rat. *J. Comp. Neurol.* **21**: 459-481, 1911.

Anderson, R. F. Cerebellar distribution of the dorsal and ventral spino-cerebellar tracts in the white rat. *J. Comp. Neurol.* **79**: 415-423, 1943.

Ariëns Kappers, C. U., G. C. Huber & Elizabeth C. Crosby. The Comparative Anatomy of the Nervous System of Vertebrates, Including Man. 2 Volumes. New York: Macmillan, 1936.

Association for Research in Nervous and Mental Disease. Cerebellum: an investigation of recent advances. The Proceedings of the Association, New York, December 28-29th, 1926. F. Tilney *et al.*, Eds. (Ser. of research papers, Vol. 6, 649 p.). Baltimore: Williams & Wilkins, 1929.

Bolk, L. Das Cerebellum der Säugetiere. Eine vergleichend anatomische Untersuchung. Haarlem and Jena: Fischer, 1906.

Bowsher, D. Introduction to Neuroanatomy. Springfield, Illinois: C. C Thomas, 1961.

Bradley, O. C. On the development and homology of the mammalian cerebellar fissures. *J. Anat. Physiol. (London)* **37**: 112-130, 1903.

Cajal, S. Ramón y. Histologie du système nerveux de l'homme et des vertébrés. Paris: Maloine, 1909-1911. (Reprinted by C.S.I.S., Madrid, 1952.)

Crosby, Elizabeth C., T. Humphrey & E. W. Lauer. Correlative Anatomy of the Nervous System. New York: Macmillan, 1962.

Dow, R. S. The fiber connections of the posterior parts of the cerebellum in the rat and cat. *J. Comp. Neurol.* **63**: 527-548, 1936.

Dow, R. S. & G. Moruzzi. The Physiology and Pathology of the Cerebellum. Minneapolis: Univ. of Minnesota Press, 1958.

Fulton, J. F. & R. S. Dow. The cerebellum: A summary of functional localisation. *Yale J. Biol. & Med.* **11**: 89-119, 1937.

Ingvar, S. Zur Phylo- und Ontogenese des Kleinhirns. *Folia neuro-biol.* **11**: 205-495, 1918.

INGVAR, S. Studies in neurology. 11. On cerebellar function. *Bull. Johns Hopkins Hosp.* **43**: 338-362, 1928.

INUKAI, I. On the loss of Purkinje cells, with advancing age, from the cerebellar cortex of albino rats. *J. Comp. Neurol.* **45**: 1-31, 1928.

JOHNSTON, J. B. Note on peduncle of flocculus and posterior medullary velum. *J. Anat. (London)* **68**: 471-479, 1934.

LARSELL, O. The morphogenesis and adult pattern of the lobules and fissures of the cerebellum of the white rat. *J. Comp. Neurol.* **97**: 281-356, 1952.

LARSELL, O. The cerebellum from myxinoids to man. (In preparation.)

PAPEZ, J. W. Comparative Neurology. 518 pp. New York: Crowell, 1929. (Reprinted by Hafner, New York, 1961.)

RILEY, H. A. An Atlas of the Basal Ganglia, Brain Stem and Spinal Cord. New York: Hafner, 1960.

SZENTÁGOTHAI, J. & K. RAJKOVITS. Über den Ursprung der Kletterfasern des Kleinhirns. *Z. Anatomie u. Entwicklungsgeschichte* **121**: 130-141, 1959.

VALVERDE, F. Reticular formation of the pons and medulla oblongata. *J. Comp. Neurol.* **116**: 71-99, 1961.

VALVERDE, F. A new type of cell in the lateral reticular formation of the brain stem. *J. Comp. Neurol.* **117**: 189-195, 1961.

VAN DER VOORT, M. R. Bijdrage tot de embryologie van het cerebellum van Mus rattus. *Ned Tijdschr. Geneesk.* **103**: 706-707, 1959.

WALBERG, F. The lateral reticular nucleus of the medulla oblongata in mammals. *J. Comp. Neurol.* **96**: 283-343, 1952.

WALLENBERG, A. Beitrage zur vergleichenden Anatomie des Hirnstammes. *Dtsch. Z Nervenheilk.* **117-119**: 677-698, 1931 (pp. 685 *et seq.* on rat).

CHAPTER VI

Mesencephalon (Midbrain)

The general form of the midbrain is less modified from the early embryonic condition than is that of either of the other primary subdivisions of the brain. Though the walls are markedly thickened and the lumen is relatively reduced, it retains the condition of a tube connecting the forebrain with the hindbrain and with only little modification of shape by greater thickening ventrally than dorsally and by the molding of the dorsal wall (*tectum*) into two eminences on each side of the colliculi anterior and posterior (*corpora quadrigemina*). Through the midbrain runs the narrow ventricle, the cerebral aqueduct (*aqueductus cerebri*). The thick wall ventral to the aqueduct constitutes the cerebral peduncles (*pedunculi cerebri*), which are divided into a thick tegmentum (containing nuclear masses and fiber tracts) in the deep position, and a pair of large flattened bands of longitudinal fibers situated superficially and ventrally, the basis or *pes pedunculi.*

The deep part of the basis is formed by a conspicuous plate of gray matter, the *substantia nigra.* Dorsal to the *substantia nigra,* the tegmentum consists of reticular formation (*formatio reticularis*) continuous with the same structure in the medulla oblongata and diencephalon, while dorsal to this again is a rather thick layer of central gray matter (*substantia grisea centralis*). Into the tegmentum may be traced many of the longitudinal tracts that have been observed in the corresponding region of the hindbrain. In the posterior part, the fibers of the lateral lemniscus (*lemniscus lateralis*) are to be seen at each side surrounding their dorsal nucleus and running anterodorsad into the tectum. From the enlarged rostral end of the dorsal nucleus of the lateral lemniscus arises a thin bundle of transverse fibers, the commissure of the lateral lemniscus (*commissura lemnisci lateralis*). After decussating, these fibers run into the corresponding nucleus of the other side and curve dorsad in the lemniscus to end in the posterior colliculus (Papez, 1929) (Fig. A12).

Ventrally the medial lemniscus (*lemniscus medialis*) continues forward in the same position that it occupied in the hindbrain, becoming more flattened dorsoventrally, however, and soon moving away from the raphe to a somewhat more lateral position, where it may be traced up into the thalamus (Figs. A12–A20).

In the dorsal part of the tegmentum, the medial longitudinal bundle (*fasciculus longitudinalis medialis*) likewise continues forward in the same position where it was observed farther back. It also becomes more flattened dorsoventrally, and it breaks up into a number of distinct, compact, little bundles. At the level of the trochlear nucleus (*nucleus trochlearis*), it forms a dorsal concavity containing the nucleus, and some of its fascicles run right through the latter. Then it swings around dorsomedially so that, at the level of the more rostral part of the oculomotor nucleus (*nucleus oculomotorius*), the tracts of the two sides enclose between them a V-shaped area of the central gray matter, in which the nerve nuclei lie. In front of these nuclei, the ventral edges of the two tracts separate a little before they continue into the hypothalamus. Here the tract disappears in relation with a small group of cells, the interstitial nucleus (*nucleus interstitialis* of Cajal), situated at the anterior extremity of the red nucleus (*nucleus ruber*) (vide infra) and just lateral to the tract itself (Fig. A14). This nucleus gives rise to the interstitiospinal tract (tract of Boyce), which in the rat is a bundle of coarse fibers running back in first the dorsal and then the medial part of the medial longitudinal fasciculus. It gives off fibers to the eye-muscle nuclei and passes on into the spinal cord, taking up a sulcomarginal position there (Papez, 1923b). In the lateral part of the medial longitudinal bundle, for a considerable distance through the midbrain, run secondary fibers from the nucleus of Deiters (*nucleus vestibularis lateralis*) to the oculomotor and trochlear nuclei.

Extending obliquely between the medial longitudinal fascicle and the lateral lemniscus, lies the cross section of the superior cerebellar peduncle (*pedunculus cerebellaris superior*), which is thick and rounded dorsomedially (*caput brachii conjunctivi*) and tapers out almost to a point ventrolaterally (*cauda brachii conjunctivi*). Passing upward, the cauda becomes less definite and the whole tract becomes a little more medial in position by the time it reaches the level of the trochlear nucleus, about the front of which it turns mediad and decussates immediately ventral to the medial longitudinal bundle. In the upper part of its course before decussating, it is less sharply marked off from the surrounding reticular formation than farther back. In man, the superior cerebellar peduncle is proportionally larger than in the rodent and the dense decussation has a considerably greater dorsoventral extent.

After decussating, the superior cerebellar peduncle runs straight forward a short distance to end largely in the red nucleus. Some of the fibers pass on and into the thalamus, while a few turn backward in the reticular formation (*brachium conjunctivum descendens*).

The red nucleus is a large constellation of large and small nerve cells which is very conspicuous in histologic sections (Nissl and luxol fast blue stains). In the human brain, it is even more prominent in myelin preparations, where it is marked off clearly from the surrounding reticular formation by a capsule made up largely of the fibers of the superior cerebellar peduncle. In the rat, however, there is no such definite capsule and a great many white fibers run between the cells, so that the nucleus is less sharply delimited in sections stained by Weigert's or the luxol fast blue method. It occupies a medial position in the tegmentum at each side, extending rostrad from a plane containing the caudal part of the oculomotor nucleus and bulging over the caudoventral diencephalic structures. A magnocellular division and dorsolateral and ventrolateral divisions composed of smaller cells may be distinguished in this nucleus, the magnocellular portion (*pars magnocellularis*) being relatively larger in the rat than in man. The large-celled part is mainly caudal, and the smaller-celled parts more rostral. In sagittal section the red nucleus is ovoid. Besides connections from the cerebellar peduncles, fibers from the neopallium (mainly striatal) also end in the red nucleus (Figs. A12–A15).

From the magnocellular division of the red nucleus, arise descending fibers which convey to the motor columns of the spinal cord the impulses received from the cerebellum, as modified by striatal influences—impulses which are believed to be important factors in muscular coordination and in the maintenance of muscle tone. These fibers pass ventromediad to cross the raphe as the ventral tegmental decussation (*decussatio tegmenti ventralis*), after which they turn caudad, forming the rubrospinal tract (*tractus rubrospinalis*) in a position ventromedial to the red nucleus. Farther caudal than this nucleus, the tract passes gradually in a lateral direction to a location just ventral to the cauda of the superior cerebellar peduncle. Papez (1929) described its descending course in the rat as "medial to the lateral lemniscus, ventral to the trigeminus, facial nucleus, etc."

From the small-celled parts of the red nucleus arise crossed and uncrossed fibers to other parts of the tegmentum and to the thalamus. From the latter, the impulses are transmitted to the corpus striatum and to the cerebral cortex. As a result of these relations, the small-celled region is found to correspond in size with the degree of development of the cerebellar hemispheres and of the cerebral cortex (especially the frontal cortex), both of which are small in the rat.

Dorsal to the ventral tegmental decussation and the decussation of the superior cerebellar peduncles, is another group of fibers crossing the raphe. These fibers arise in the tectum, whence they curve around the central gray matter to its ventral surface (fountain-like radiation of Meynert) and form the dorsal tegmental decussation (*decussatio tegmenti dorsalis*). They then turn directly caudad in the ventral medial part of the medial longitudinal bundle as the medial tectospinal tract (*tractus tectospinalis medialis*), which has already been observed in the hindbrain. Some of the fibers are said by certain authors not to decussate but to pass caudad on the same side along with the lateral lemniscus. After giving off fibers to the oculomotor and trochlear nuclei, the medial tectospinal tract suddenly becomes more scattered near the caudal end of the decussation of the superior cerebellar peduncles, some of its fibers as they continue back being mingled with the medial longitudinal bundle and with the medial lemniscus (Papez, 1929). The medial tectospinal fibers arise mainly in the medial part of the tectum and end in the cervical spinal cord to influence the muscles of the neck. There is also a lateral tectospinal tract arising in the more lateral parts of the tectum and descending through the homolateral reticular formation.

The central gray matter surrounding the cerebral aqueduct contains several more or less distinct cell masses. Among the most evident of these are the nuclei of the oculomotor and trochlear nerves, which lie in the ventral part of the central gray, directly dorsal to the medial longitudinal bundle (Figs. A10–A12).

The trochlear nucleus (*nucleus n. trochlearis*) is a small group of large cells near the level of the rostral end of the inferior colliculus. In the rat, it lies actually between the fascicles of the medial longitudinal bundle, suggesting the intimacy of its relation to this tract, from which it receives most of its afferent fibers. The axons arising from this nucleus may be traced caudolaterad and dorsad, running backward at the boundary between the central gray and the surrounding tissue. This course takes the nerve root to the anterolateral region of the anterior medullary velum, in which the fibers decussate to emerge as the cranial nerve roots. Occasionally an accessory trochlear nucleus occurs on one side, caudal to the main group.

The oculomotor nucleus (*nucleus n. oculomotorii*) appears as a complex directly rostrad to the trochlear nucleus and practically continuous with it, but slightly more medial and entirely dorsal to the medial longitudinal bundle. The complex extends up to near the anterior end of the midbrain. The chief oculomotor nucleus is composed of rather large multipolar cells forming a mass very close to the median plane. In this mass there are two parts, but they are indistinguishable in rodents (Gillilan, 1943). In man, the oculomotor nuclei include a median center (nucleus of Perlia) and paired lateral nuclei, but the former is absent in rodents. The root fibers of the oculomotor nerve pass ventrad in small fascicles which emerge along the medial margins of the cerebral peduncles (Figs. A12, A15, and A35), a few of them first decussating between and dorsal to the nuclei and joining the root of the other side.

Immediately dorsal and anterior to the oculomotor nuclei proper is a mass of small cells the axons of which also emerge in the oculomotor nerve. This is the nucleus of Edinger-Westphal* (*pars rostralis*), which is the origin of the general visceral fibers in the oculomotor nerve. It is continuous across the median plane in the rodents, but in man is distinctly paired. Gillilan recognizes in the rat a *pars rostralis* (*nucleus medianus anterior*), and a main or caudal Edinger-Westphal nucleus, the latter incompletely paired.

Various nuclei also occur in the tegmentum; of these, two important centers are the dorsal and ventral tegmental nuclei (*nucleus tegmenti dorsalis* and *ventralis*, or *nucleus medialis profundus*). These are located at the extreme

---

* *Nucleus medianus anterior*, of oculomotor complex.

posterior end of the midbrain and are better developed in the rodents than in man. The dorsal tegmental nucleus lies immediately dorsal to the medial longitudinal bundle, a little behind the trochlear nucleus, and extends caudad as far as the rostral end of the motor V nucleus of the trigeminal nerve. Between the levels of Figs. A8 and A9 it appears as a large rounded mass composed of very small cells and rather clearly outlined by a diffuse capsule of fine fibers. It receives fibers from the interpeduncular nucleus (*nucleus interpeduncularis*) through the tegmental tract of that center and from the mamillary body through the mamillotegmental fascicle (*fasciculus mamillotegmentalis*). Some of its axons join the *fasciculus longitudinalis dorsalis* (a periependymal longitudinal tract) which extends back from the hypothalamus. It is most distinct at, and caudal to, the level of this nucleus. A recent study in the rat demonstrates fibers from this nucleus in the mamillary peduncle distributed to mamillary nuclei, in the medial forebrain bundle to the nucleus of the *gyrus diagonalis* (band of Broca) and medial septal nucleus, and others. A more diffuse mass of medium-sized cells lateral and rostral to the dorsal tegmental nucleus is the laterodorsal tegmental nucleus.

The ventral tegmental nucleus is a conspicuous mass of multipolar cells ventral to the medial longitudinal bundle, in which also many mamillotegmental fibers end. These nuclei are apparently relay stations on a reflex pathway from the hypothalamus to the motor nuclei of the hindbrain. The mamillotegmental fasciculus is difficult to distinguish in the lower part of its course in transverse sections prepared by Weigert's method. It is a group of fine fibers which curve backward in a vertical plane after leaving the mamillary body and run dorsocaudad through the tegmentum on each side of the raphe to end in the nuclei just described.

Other correlation centers are the dorsal nucleus of the raphe which lies in the median plane just dorsal to the trochlear nuclei, some groups of cells in the raphe posterior to the decussation of the superior cerebellar peduncle, and a number of nuclei in various parts of the reticular formation which are not usually distinct in Weigert sections.

The cells of the reticular formation are so diffusely scattered among its fibers that there has been a tendency to neglect them, but they include correlating and activating elements of great functional importance. In the caudal part of the midbrain, medium-to-large reticular cells, ventrolateral to the medial longitudinal bundle and ventromedial to the superior cerebellar peduncle, are designated as the deep lateral tegmental nucleus. A dorsolateral tegmental nucleus, a ventral tegmental area, a cuneiform area, and others are recognized besides cell groups associated with the various large fiber bundles and decussations. Among the last of these, there must be mentioned particularly the *nucleus Darkschevitch*.* This mass of small cells is situated at about the level of

* Variously spelled in English as Darkshevich, Darkshevitch, Darkscheivitsch.

the anterior end of the medial longitudinal bundle, to which it may contribute some fibers. It lies just dorsal to the interstitial nucleus and serves as a bed nucleus of the posterior commissure.

Situated in a median position at the ventral surface of the tegmentum lies the interpeduncular nucleus (*nucleus interpeduncularis*) (Figs. A12, A13, and A15), a mass of gray matter occupying the posterior perforated space of human anatomy, which lies at the bottom of the interpeduncular fossa. It extends from the caudal end of the mamillary body caudad as far as the ventral pontine nuclei, its size being greatest at levels just behind the emergence of the oculomotor nerve. The cell bodies are mostly small. This center receives a large fiber bundle, the *fasciculus retroflexus* (Figs. A18, A19), from the habenular nuclei of the diencephalon, as well as fibers from the mamillary body and from bulbar visceral centers, and gives off fibers, as already mentioned, which run to the dorsal tegmental nucleus as the tegmental tract of the interpeduncular nucleus. This is a group of very fine fibers which may be observed to leave the dorsal surface of the interpeduncular nucleus and to run dorsocaudad on each side of the raphe. These structures, possibly being concerned with the correlation of olfactory with other, chiefly somatic, impulses, are largest in animals having a highly developed sense of smell. They are considerably larger in the rat than in man, whose olfactory sense is rather poorly developed.

In the deep part of the *basis pedunculi,* just in front of the anterior border of the pons, there appears a mass of gray matter separating the tegmentum from the ventrally situated tracts of the *pes pedunculi.* This mass, the *substantia nigra,* has the form of a broad, thick band extending forward into the hypothalamus, becoming thicker and rounded in cross section as it extends (Figs. A12–A15). It receives fibers from the cerebral hemispheres and also from the tectum and probably from the cerebellum, and it gives rise to others which run through the tegmentum, but its precise connections and function are not yet clearly understood. It has received its name on account of its dark color in the human brain, where it stands out conspicuously when examined in gross material. This color is due to the presence in many of the cell bodies of melanin pigment. There is less pigmentation in lower mammals than in higher ones (Ariëns Kappers *et al.*, 1936; Innes and Saunders, 1962), however, and in the rat it is practically or entirely absent.

The *substantia nigra* is considered to comprise three regions, differing in the size, grouping, and staining reactions of the cell bodies (Gillilan, 1943). The most ventral is the *zona reticulata,* partly mingled with the fibers of the *pes pedunculi,* and dorsal to it are a *zona compacta* and a *pars lateralis.* The emerging roots of the oculomotor nerve cut across the medial part of the *zona compacta* caudally and break it up into patches of deep-staining cells.

Superficial to the *substantia nigra,* the *basis pedunculi* is composed of a broad band of closely grouped longitudinal fibers running along each side of the ventral surface of the midbrain and appearing roughly crescentic in cross section. The fibers originate in the cerebral cortex and pass through the internal capsules to form these bands, which converge toward the upper edge of the pons and penetrate into it. These large bundles gradually decrease in size as they descend, giving off fibers to various parts of the brain; analysis shows that they are composed of several distinct tracts. In man the medial fifth of the bundle is composed of fibers running from the frontal cortex to the pontine nuclei, which constitute the frontopontine tract (*tractus frontopontinus*), but this portion may be presumed to be very small in the rat if it is present, since the frontal cortex is developed to a very slight extent. The lateral fifth in man is made up of fibers from the temporal and occipital lobes to the same nuclei—the temporopontine tract (*tractus temporopontinus*). Between these lies the large corticospinal tract (*tractus corticospinalis*), with which are mingled many corticobulbar fibers. Many of the latter, however, are grouped in the midbrain into two distinct bundles which pass to the nuclei of the cranial nerves.

As might be expected, the *basis pedunculi,* consisting of fibers of neocortical origin, varies in size in different animals according to the development of the neocortex. It is largest in man, where the neocortex is most highly developed, and is considerably smaller in the rat. It has been shown that in the rat, from medial to lateral across the peduncle there are fibers from cortical centers for head and neck, then upper extremity, and then lower extremity. A considerable number of the fibers for the head region separate in the midbrain and pons as an aberrant pyramidal system.

A number of small fascicles separate from the optic tract at the ventrorostral tip of the medial geniculate body and run caudomediad over the surface of the cerebral peduncle. This is the basal optic root (*tractus opticus basalis*) (Fig. A14). In the latter half of their course the fascicles assemble as a compact bundle, which turns dorsad around the medial edge of the *pes pedunculi* to end in a distinct nucleus associated with the medial part of the compact zone of the *substantia nigra,* the basal optic nucleus (ectomamillary nucleus). Most of the fibers are very finely myelinated. Kosaka and Hiraiwa believed that the root contains both crossed and uncrossed fibers in the rat; Chang (1936) considered it to be composed of collaterals from crossed optic fibers; and Gillilan (1941) maintains that it is entirely crossed. A few of the fibers pass through the nucleus to end in the *substantia nigra,* and some also pass to the lateral reticular gray of the tegmentum, and others to the oculomotor nucleus. Secondary fibers from the nucleus also run to these regions.

Associated with the basal optic root are scattered fine fibers that separate to penetrate the peduncle and enter the ventrolateral part of the subthalamic nucleus. These constitute the anterior accessory optic tract, very poorly developed in the rat.

The tectum is the dorsal portion or roof of the midbrain. In the lower vertebrates, it is molded into two rounded optic lobes, where most of the fibers of the optic nerve terminate, while the posterior part of its ventrolateral portion contains a more or less massive auditory correlation center. In the mammals, the latter center has acquired a more dorsal situation and appears as a second, usually smaller eminence behind the reduced optic lobe. Hence the optic lobes have come to be known in mammals as the anterior colliculi (*colliculi anteriores*), while the phylogenetically new eminences are the posterior colliculi (*colliculi posteriores*). In the rat and other lower mammals, the latter are considerably smaller than the former, whereas in man they are more nearly alike in size. This difference in proportion is due chiefly to a decrease in the functional importance and consequently in the relative size of the anterior colliculi in man, a much larger percentage of the optic fibers ending in the diencephalon, whence their impulses are sent to the cerebral cortex.

As seen in sections, the posterior colliculi appear simpler in structure than the anterior ones. Each contains a large, somewhat rounded mass of gray matter, the nucleus of the posterior colliculus, which is the end station of the greater part of the lateral lemniscus. Most of the fibers of this tract may be seen to plunge directly into the nucleus. Some of them, however, pass around it, forming a capsule before entering its substance. A certain proportion of these may decussate to end in the nucleus of the other side, but Papez (1923a,b) found no evidence of this in his studies of degeneration in the brain of the rat.

Separated from the nucleus of the posterior colliculus by the deep portion of its capsule lies a thick layer of central gray matter. Dorsal to this, the space between the right and left nucleus is filled by internuclear cortex or laminated gray matter of the tectum (*laminae tecti*), which is penetrated by a great many white fibers, and superficial to the nucleus is a capsular zone of gray, or outer cortex, also mingled with many white fibers. Huber and Crosby (1943) have shown that the chief nucleus is an enlargement of the lateral part of the original periventricular gray matter, continuous with that area in the anterior colliculus, and that the capsular gray is continuous with the much more highly developed laminae of the anterior colliculus between its *stratum profundum* and the optic tract (see below).

The tectum, being composed of important correlation centers, receives many different kinds of fibers coming from the spinal cord, the medulla oblongata, and the forebrain, perhaps including corticotectal connections. Most of these, however, are not easily traced in ordinary sections of normal material. Not all the fibers of the lateral lemniscus end in the posterior colliculi. Some divide before terminating there and send a branch into the anterior colliculus, and it may be that a few such fibers end in the latter region without previously dividing. A considerable number of the fibers terminating in the colliculi are, moreover, collaterals from axons which continue their course further up the brain along with some that have no connection in the midbrain. These form a distinct tract on the lateral aspect of the tectum, which is the direct continuation of the lateral lemniscus but which is now known as the brachium of the posterior colliculus (*brachium colliculi posterioris*). The fibers that end in the tectum form the chief reflex auditory pathway, according to the usual view, and the brachium is the cortical pathway up which pass auditory impulses destined to enter consciousness. The fibers of the latter group end in the medial geniculate body, whence new axons pass to the auditory cortex. The brachium contains also fibers arising in the posterior colliculi, and some of cortical origin which terminate in these centers.

It is usually considered that the tectospinal tracts in most mammals include fibers from the posterior colliculi. Papez (1923a,b), however, could find in Marchi preparations of rat brains no demonstrable descending tract from the posterior colliculi and concluded that these cannot be regarded as reflex centers. Many of the fibers originating in a colliculus decussate between the two pairs of colliculi as the commissure of the posterior colliculi and Papez found these to end entirely in the opposite colliculus. Along with the commissure of the lateral lemniscus and the incomplete decussation of the *corpus trapezoideum*, they provide for bilateral representation of auditory stimuli in the posterior colliculi and in the medial geniculate bodies (*corpora geniculata medialia*). Most of the fibers arising in each posterior colliculus, however, enter its brachium to ascend to the thalamus and terminate in the medial geniculate body.

The nucleus and fibers of the mesencephalic root of the trigeminal nerve (*nucleus tr. mesencephali n. trigemini*), which lie in the lateral part of the tectum at the outer border of the central gray matter, have already been described. The cell bodies become fewer as they are traced forward through the midbrain and disappear near the rostral level of the oculomotor nucleus.

The anterior colliculi present fundamental differences from the posterior bodies, differences of a highly significant character since they illustrate two ways in which higher correlation centers may develop. The chief nucleus of the posterior colliculus increases in size but not in complexity with increase in the ascending auditory paths. "The superior collicular pattern is a secondary differentiation from the primitive periventricular gray through the peripheral migration of neurons during embryonic development to form the layers external to the main efferent layer, *stratum album profundum*. Such migrations occur embryologically and probably phylogenetically under the influence of afferent tectal tracts and . . . the layering . . . favors localization and permits specificity of reception and projection of impulses" (Huber and Crosby, 1943). Lamination is found in the optic lobes of all vertebrates except cyclostomes and tailed amphibians. In mammals it is actually less complex than in many lower forms, the changes reflecting a shift of function from that of being largely a way station to the dorsal thalamus to that of being a station largely on descending paths, particularly from the cerebral cortex. Terminology of the layers has varied widely.

The cortex of the anterior colliculi is covered by a very thin layer of fibers, the *stratum zonale*, derived mainly from the homolateral striate area of the cerebral cortex, and so less well developed in the rat than in man. The fibers turn inward and end in the two subjacent layers (Figs. A12–A18).

Beneath the zonal layer lies the much thicker *stratum griseum superficiale,* which contains very few myelinated fibers; and this is followed by the *stratum opticum,* also of considerable thickness and occupied largely by coarse fascicles of optic fibers. These fibers may be observed rostrolaterally entering this layer from the terminal portion of the optic tract (brachium of the anterior colliculus). In the deeper part of the same layer is an internal corticotectal system forming a rather distinct zone. The optic fibers end particularly in the underlying layers. Chang believed that he demonstrated a localization of optic terminals in the colliculus of the rat, fibers from the upper quadrant of the retina ending caudolaterally, fibers from the lower quadrant mediorostrally, those from the temporal portion laterally, and those from the nasal portion medially.

Next follow in order the *stratum griseum intermediale,* the *stratum album intermediale,* and the *stratum griseum profundum,* all three of which have sometimes been regarded as subdivisions of a single *stratum lemnisci.* Here ascending systems are received and correlated with optic and cortical terminals.

The *stratum album profundum* separates the deepest of the preceding layers, from which it is not very sharply differentiated, from the central gray matter. It is composed chiefly, perhaps entirely, of efferent and commissural fibers rising from cells in the gray matter both external and internal to it. The efferent fibers mostly enter the dorsal tegmental decussation; after crossing in it they form the tectobulbar and tectospinal tracts, though some of these fibers are stated to descend without crossing. Tectopontal tracts are reported to arise particularly in the caudal part of the colliculus and terminate in the tegmentum and the lateral nucleus of the pons. In the rat and other lower mammals, a tectogeniculate tract, associated with the brachium of the anterior colliculus, passes to the ventral nucleus of the lateral geniculate body, but both the tract and the nucleus are reduced or lost in higher animals.

At the anterior boundary of the tectum, where it continues into the thalamus, lies the large posterior commissure (*commissura posterior*) which appears as an anterior extension of the *stratum profundum* of the anterior colliculi (Figs. A16–A18). This commissure is apparently a rather fundamental structure as it is very constant throughout the whole vertebrate series and develops early in ontogeny. At each side of the commissure, its fibers spread out ventrally and caudally in a large mass of cells, which has been called the nucleus of the posterior commissure, and in which several subdivisions have been described. In the rat the medial nucleus of the posterior commissure passes over into the pretectal nucleus (posterior nucleus of the thalamus) so that it is difficult to distinguish them, and both nuclei seem to give rise to fibers of the commissure. The nucleus of the posterior commissure receives optic tract fibers and gives rise to a large part of the commissure itself in the rat. Many of the fibers terminate in the interstitial nucleus and in the nucleus of Darkschevitch, thus leading from the optic tract to the heterolateral interstitiospinal tract. Spinotectal fibers probably enter the nucleus of the posterior commissure and it has been claimed that another important constituent of the commissure is probably made up of ascending vestibular fibers from the lateral part of the medial longitudinal bundle. There are also contributions from the nucleus of Darkschevitch.

The subcommissural organ (*corpus subcommissurale*) is present in all vertebrates and some particular study has been made of rodents including the rat. It is more conspicuous in human infants and fetuses than in adults (Keene and Hewer, 1935). It consists of a thickening of ependymal lining of the ventricular roof around the posterior commissure at the transition from the third ventricle to the aqueduct. This body is seen as a kidney-shaped, but not otherwise identified, structure immediately rostral to the posterior commissure in Fig. A38. It is composed of a high, well-developed and deeply staining columnar epithelium, differing from ordinary ependyma (Fig. 12, and Wislocki and Leduc, 1954). The lining extends into the dorsal recess which becomes well outlined during the embryonic development of most vertebrates and persists in some adult forms as the *recessus postcommissuralis* or mesocelic recess, located in the midline at the caudal end of the posterior commissure. An individually variable vestige of this recess, lined by typical high columnar epithelium of the subcommissural organ, may persist in the human brain and form a blind tubule between the fascicles of the posterior commissure, and it occasionally communicates with the cerebral aqueduct. The rostral end of Reissner's fiber has been found attached to the subcommissural organ. This fiber is a non-nervous fibrillary structure which may run through the entire ventricular system and down to the termination of the spinal central canal; it occurs in all vertebrate classes. It may be related to ependymal cilia, or represent a secretion of the subcommissural organ. It has not been described in the human adult brain, but Keene and Hewer (1935) identified it in a fetus of 15 weeks. Wislocki and Leduc (1954) reported that the subcommissural organ in rodents including the rat, and Reissner's fiber, both stained selectively with the alum-hematoxylin component of Gomori's stain. These authors suggested that the columnar cells of the subcommissural organ are secretory and that they produced Reissner's fiber. Bargmann and Schiebler (1952) studied the subcommissural organ of dogs and cats and assumed that this organ may secrete into the cerebrospinal fluid a Gomori-positive substance which also displays a strong periodic acid-Schiff reaction and thus might be a mucopolysaccharide. However, nothing is known with certainty concerning the functional significance of the subcommissural organ or of Reissner's fiber, but the constancy of these structures throughout the vertebrate kingdom is noteworthy.

These concepts are challenged by the recent observations of Gilbert (1960), who found that the subcommissural organ may produce hormones instrumental in the control of water metabolism which act apparently antagonistic to the supraoptico- and paraventriculohypophysial system.

References

Ariëns Kappers, C. U., G. C. Huber & Elizabeth C. Crosby. The Comparative Anatomy of the Nervous System of Vertebrates, Including Man. 2 Volumes. New York: Macmillan, 1936.

Bargmann, W. & Th. H. Schiebler. Histologische und cytochemische Untersuchungen am Subcommissuralorgan von Säugern. *Z. Zellforsch.* **37**: 583-596, 1952.

Cajal, S. Ramón y. Histologie du système nerveux de l'homme et des vertébrés. Paris: Maloine, 1909-1911. (Reprinted by C.S.I.S., Madrid, 1952.)

Chang, H. T. The primary connections of the optic nerve in the albino rat. *Chinese J. Zool.* **2**: 17-30, 1936.

Crosby, Elizabeth C., T. Humphrey & E. W. Lauer. Correlative Anatomy of the Nervous System. New York: Macmillan, 1962.

Gilbert, G. J. The subcommissural organ. *Neurol.* **10**: 138-142, 1960.

Gillilan, Lois A. The connections of the basal optic root (posterior accessory optic tract) and its nucleus in various mammals. *J. Comp. Neurol.* **74**: 367-408, 1941.

Gillilan, Lois A. The nuclear pattern of the non-tectal portions of the midbrain and isthmus in rodents. *J. Comp. Neurol.* **78**: 213-252, 1943.

Herrick, C. Judson. An Introduction to Neurology. 5th Ed. Philadelphia: Saunders, 1931.

Huber, G. C. & E. C. Crosby. A comparison of the mammalian and reptilian tecta. *J. Comp. Neurol.* **78**: 133-190, 1943.

Innes, J. R. M. & L. Z. Saunders. Comparative Neuropathology; p. 660. New York: Academic Press, 1962.

Keene, M. F. L. & E. E. Hewer. Subcommissural organ and mesocoelic recess in human brain, together with note on Reissner's fibre. *J. Anat. (London)* **69**: 501-507, 1935.

Kosaka, K. & K. Hiraiwa. Zur Anatomie der Sehnervenbahnen und ihren Zentren. *Folia neurobiol.* **9**: 367-389, 1914.

Kuhlenbeck, H. & R. N. Miller. The pretectal region of the rabbit's brain. *J. Comp. Neurol.* **76**: 323-365, 1942.

Morest, D. K. Connexions of the dorsal tegmental nucleus in rat and rabbit. *J. Anat. (London)* **95**: 229-246, 1961.

Olzewski, J. *In*: Brain Mechanisms and Consciousness. (E. D. Adrian, F. Bremer, H. H. Jasper & J. F. Delafresnaye, eds.), p. 54. Springfield, Illinois: C. C Thomas, 1954.

Papez, J. W. The mammillary peduncle, Marchi method. *Anat. Rec.* **25**: 146, 1923a.

Papez, J. W. The rubrospinal tract, Marchi method. *Anat. Rec.* **25**: 147, 1923b.

Papez, J. W. Comparative Neurology. 518 pp. New York: Crowell, 1929. (Reprinted by Hafner, New York, 1961.)

Papez, J. W. & G. LaVerne Freeman. Superior colliculi and their fiber connections in the rat. *J. Comp. Neurol.* **51**: 409-440, 1930.

Riley, H. A. An Atlas of the Basal Ganglia, Brain Stem and Spinal Cord. New York: Hafner, 1960.

Shintami, Y. K. The nuclei of the pretectal region of the mouse brain. *J. Comp. Neurol.* **113**: 43-60, 1959.

Van Valkenburg, C. T. On the mesencephalic nucleus and root of the nervus trigeminus. *Proc. Koninkl. Akad. Wetens. Amsterdam*: 25-42, 1911.

Weinberg, E. The mesencephalic root of the fifth nerve. A comparative anatomical study. *J. Comp. Neurol.* **46**: 249-405, 1928.

Wislocki, G. B. & Elizabeth H. Leduc. The cytology of the subcommissural organ, Reissner's fiber, periventricular glial cells, and posterior colliculus recess of the rat's brain. *J. Comp. Neurol.* **101**: 283-309, 1954.

CHAPTER VII

Prosencephalon (Forebrain)

The forebrain is that part of the central nervous system which is derived from the prosencephalic vesicle. With ascending phylogeny, nervous mechanisms become more and more localized in the forebrain. Consequently, the mammalian forebrain harbors most of the mechanisms subserving the higher functions of life, such as we commonly call the "mind," and, in addition, mechanisms for motor function, sensory perception, and "homeostasis." The latter may be defined as the maintenance of steady states in the entire organism, involving all organs, such maintenance being necessary for the proper execution of all but the most primitive functions of life.

On account of its dominating role over the organism as a whole, the forebrain has received the attention of innumerable scientists representing practically every discipline of scholarly endeavor. Nevertheless, relatively little is known as to how the forebrain exercises its functions, even though a prodigious amount of information has accumulated over the past decade. In general, the old hypothesis of "parcellated" representation of specific functions in circumscribed, anatomically defined, regions of the forebrain, forcefully promoted by Franz Joseph Gall (1758–1828) as "phrenology," has given way to more dynamic concepts based upon information and communication theory and on electronic models. Consequently, finite anatomically defined forebrain structures are viewed as integral parts of larger and more complex mechanisms, and their functional significance is expressed relative to the function of the whole rather than in terms of individual performance.

This scheme of operation has few exceptions. While repeated electrical stimulation of a specific point in the motor cortex of the frontal lobe elicits reproducible movements, the destruction of the stimulated area does not necessarily abolish this effect. Instead, the same movement can be elicited by stimulation of a neighboring region. This is an example of the "plasticity" of the nervous system and serves to illustrate the dynamic organization of forebrain function. On the other hand, destruction of a ventral horn cell in the spinal cord is invariably followed by degeneration of the muscle fibers innervated by the destroyed cell, and restoration of function by collateral innervation is, at best, partial.

Obviously, in the forebrain functional mechanisms are not always as closely tied to morphologic structures as they are in the spinal cord. Nevertheless, structural neuroanatomy is indispensable as a basis for the understanding of forebrain functions. Consequently, neuroanatomical information is here presented by the traditional approach. Functional implications are discussed whenever known.

Anatomically, the forebrain is divided into the *diencephalon* (interbrain) and the *telencephalon* (endbrain). In the latter, two major divisions are recognized in higher vertebrates, the *rhinencephalon* (olfactory or smell brain) and the nonolfactory *telencephalon* which, in mammals, are separated from each other by the rhinal fissure. During early embryogenesis the prosencephalon is a vesicle, the lumen of which is retained in the form of the ventricles in the fully developed forebrain. The telencephalon forms paired symmetrical "hemispheres," each of which contains a lateral ventricle. The diencephalon occupies a central and ventral position forming around the third ventricle. Broadly speaking, the diencephalon is the connecting link between the rostrolaterally located telencephalic hemispheres and the caudally extending mesencephalon.

The anatomical structures which connect diencephalon and telencephalon are massively developed fiber tracts, running at a more or less obliquely parasagittal plane and shaped like a "C" on a horizontal plane. These fiber systems, as they radiate into the telencephalic hemispheres, are known as *corona radiata;* they are made up of fibers which connect various subcortical nuclei with their telencephalic cortical projection areas, the corticopetal fibers. These are intermingled with efferent cortical axons, the corticofugal fibers, which connect with diencephalic, mesencephalic, and other lower centers of the central nervous system. The convergence of the *corona radiata* in a dorsoventral direction leads to the formation of a compact fiber system called the internal capsule (*capsula interna*), which surrounds the lateral aspects of the diencephalon and separates the *corpus striatum* from the latter.

At the caudal end, the diencephalon is continuous with the mesencephalon (Fig. A37). Microscopically, however, most of the nuclear masses have been identified as to their mesencephalic or diencephalic origin, respectively, so that a diencephalic-mesencephalic border may be considered to exist. This junction is traversed by numerous fiber tracts, the most conspicuous of which is the *pes pedunculi,* a direct continuation of the posterior limb of the internal capsule. Moreover, two continuous gray masses can be traced through the diencephalic-mesencephalic junction. Surrounding the aqueduct is the periaqueductal gray matter (*substantia grisea periventricularis*) which is anatomically and functionally a continuation of the periventricular systems of thalamus and hypothalamus. In the tegmentum lies the reticular formation (*formatio reticularis*) which extends from the medulla oblongata through pons and midbrain into the ventrolateral regions of the thalamus.

A. DIENCEPHALON (INTERBRAIN)

Anatomically, the diencephalon consists of five more or less well delimited complexes. The epithalamus occupies the dorsal midline region. The hypothalamus forms the ventral region around the base of the third ventricle. In between these two extends the thalamus, dorsolaterally bounded by the metathalamus and ventrolaterally by the subthalamus.

1. Epithalamus

The epithalamus comprises the thin membranous roof of the third ventricle, termed *velum interpositum,* which supports the chorioid plexus of the third ventricle, the pineal body (*epiphysis*), and the habenular complex (*habenula*). The pineal body is a small glandular organ which projects caudad between the anterior colliculi (*colliculi anteriores*) (Figs. 7, 25). It is wedged between the posterior portions of the cerebral hemispheres and is attached to the posterior roof of the third ventricle by a hollow stalk containing a funnel-shaped extension of the third ventricle, called the pineal recess (Fig. 12). The pineal gland secretes melatonin (5-methoxy-*N*-acetyltryptamine) which, injected daily in microgram amounts, decreases incidence of estrus in rats (Wurtman and Chu, 1963).

It may be significant that in man primary neoplasms arising from the pineal body frequently show features of teratoma, i.e., a malignancy containing tissues of all three germinal layers. Comparative anatomy considers the pineal body as the homologue of the rudimentary parietal eye of lower vertebrates.

The habenular complex forms a fusiform ridge along the dorsal edges of the walls of the third ventricle. It consists of a medial and a lateral nucleus (*nucleus habenularis medialis et lateralis*) covered by a dorsal layer of medullated nerve fibers, the *stria medullaris thalami* (Figs. A18–A22, A23–A29, A35, and A38). Most of the fibers of the *stria medullaris* run in an anteroposterior direction and terminate in the habenular nuclei and also in the *nucleus parataenialis thalami,* which accounts for the caudally decreasing size of the *stria medullaris.* Some fibers, however, pass the habenular nuclei, then turn sharply dorsad and mediad and cross in the habenular commissure (Fig. A18), which is directly dorsal to the posterior commissure but separated from the latter by the pineal recess. These crossed fibers terminate in the heterolateral habenular nuclei. The different components of the *stria medullaris* unite near the mediodorsal angle of the rostral end of the thalamus. Their origin, which has been extensively studied by Herrick, Johnston, Gurdjian, and others, is widely scattered throughout the forebrain. On the basis of these studies, the following components of the *stria medullaris* are known.

Medial corticohabenular tract. The fibers of this bundle originate in the hippocampus. They run in the postcommissural fornix and join the *stria medullaris* at its rostral end.

Lateral corticohabenular tract. These fibers arise from the deep layers of the temporal prepyriform cortex and cross through the medial forebrain bundle where they join with the lateral olfactohabenular tract. Fascicles of this bundle cross in the habenular commissure. It is possible that efferent fibers from the globus pallidus reach the habenula by way of this tract.

Lateral olfactohabenular tract. The fibers of this tract originate in the caudal part of the *tuberculum olfactorium* and the rostral part of the preoptic area. They course through the anterior part of the medial forebrain bundle and then join the lateral corticohabenular tract.

Septohabenular tract. According to Gurdjian (1926), these fibers arise from all parts of the septal area. Young (1936) found in the rabbit that the *nucleus fimbrialis septi* gives rise to this tract.

Stria terminalis component. This bundle of fibers originates in the anterior region of the amygdala whence it runs rostrad in the *stria terminalis* and joins the *stria medullaris* at the bed nucleus of the *stria terminalis,* probably picking up additional fibers from this nucleus.

In addition to these well-defined bundles, the *stria medullaris* contains fibers arising in the thalamus and hypothalamus, but their course has not been fully traced as yet.

Another afferent pathway to the habenula originates in the interpeduncular nucleus (Massopust and Thompson). This interpedunculodiencephalic pathway sends fibers with the *fasciculus retroflexus* to the lateral nucleus of the habenula, and to the dorsolateral and dorsomedial thalamic nuclei. A few fibers of this bundle continue anteriorly through the *stria medullaris* and terminate in the anterior hypothalamic area. Destruction of this tract leads to a loss of learned kinesthetic, auditory and discrimination habits.

The efferent fibers of the habenular complex emerge ventrally, forming a conspicuous bundle, the *fasciculus retroflexus* (Meynert) or the *tractus habenulo-interpeduncularis,* which takes a straight course in a ventrocaudal direction and terminates in the interpeduncular nucleus (*nuc. interpeduncularis*) of the mid-brain. This nucleus emits many fibers, the pedunculotegmental fibers, to the *nuc. tegmenti dorsalis.* The habenular nuclei also connect directly with the dorsal tegmental nucleus, i.e., without synapsing in the interpeduncular nucleus, via the habenulotegmental tract. Fibers emerging from the dorsal tegmental nucleus form part of the dorsal longitudinal fascicle.

By virtue of its fiber connections, the habenular complex is usually considered to represent an "olfactosomatic correlation center" (Kuhlenbeck, 1954a). MacLean includes it among the subcortical cell stations of the limbic system (see Chapter VIII), which is not contradictory to the above interpretation.

2. Hypothalamus

The anatomical delineation of the hypothalamus is still a matter of controversy. Kuhlenbeck, for instance, includes in this part of the diencephalon the entire subthalamus and the *globus pallidus,* because they are derivatives of the primordial hypothalamic longitudinal zone. In the present account we follow the practice of standard texts, i.e., we do not discuss subthalamus and globus pallidus as hypothalamic structures.

The hypothalamus is shaped somewhat like a rectangular open box, the cavity being the ventral portion of the third ventricle (*ventriculus tertius*). The anterior wall is formed by the preoptic area and the posterior wall by the mamillary complex. Sides and bottom contain a number of nuclei some of which are not very clearly defined. The bottom part, i.e., the floor of the third ventricle between the optic chiasma and the mamillary bodies, is known as the *tuber cinereum* (gray swelling). In its center is a small hole which opens into a funnel-shaped extension, the infundibulum. That part of the tuber cinereum which, as a circular wall, surrounds the orifice of the infundibulum, the median eminence, protrudes into the ventricular lumen. The infundibulum extends in a ventrocaudal direction and its cavity terminates blindly in the neurohypophysis or posterior pituitary lobe, which is anatomically and functionally an extension of the infundibulum (Fig. 12).

The nomenclature of the various hypothalamic nuclei has varied greatly from one species to another, but even within one and the same species various authors employ different terms. To alleviate the resulting confusion, Rioch, Wislocki, and O'Leary (1940) have established a uniform terminology applicable to all mammalian species, which is used in the following.

Anatomically, the hypothalamus can be divided into an anterior part containing a few myelinated and many unmyelinated fibers, represented by the tuber cinereum and the nuclei in the lateral walls of the third ventricle as well as the preoptic area. Included also in this part of the hypothalamus are the infundibulum and the posterior lobe of the pituitary. In contrast, the posterior wall of the hypothalamus, comprising the mamillary complex, contains a wealth of myelinated fiber systems. This morphologic schism, which is an oversimplification, nevertheless has functional implications that justify a separate discussion of these two parts. Thus the poorly myelinated part is the final common pathway for neural influence on the hypophysis, whereas the mamillary bodies exert no direct control over this endocrine gland. Accordingly, the poorly myelinated part of the hypothalamus is termed the vegetative hypothalamus (Figs. A21, A24–A26, A28–A37).

a. *Vegetative Hypothalamus.* In a rostrocaudal direction we encounter the lateral and medial preoptic area (*area preoptica lateralis et medialis*), formerly called *nucleus preopticus lateralis et medialis.* There is disagreement as to the precise ontogenetic and morphologic position of the preoptic area. In Craigie (1925), it was identified as median telencephalon (*pars optica hypothalami*). In their précis on the preoptic, hypothalamic, and hypophysial terminology, Rioch *et al.* (1940) do not elaborate on the controversy. Kuhlenbeck (1954a), on the other hand, divides the preoptic region into a telencephalic and a diencephalic portion. Riley states that this area ontogenetically represents the telencephalodiencephalic junction which belongs to the unevaginated median telencephalon, and which is anatomically closely related to the hypothalamus. Whatever its derivation, the preoptic area provides an anatomical and functional link between the limbic centers of the telencephalon and the vegetative hypothalamus. Ventral and slightly lateral to the preoptic area is the very distinct supraoptic nucleus (*nuc. supraopticus*) which hugs the *tractus opticus* on its dorsal aspects (Figs. A25 and A26). On either side of the midline is a tiny but distinct nuclear mass, the *nuc. suprachiasmaticus,* and slightly caudal to this is the anterior hypothalamic area, an accumulation of diffusely strewn nerve cells intermingled with unmedullated fibers. Dorsally we find the *nuc. paraventricularis hypothalami* (*nuc. filiformis* of the old nomenclature). The *nuc. dorsomedialis* and *nuc. ventromedialis hypothalami,* which are arranged in a dorsoventral sequence to each other, follow immediately. Over the dorsocaudal aspects of the dorsomedial nucleus extends the *nuc. posterior hypothalami.* The *nuc. arcuatus hypothalami* forms a continuous mass of gray matter around the floor of the third ventricle, whereas the upper walls are surrounded by the periventricular gray matter which continues caudally as the periaqueductal gray matter (*substantia grisea periventricularis*) of the midbrain. The outer wall of the hypothalamus, lateral to the dorso- and ventromedial nuclei, is formed by the lateral hypothalamic area (*area lateralis hypothalami*), a poorly delimited mass of nerve cells between which the fibers of the medial forebrain bundle pass in a parasagittal horizontal plane. In the median eminence are located the *nuclei tuberales.* Infundibulum and neurohypophysis do not contain discernible nerve cell bodies. Rather they are made up of special glial elements, the pituicytes, and of nerve fibers representing the supraopticohypophysial and paraventriculohypophysial tracts.

A most important afferent, efferent, and interconnecting fiber system for the hypothalamus is the medial forebrain bundle (*fasciculus medialis telencephali*). This tract of thinly myelinated and unmyelinated fibers stretches parallel to the lateral border of the hypothalamus from the olfactory tubercle through the base of the forebrain and extends into the mesencephalon (Figs. A21–A28). It contains afferent descending fibers to the hypothalamic nuclei, originating from many centers of the olfactory telencephalon (to be discussed later), as well as ascending fibers from the tegmental nuclei and the reticular formation. In addition, the medial forebrain bundle connects the various parts of the hypothalamus with each other. Finally, it carries efferent fibers from the preoptic, anterior, lateral, and posterior hypothalamic areas to midbrain, rhombencephalon, and spinal cord, subserving sympathetic and parasympathetic functions. The complexity of this association system is beyond the scope of this book, and reference should be made to the studies of Krieg, Nauta, Green, and others, some of which, however, do not refer to the rat brain. Another longitudinal associational fiber system lies in the periventricular gray matter, the so-called diencephalic periventricular system (Crosby and Woodburne, 1940), which is continuous with the *fasc. dorsalis longitudinalis* of the midbrain and hindbrain (Figs. A13–A15).

Fibers from the amygdala (*nuc. amygdalae*) reach the hypothalamus through the compact *stria terminalis* and the diffuse ventral amygdalofugal pathway (Fig. 37). In lower vertebrates, a sizable number of optic nerve fibers connect with the hypothalamus, apparently representing a mechanism for changes in skin color in chameleon and for similar adaptive effects. Finally, there are afferent fiber systems from neopallium and basal ganglia to the hypothalamus, but their localization in the rat brain is not well defined.

The vegetative hypothalamus is the most important nervous center for autonomic and endocrine control of the entire organism, as clearly demonstrated by the Nobel Prize winning studies of W. R. Hess. Some of the most outstanding scientists in the field, such as Cannon, Bard, Ranson, and more recently Houssay and Harris, to name but a few, have made significant and often exciting contributions to the knowledge of hypothalamic function. The hypothalamus exerts its influence on vegetative control in two ways. First, it gives rise to thinly myelinated fibers which apparently originate in the preoptic area, the anterior, lateral, and posterior hypothalamic areas, and which descend through the midbrain in medial bundles, the dorsal longitudinal fascicle, and in lateral bundles which pass through the mamillary bodies to reach the intermediolateral cell columns of the spinal cord. These fibers, representing the afferent pathways to the paravertebral sympathetic chain and to parasympathetic centers in the neuraxis, mediate impulses for vasomotor and respiratory control and for a variety of other autonomic effects—pupillary tonus, erection of hair, secretory activity, and genital functions, plus many others. In general, sympathetic autonomic reactions are elicited by stimulation of the posterior hypothalamus whereas stimulation of the anterior part results in parasympathetic responses.

Apart from these responses involving the efferent mediation of nervous impulses, the hypothalamus exerts its control over metabolism, endocrine activity, sexual activity, and other vegetative functions on a humoral basis, by elaborating active substances of hormone character. These substances are conducted to the hypophysis. It is established that the nerve cells of the supraoptic and paraventricular nuclei secrete antidiuretic hormone (ADH), which flows along the supraoptico- and paraventriculohypophysial tracts through the infundibulum into the posterior pituitary lobe. The extraordinary richness of the capillary bed in the supraoptic and paraventricular nuclei (Table I, p. 39) is probably significant in this connection. Disturbance of this system results in diabetes insipidus. There is circumstantial evidence that the ventrodorsal and ventromedial nuclei, and maybe others also, produce active humoral substances (Tonutti, 1958; Harris, 1958; Bovard, 1961). These, however, reach the anterior pituitary gland via the blood stream through the hypophysial-portal system, where they elicit thyrotropic and gonadotropic effects. ACTH is released from the anterior pituitary lobe, probably under the influence of a chemical transmitter carried from the median eminence through the portal system. It is, however, not clear by which means stimulation of the posterior hypothalamus results in the production of this chemical transmitter. The *nuclei tuberales* have been functionally linked to sexual activity, but it has been shown that lesions in the region of the median eminence also result in changes of eating and drinking habits.

The neurosecretory activity of the nerve cells of certain hypothalamic nuclei is one of the most fascinating recent discoveries, partly because it was entirely unexpected. Yet, it would be wrong to assume that all hypothalamic mechanisms subserving vegetative functions depend on the elaboration of humoral factors. This is implicitly shown by studies in which electric stimulation of minute hypothalamic regions yields immediate responses in the form of voracious eating and drinking, sneezing, yawning, urination, defecation, ovulation, attack, withdrawal, and a host of other reflex actions. These experiments, utilizing implanted electrodes, have also shown that evoked responses of identical nature, such as those enumerated above (and many others, for instance, changes in blood pressure, respiratory rate, gastric motility), can be elicited from different hypothalamic regions. On the other hand, reproducible responses from one and the same site of stimulation can be altered or even completely abolished by simultaneous stimulation of a different region. These observations again testify to the dynamic rather than static organization of neural mechanisms in the forebrain.

The hypothalamus receives afferent stimuli not only through neuronal circuits, but also chemically by circulating hormones elaborated in the peripheral endocrine glands. The mechanism involved in this hormonal stimulation operates on the general principle of "feedback," controlling the activity levels of these hormones by appropriate efferent humoral stimulation of the anterior pituitary gland via the hypophysial–portal system.

b. *Mamillary Complex.* In contrast to the higher mammals, in particular the primates, which have well shaped bosom-like pairs of mamillary bodies, the rat has the mamillary complex fused in the median plane. Thus, it really is not reminiscent of what the name implies (Fig. 8).

Superficially, the mamillary complex is covered by a very thin layer of white fibers. Each half consists of two main nuclei, a larger medial and a smaller lateral one (*nuc. mamillaris medialis et lateralis*), and between these penetrate a number of fibers of the medial forebrain bundle. Some of these fibers end in the mamillary nuclei. Others cross over diffusely in the supramamillary commissure (*commissura supramamillaris*) (Fig. A17), after which they descend through the tegmentum. Caudally this commissure blends with the ventral tegmental decussation (*decussatio tegmenti ventralis*) of Forel (Fig. A15). In addition to descending fibers of the medial forebrain bundle, descending fornix fibers also cross in the supramamillary commissure. The largest part of the crossing fibers of this commissure connects the subthalamic bodies and the red nuclei. The ventral tegmental nuclei are connected by commissural fibers which cross in the posterior part of the supramamillary commissure and the ventral tegmental decussation.

In the immediate vicinity of the medial and lateral mamillary nuclei a number of other nuclei can be discerned. Caudally is the *nucleus mamillaris posterior* (*nucleus mamillaris medialis pars posterior*), an extension of the medial nucleus, and dorsal to it the supramamillary area. Rostral to the mamillary nuclei are the dorsal and ventral premamillary nuclei. The latter forms a bed nucleus for the diencephalic periventricular systems and belongs functionally to the vegetative hypothalamus (Gurdjian, 1926).

Most of the connecting fiber systems of the mamillary complex are myelinated and very conspicuous in stained sections. An efferent system originating in the tegmental nuclei (Guillery, 1957), probably in part in the *substantia nigra* (Papez, 1923a), is the mamillary peduncle (*pedunculus mamillaris*) (Figs. A17, A19, and A35). At the level of the interpeduncular nucleus this fascicle is traversed and then laterally bordered by the root of the *nervus oculomotorius* (Fig. A15). The mamillary peduncle enters the mamillary complex dorsolateral to the column of the fornix (*columna fornicis*), where it bifurcates, sending many transverse fibers via the fornix into the medial nucleus while others pass ventrad into the lateral mamillary nucleus. Some fibers of the mamillary peduncle continue rostrad in the medial forebrain bundle. Some of them terminate in the *nuc. tuberales hypothalami,* and others can be traced to the diagonal band of Broca and the medial septal nucleus (Guillery). Other afferent fibers are received through the medial forebrain bundle as described above. The most conspicuous afferent system (Nauta, 1956) is represented by the fornix column in which many fibers of the ipsilateral *fimbria hippocampi* collect. Roughly one-half of the fornix fibers terminate in the mamillary nuclei which are entered from a dorsolateral position.

The efferent systems of the mamillary body leave the anterodorsal part of the medial nucleus as a group of compact bundles forming a conspicuous tract in a vertical plane which bifurcates about 1.5 mm above the medial mamillary nucleus. The majority of fibers turn rostrad here and run in an anterodorsal direction, taking a straight course to the anterior nuclei of the thalamus. This mamillothalamic tract (*tractus mamillothalamicus* or bundle of Vicq d'Azyr) breaks up into small scattered bundles before it terminates in the three anterior thalamic nuclei, whence secondary fibers project to the cingulate cortex. These connections are highly ordered, demonstrated by Pilleri for human beings and by Powell for the rat (Fig. 32) i.e., the *pars medialis* of the medial mammillary nucleus projects to the anteromedial nucleus of the thalamus and from there to the anterior cingulate cortex. The *pars lateralis* projects to the anterodorsal nucleus. The other part of the efferent mamillary fibers lies at first lateral to the mamillothalamic fibers. At the bifurcation, this bundle breaks away caudally at a right angle and soon loses its compactness. This mamillotegmental fascicle (*fasciculus mamillotegmentalis*) sends fibers to motor nuclei in the tegmentum and medulla oblongata (Figs. A11, A12, and A35). It also connects with neurons of the reticular formation which give rise to ascending reticular pathways and to the descending reticulospinal tracts.

The intimate connection of the mamillary bodies with the hippocampus and the anterior nuclei of the thalamus has prompted their inclusion among the structures representing the limbic system, a mechanism subserving affective behavior (see Chapter VIII). Destruction of the mamillary bodies in man pro-

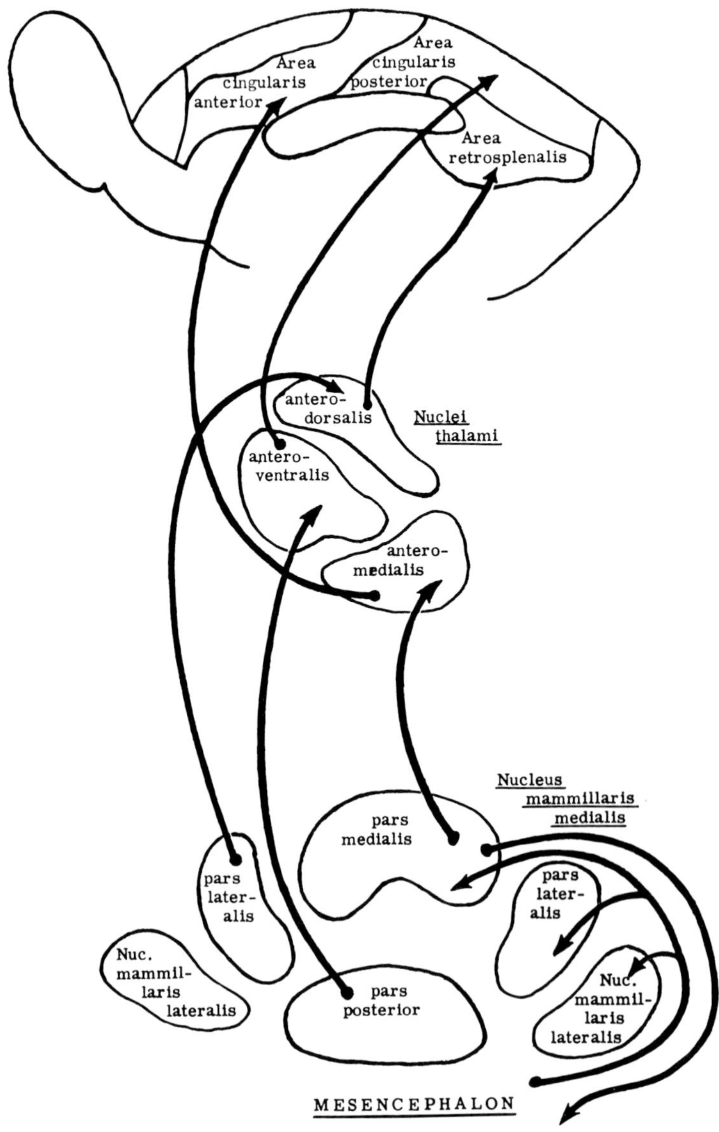

FIG. 32. Mamillo-thalamic-cingulate projection system. (Diagram redrawn from Powell.)

duces severe psychological disturbances in the form of alterations of affective behavior and disorientation (Korsakoff's psychosis).

3. THALAMUS

The largest part of the diencephalon is represented by the thalamus. Originally it was considered to play an important role in the mechanism of vision, and therefore it was referred to as *thalamus opticus*. This notion, however, is no longer tenable. Only the lateral geniculate body, a part of the metathalamus, and the pretectal nuclear group receive optic fibers, whereas the largest part of the thalamus serves as a relay and connection center for practically every conceivable aspect of sensory and motor function, as well as for behavioral control.

Since the thalamus has been studied by investigators belonging to different schools, who worked on different species, a complex nomenclature with numerous confusing synonyms has been evolved, and many discrepancies in the subdivision of the thalamic nuclear masses are evident. The basis of these difficulties is thus a historical one and also one of questionable identity of homologies among the various vertebrate species. Furthermore, outright errors have crept into the literature, and above all the human element of subjective evaluation has further compounded these problems. What one author considers to represent a distinct and identifiable nuclear mass may be interpreted by another as part of a different nucleus. Likewise, the fiber connections of the thalamic nuclei are a matter of controversy. This is easily understood if one studies the extremely rich and complicated fiber tracts within the thalamus as well as in its surroundings. The latter form the *corona radiata thalami*, of which numerous subdivisions are identified.

Riley's atlas contains a very useful compilation of synonyms of thalamic nuclei and of all other neuroanatomical terms, but even this listing cannot be considered to be complete. In the present book, no attempt has been made to outline more than the least equivocal anatomical landmarks, and the reader needing more detail is referred to the excellent reviews and studies of Le Gros Clark, Gurdjian, Krieg (1944), Lashley, Waller, and Kuhlenbeck.

A subdivision of the thalamic nuclei has been attempted in different ways. The simplest approach is the phylogenetic, in which the development of certain parts of the thalamus is correlated with that of the neopallium. In following this approach, one finds that those thalamic structures which are located close to the midline and account for the formation of the *massa intermedia* remain relatively constant during ascending phylogeny, and are therefore considered to represent a phylogenetically old part expressed in the term "paleothalamic nuclei." On the other hand, there are those nuclei that increase in size commensurately with the development of the neopallium. They are found in the ventrolateral region and in the posterior part of the thalamus, including the pulvinar, and are collectively referred to as neothalamic nuclei. Elegant as it may appear, this approach, however, has not provided clear-cut answers for such distinct nuclei as the anterior group; moreover, it fails to provide a rationale for the delineation of anatomically well-delimited structures. Consequently, the morphologic approach is most widely employed, and the following criteria are used: (1) homotypy of perikarya, i.e., it is assumed that each distinct nucleus is populated by nerve cells of uniform morphology; (2) delineation by zones of myelinated fibers, i.e., a nucleus is usually considered to consist of closely packed perikarya separated from surrounding structures by zones of fibers or by tissues containing few perikarya. Even if these criteria are applied, outlining of nuclei by the examination of histologic sections is difficult unless a three-dimensional reconstruction is made, a method which has been successfuly employed by Krieg (1944).

Steering a middle course between the views proposed by various recent authors, one can conveniently subdivide the thalamic nuclei into a number of groups which, with the exception of the midline group, are bilaterally symmetrical.

The midline group extends throughout the entire thalamus from its rostral end, at the hippocampal commissure, to the indistinct diencephalic-mesencephalic junction at the level of the posterior commissure. Occupying a dorsal position underneath the ventricular lumen is the *nuc. paraventricularis thalami* which is subdivided by Krieg (1944) into two distinct nuclei based upon cytomorphology. Ventral to this nucleus is the *nuc. reuniens* which also extends throughout the length of the thalamus. In its middle third, however, the *nuc. reuniens* is separated from the paraventricular nucleus by the *nuc. rhomboideus* and in part by the *nuc. medialis thalami* (Figs. A19–A25, A37).

The midline nuclei, as can readily be seen, account for the formation of the *massa intermedia,* the structure which connects the thalami of the two sides across the third ventricle. In the human brain, the *massa intermedia* has about the same absolute size as in the rat brain. Thus, it represents only a very small part of the entire thalamus in man and has not increased parallel with neopallial development, a fact which places the midline nuclei distinctly into the group of paleothalamic nuclei.

The medial group of nuclei is anatomically and functionally related to the midline group. In general, these nuclei assume a lateral and ventral position in relation to the midline group. In the anterior thalamus, we find the *nuc. parataenialis* wedged between the *nuc. paraventricularis,* the *stria medullaris,* and the anterior nuclei. In the middle sector of the thalamus, the *nuc. medialis thalami* (frequently referred to as *nuc. mediodorsalis*) is recognized, which connects through the *massa intermedia* dorsal to the *nuc. rhomboideus.* At the caudal end of the thalamus is the *nuc. parafascicularis* in a similar topographic relationship to the *nuc. paraventricularis* as the *nuc. parataenialis* in the anterior thalamus. The parafascicular nucleus extends around the dorsal and lateral aspects of the fasc. retroflexus, which accounts for its name. In addition to the mentioned nuclei, the *nuc. gelatinosus thalami,* situated between the *nuc. reuniens* and *nuc. rhomboideus* in a paramedian position and ventral to the *nuc. medialis,* and the *nuc. centri mediani* (*centre médian* of Luys, *nuc. centromedialis thalami*) are included among the medial group by Krieg (1944). The centromedial nucleus is found lateral to the *nuc. gelatinosus* at about the same level (Figs. A19–A23, A37, A38).

The above-mentioned thalamic nuclei are separated from the remainder of the thalamic structures by a layer of medullated fibers, the *lamina medullaris interna*. This fiber system is rather distinct in the primate but is not conspicuous in the murine brain. Consequently, it provides a continuous source of controversy for neuroanatomists. Within the medullary lamina, some authors have identified nuclear masses which are collectively referred to as the intralaminar thalamic nuclei. Krieg (1944) feels that only the *centre médian* can be designated an intralaminar nucleus. The school of Le Gros Clark, in particular Powell, however, describe three intralaminar nuclei and identify them as (1) the centromedial nucleus (*nuc. centri mediani, centre médian*); (2) the *nuc. parafascicularis*, which Powell *et al.* (1957) depicts in a position medial to the latter; and (3) the *nuc. centralis lateralis* in the dorsal part of the lamina. The latter nucleus, as identified by Powell, could be part of the *nuc. parafascicularis* described by Krieg (1944). This opinion differs from that of Kuhlenbeck, who surmises that in man the *nuc. centri mediani* (*centre médian*) represents a lateral differentiation of the *nuc. parafascicularis* of lower mammals.

All the nuclei which have been mentioned up to this point are usually considered to be paleothalamic in nature, i.e., that they do not have extensive direct neopallial connections. This has, however, been disputed by Le Gros Clark, who found efferent projections from the *nucleus medialis* to the neocortical frontal pole.

The midline nuclei (*nuc. reuniens, rhomboideus, paraventricularis*, and probably also part of the *nuc. parafascicularis*) form the thalamic portion of the periventricular system (*substantia grisea periventricularis*) into which they send numerous fibers forming the descending dorsal longitudinal fascicle. The intralaminar nuclei, according to Powell, project via the inferior thalamic radia[illegible]n to the medial cortex of the hemisphere and to the neostriatum, i.e., the [illegible]nen and caudate nucleus. There are no direct connections to the septum [illegible]ory tubercle, medial and anterior olfactory nuclei, or amygdala. Physiol[illegible]a-tions have shown that the midline and intralaminar nuclei upon [illegible]-ulation produce "recruiting responses" over large areas of th[illegible]t according to Powell and others no direct thalamocortical pro[illegible]re involved. Instead, the response is elicited by impulses tr[illegible]ti-synaptic pathway involving the neostriatum, whence, [illegible]ute perhaps passing through the sub- and hypothalamus. [illegible]tem, they are projected to the cortex.

The afferent fibers to the medial and midline group originate partly within other parts of the thalamus (intrinsic thalamic system) and are believed to be generally connected to ascending pathways from the reticulothalamic, tegmento-thalamic, and tectothalamic tracts (Papez, 1956). Krieg (1944) described afferent fibers from the medial lemniscus to the *nuc. medialis,* but it should be remembered that most of the lemniscal fibers connect with the ventrolateral group of thalamic nuclei. The centromedial nucleus receives fibers from the emboliform nuclei of the cerebellum (Jung and Hassler, 1960).

There is little doubt among physiologists, clinicians, and neuroanatomists that the paleothalamic nuclei play an important role in forming connecting links between the reticular activating and the limbic system, and also the extrapyramidal motor system. The complexity of the fiber connections involved, however, has thus far precluded their precise and complete anatomical demonstration.

The anterior group of thalamic nuclei is located in the rostrodorsal region of the thalamus. The *nuc. anteroventralis* is lodged between the *stria terminalis* and the *stria medullaris,* and, farther caudad, is medially bordered by the *nuc. anterodorsalis.* Ventral and medial to these nuclei, sweeping around the *nuc. parataenialis* and *paraventricularis* is the anteromedial nucleus on the base of which the mamillothalamic tract breaks up into smaller bundles. The anterior nuclei are connected by commissural fibers with their contralateral counterparts. They constitute the terminals for the fibers of the mamillothalamic tract, which has already been described (Figs. A25, A26, A35–A38). They also receive afferent fibers from the hippocampus through the postcommissural fornix. The anterior thalamic nuclei project to the cingulate cortex. Both afferent and efferent connections of these nuclei display a high degree of spatial organization, as depicted in Fig. 32. Their function is not well understood, but their central position between the limbic cortex and the diencephalon has prompted Papez (1937) to propose that they play an important role in the mechanism of emotive processes. In man, surgical elimination of the anterior thalamic nuclei has favorably influenced emotional disturbances in some instances.

At the periphery of the internal medullary lamina, the ventrolateral group of thalamic nuclei extends as a curved structure, the basis of which is formed by the medial lemniscus, its most important afferent fiber tract (Figs. A19–A22, A23, A37, A38). The *nuc. ventralis thalami* is divided into a number of subnuclei. The *pars medialis* and the *pars dorsalis* receive the bulk of the fibers of the medial lemniscus, the gracilothalamic and cuneothalamic tracts, as well as the trigeminal and spinal lemnisci. The efferent fibers of these nuclei project by way of the dorsal thalamic radiation to the parietal area of the neocortex, the so-called somesthetic cortex. The *pars ventralis* is also a terminal of lemniscal fibers but receives afferent fibers from the superior cerebellar peduncle through the *fasciculus thalamicus.* This bundle is poorly demarcated in the rat. It also contains efferent fibers from the *globus pallidus* connecting with the *pars lateralis* of the ventral nucleus. These fiber connections suggest that the *pars lateralis* is concerned with motor function. In man, the surgical destruction of this nucleus, known as thalamectomy, is an established treatment for the alleviation of Parkinsonian tremor and other hyperkinesias, but it is not clear whether a similar mechanism exists in the rat brain. In the human thalamus, a posterolateral division of the ventral nucleus is known which receives the spinothalamic and bulbothalamic tracts and thus serves as a relay center for painful stimuli. It projects again to the somesthetic parietal cortex, but possibly also to the frontal lobe. In the rat, it is not well defined, and it is believed by Kuhlenbeck that its homologue is represented by the *pars lateralis.* The region labeled *pars ventromedialis* in Fig. A19 is congruent with that division of the *nucleus ventralis* which relays taste impulses to the somatic sensory face area 13 in the insular region, immediately dorsal to the rhinal fissure (Benjamin and Akert) (Fig. 38).

The *nuc. lateralis thalami* is a distinct structure in the rat brain where it is found at the floor of the lateral ventricle between the anterior group and the *nuc. reticularis thalami* (Figs. A19–A23). It extends caudad to the level of the lateral geniculate body. Its caudal continuation beyond this point is known as the *pars posterior* of the *nuc. lateralis thalami.* The lateral nucleus is said to receive afferent fibers from the thalamus, the subthalamus, and some adjacent thalamic nuclei, such as the ventral nucleus, which forms much of its ventral border, and to project to the parietal, temporal, and occipital lobes. The *pars posterior,* however, is intimately connected with the optic system, both through afferent optic tract fibers and by way of a reciprocal projection system with the occipital cortex. On account of these fiber connections, the *pars posterior* has been considered to be the homologue of the primate *pulvinar,* which is not discernible in the rat brain. With this evolution, there is apparently a change in functional significance of the lateral nucleus. Thus, it was recently suggested that the human *pars posterior* of the lateral nucleus projects to the cingulate cortex, the destruction of which results in a retrograde degeneration of this nucleus (Locke, Angevine, and Yakovlev). The human lateral nucleus, according to Riley, has strong connections with the neopallium, the striatum, and the subthalamus; it is therefore considered to represent a pallial-striatal relay center.

In the caudal end of the dorsal thalamus are a number of small nuclei referred to as the pretectal cell group. They lie in the diencephalic-mesencephalic border zone and are therefore sometimes included with the mesencephalic tectal nuclei. The *area pretectalis* contains several small nuclei which have been identified by Bucher and Nauta and are not further enumerated here. The *nuc. posterior thalami* belongs anatomically to this group and so does the *nuc. suprageniculatus.* As shown by Nauta and Bucher, all these nuclei are related to each other both functionally and by fibers. They receive fibers from the medial lemniscus, from the optic tract, from the *area striata* (occipital area 17), and also from the cerebellum and the extrapyramidal motor centers of tegmentum and subthalamus. All these connections are relatively diffuse and therefore not traceable in normal preparations. On account of these fiber connections, it can be safely assumed that this region provides a mechanism for the integration of visual and tactile impressions for appropriate motor responses.

4. Metathalamus

The metathalamus comprises the *corpora geniculata laterale* and *mediale*, each of which is composed of a dorsal and a ventral nucleus. They lie dorsal and lateral to the thalamus, and this topographical relation is expressed by the prefix "meta-" which in anatomy denotes "dorso-" (Figs. A13, A21, and A38). Over its dorsolateral aspects, the metathalamus is in superficial contact with the hippocampus, from which it is separated by the *fissura chorioidea* (Fig. 10). In primates, however, the geniculate bodies and the hippocampus are displaced ventrad by the markedly developed neopallium. Therefore, the term metathalamus is rarely used in human anatomy. Kuhlenbeck, for instance, lists the geniculate bodies among the posterior group of thalamic nuclei.

The lateral geniculate body forms a curved structure at the rostral end of the metathalamus; its surface is covered by a layer of white matter. These fibers are largely derived from the optic pathways. The latter consist of the optic nerves caudally followed by the optic chiasma and the optic tracts. As shown by Polyak, 90% of the optic fibers of the rat cross in the optic chiasma and continue in the contralateral optic tract. The optic tract begins as a compact bundle which runs in a dorsocaudal direction and reaches the ventral border of the lateral geniculate body. At this point the fibers spread out and many of them dip into the lateral geniculate body, where they terminate in both the ventral and the dorsal nucleus. A number of fibers, however, continue to enter the various structures of the pretectal area, including the *nuc. lateralis thalami pars posterior*, and to the anterior colliculus of the tectum. According to Tsang (1937a,b), the lateral geniculate body of the rat receives only collaterals of optic fibers which terminate ultimately in the anterior colliculus. This would then explain that rats, after a generous bilateral ablation of area 17, are still able to respond to visual cues in avoidance experiments (Meyer *et al.*).

The dorsal nucleus of the lateral geniculate body projects its fibers through the optic radiation into occipital cortical area 17, the primary visual cortex. Consequently, only those fibers of the optic tract that send collaterals to the dorsal nucleus of the lateral geniculate body carry visual impulses to the cortex, whereas those terminating in the ventral nucleus are believed to subserve pupillary reflex mechanisms. Lashley (1934) found a region in the ipsilateral dorsal nucleus of the lateral geniculate body which he could identify as the probable site concerned with binocular vision, because it receives afferent fibers from the ipsi- and the contralateral optic nerves. For such studies, the rat brain is advantageous since only a small part of its retinal fibers remain uncrossed in the optic chiasma. The lateral geniculate body receives projection fibers from area 17, most of which go to the ventral nucleus (Nauta and Bucher). With ascending phylogeny, the dorsal nucleus becomes larger and lamellated, so that in simian primates and man the term lateral geniculate body applies only to the homologue of the dorsal nucleus. The ventral nucleus becomes relatively smaller, displaced anteriorly, and separated from dorsal nucleus by the visual fibers. The human homologue of the ventral nucleus is termed *nuc. pregeniculatus.* It is poorly delimited from the *zona incerta.*

The visual pathways from the retina to area 17 display a high degree of spatial organization. This means that optic nerve fibers, originating from given points in the retina, will maintain an ordered topographic relationship to each other for their entire course to the dorsal nucleus of the lateral geniculate body. The nerve cells of the latter, their efferent axons and their final termination points in the visual cortex, are organized on the same principle.

Those optic fibers which pass the lateral geniculate body and terminate in the pretectal area and in the *colliculus anterior* form the *brachium colliculi anterioris,* which is a continuation of the optic tract. There is no precisely defined boundary between these two segments of the optic fibers. Shortly before reaching the lateral geniculate body, a group of the optic fibers splits off in a ventromedial direction to form the *tractus opticus basalis* which terminates in the *nuc. tr. opticus basalis* of the midbrain (Gillilan). Still other optic fibers leave the optic pathways at the chiasma, where they form the hypothalamic optic root, which terminates in the region of the median eminence of the hypothalamus.

The medial geniculate body is located ventrally, medially, and caudally to the lateral body. This nucleus receives most of its afferent fibers through the *brachium colliculi posterioris* from the posterior colliculus. Since the latter is a terminal for the lateral lemniscus, the "central auditory tract," the medial geniculate body receives auditory impulses which it transmits through the "auditory radiation" of the *corona radiata* to the temporal neocortex, area 41 (Fig. 38, p. 160). The spatial organization of the auditory pathways is based on frequency and tone intensity, thus permitting "localization" of the stimulus source (Rose *et al.,* 1963).

It is usually stated that some fibers emitted by the medial geniculate body pass rostrad to the region of the optic chiasma where they cross in the commissure of Gudden (*commissura supraoptica ventralis*), and then run back to the contralateral medial geniculate body. Bucher and Bürgi, however, doubt this. Although their studies were performed on the cat, it is safe to assume that the results apply to the murine brain as well. Since two other supraoptic commissural systems are located in the dorsal region of the optic chiasma, all three will be considered together. Besides the ventral supraoptic commissure, the older literature lists a dorsal supraoptic commissure, the ventral part of which is known as Meynert's commissure and the dorsal part as Ganser's commissure. Bucher and Bürgi found that the commissure of Ganser forms a distinct structure, the *commissura supraoptica dorsalis,* the fibers of which ascend through the midbrain in the medial longitudinal fascicle and, after crossing, terminate in the reticular nucleus of the thalamus. According to the same authors, the ventral supraoptic commissure, which is distinct in sections of the normal rat brain, since its fibers stain less deeply than the optic ones, forms one anatomical structure, i.e., it contains both the commissures of Gudden and of Meynert, which cannot be separated from each other. The fibers of this commissure run in opposite directions. Those of the *pars tectopetalis* ascend in the region of the lateral *tegmentum* and, after crossing, terminate in the region ventral to the medial geniculate body and the superior colliculus. The fibers of the *pars tectofugalis* can be traced in the reverse direction, from the optic tectum to the region below the opposite medial geniculate body and possibly into the tegmentum. From this study, it follows that the supraoptic commissures are actually decussations.

5. Subthalamus

The subthalamus is located at the ventral and lateral aspects of the thalamus from which it is separated by the *lemniscus medialis*. The *pedunculus cerebri* forms its ventral border. Medially, the subthalamus blends with the lateral hypothalamic region. Through the subthalamus pass numerous thalamofugal and thalamopetal fibers on their way to and from the telencephalic cortex. They are particularly dense in the rostral extreme, where they form the *radiatio thalamostriatalis* (Fig. A25), a part of the inferior thalamic radiation often called ventral thalamic peduncle. These fibers cause the rostral part of the *zona incerta* to become rather indistinct, and this part is known as *"regio innominata,"* a term which is rarely used at present.

The subthalamus contains a conspicuous and large nuclear mass, the *zona incerta,* and, ventral to the latter, a somewhat indistinct and much smaller nucleus, the *corpus subthalamicum* (body of Luys). The latter, however, is quite prominent in the primate brain, where it appears as a lens-shaped nucleus immediately dorsal to the *pes pedunculi.* In between, and also surrounding, these structures, extend myelinated fibers which are somewhat indistinct in the rat brain, but which form characteristic fiber tracts in the human brain. From the ventromedial angle of the *globus pallidus* emerges a fiber bundle, the *ansa lenticularis* (*radiatio thalamostriatalis, radiatio corporis striati pars pallidothalamica*) in a medial direction. The tract forks almost immediately after its formation into a dorsal bundle, the field H_1 and a ventral bundle, the field H_2 and between these extends the *zona incerta.* The fibers of field H_1 connect with the ventral thalamic nucleus, forming the *fasciculus thalamicus.* Field H_2 is composed of fibers connecting the *globus pallidus* with the *corpus subthalamicum,* the *zona incerta, substantia nigra,* and *nucleus ruber.* This fiber system provides reciprocal connections, i.e., fibers run in opposite directions between the *globus pallidus* and some parts of the *putamen* on the one hand and the mesencephalic and subthalamic nuclei on the other. Contralateral connections between the *corpora subthalamica* and the *zonae incertae* run via the supramamillary commissure. Apart from the pallidal fibers, the subthalamus receives fibers from the nuclei of the ventral thalamus, the substantia nigra, the red nucleus, and the tegmental nuclei of the midbrain. The *corpus subthalamicum* receives afferent fibers from neocortex and cerebellum, but similar connections have not been demonstrated for the *zona incerta* (Figs. A17, A22–A25).

The efferent fibers of the *corpus subthalamicum* connect substantially with the *substantia nigra,* but also with numerous other diencephalic, mesencephalic and telencephalic centers. The distribution of the fibers originating in the *zona incerta* is similar, except that this structure also connects with the inferior olivary body.

The entire subthalamus is chiefly involved in motor function, and, together with the telencephalic basal ganglia, the red nucleus and the substantia nigra, forms the so-called extrapyramidal motor system or paleostatic and paleokinetic system. Destruction of the *corpus subthalamicum* in man will result in contralateral hemiballism, but this has not been observed in the rat.

Some authors include the *nuc. reticularis thalami* with the subthalamus. This nucleus forms a dorsal medially concave continuation of the *zona incerta* over its entire anteroposterior extension. The nucleus is traversed by many conspicuous bundles of corticothalamic and thalamocortical projection fibers which give it a characteristic appearance in Weigert sections and account for its name. These fibers are known as the *lamina medullaris thalami lateralis.* Little is known about the fiber connections and functions of this nucleus. In man, it receives afferent impulses from the hypothalamus and subthalamus and projects to the parietal, occipital, and temporal lobes (Riley), and in this respect is similar to the lateral nucleus of the thalamus.

References

ARIËNS KAPPERS, C. U., G. C. HUBER & ELIZABETH C. CROSBY. The Comparative Anatomy of the Nervous System of Vertebrates, Including Man. 2 Volumes. New York: Macmillan, 1936.

BENJAMIN, R. M. & K. AKERT. Cortical and thalamic areas involved in taste discrimination in the albino rat. *J. Comp. Neurol.* **111**: 231-259, 1959.

BOVARD, E. W. A concept of hypothalamic functioning. *Perspectives in Biol. and Med.* **5**: 52-60, 1961.

BUCHER, V. M. & S. M. BÜRGI. Some observations on the fiber connections of the di- and mesencephalon in the cat. Part III. The supraoptic decussations. *J. Comp. Neurol.* **98**: 355-379, 1953.

BUCHER, V. M. & W. J. H. NAUTA. A note on the pretectal cell groups in the rat's brain. *J. Comp. Neurol.* **100**: 287-295, 1954.

CAJAL, S. RAMÓN Y. Histologie du système nerveux de l'homme et des vertébrés. Paris: Maloine, 1909-1911. (Reprinted by C.S.I.S., Madrid, 1952.)

CHANG, H. T. The primary connections of the optic nerve in the albino rat. *Chinese J. Zool.* **2**: 17-30, 1936.

CLARK, W. E. LE GROS. An experimental study of thalamic connections in the rat. *Phil. Trans. Roy. Soc. London* **222B**: 1-28, 1932a.

CLARK, W. E. LE GROS. The structure and connections of the thalamus. *Brain* **55**: 406-470, 1932b.

CLARK, W. E. LE GROS & R. H. BOGGON. On the connections of the anterior nucleus of the thalamus. *J. Anat. (London)* **67**: 215-226, 1933.

CRAIGIE, E. H. An Introduction to the Finer Anatomy of the Central Nervous System Based upon that of the Albino Rat. Toronto: University Press, 1925a.

CROSBY, ELIZABETH C. & R. T. WOODBURNE. The comparative anatomy of the preoptic area and the hypothalamus. *In:* The Hypothalamus and Central Levels of Autonomic Function (J. F. Fulton, S. W. Ranson & A. M. Frantz, eds.), pp. 52-169. Baltimore: Williams & Wilkins, 1940.

CROSBY, ELIZABETH C., T. HUMPHREY & E. W. LAUER. Correlative Anatomy of the Nervous System. New York: Macmillan, 1962.

ENGELHARDT, FR. & R. DIEPEN. Veränderungen am supraoptico-hypophysären System nach Koagulationen im Tuber cinereum der Ratte. *In:* Hormone und Psyche die Endokrinologie des alternden Menschen. 5. Symposion der Deutschen Gesellschaft für Endokrinologie Freiburg, 7. bis 9. März 1957, pp. 246-268. Berlin-Göttingen-Heidelberg: Springer, 1958.

GILLILAN, LOIS A. The connections of the basal optic root (posterior accessory optic tract) and its nucleus in various mammals. *J. Comp. Neurol.* **74**: 367-408, 1941.

GLOOR, P. Telencephalic Influences upon the Hypothalamus. Hypothalamic-Hypophysial Interrelationships (W. S. Fields, R. Guillemin & C. A. Carton, eds.), pp. 74-114. Springfield, Illinois: C. C Thomas, 1956.

GREEN, J. D. Neural pathways to the hypophysis. *In*: Hypothalamic-Hypophysial Interrelationships (W. S. Fields, R. Guillemin & C. A. Carton, eds.), pp. 3-16. Springfield, Illinois: C. C Thomas, 1956.

GROOT, J. DE. The rat forebrain in stereotaxic coordinates. *Verhandl. Koninkl. Nederl. Akad. Wetensch. afd. Natuurkunde,* Tweede Reeks, Deel LII, No. 4, 1959.

GUILLERY, R. W. Degeneration in the post-commissural fornix and the mamillary peduncle of the rat. *J. Anat. (London)* **90**: 350-370, 1956.

GUILLERY, R. W. Degeneration in the hypothalamic connexions of the albino rat. *J. Anat. (London)* **91**: 91-115, 1957.

GURDJIAN, E. S. The hypothalamus in the rat. *Anat. Rec.* **32**: 208, 1926.

GURDJIAN, E. S. The diencephalon of the albino rat. Studies on the brain of the rat. No. 2. *J. Comp. Neurol.* **43**: 1-114, 1927.

HARRIS, G. W. The reticular formation, stress, and endocrine activity. *In*: Reticular Formation of the Brain (H. H. Jasper, L. D. Proctor, R. S. Knighton, W. C. Noshay & R. T. Costello, eds.), pp. 207-222. Boston and Toronto: Little, Brown, 1958.

HAYHOW, W. R., C. WEBB & A. JERVIE. The accessory optic fiber system in the rat. *J. Comp. Neurol.* **115**: 187-211, 1960.

HERRICK, C. J. Brains of Rats and Men. A Survey of the Original and Biological Significance of the Cerebral Cortex. Chicago: Univ. of Chicago Press, 1926.

HERRICK, C. J. An Introduction to Neurology. 5th Ed. Philadelphia: Saunders, 1931.

HESS, W. R. The Diencephalon. New York: Grune & Stratton, 1954.

JOHNSTON, J. B. The morphology of the septum, hippocampus and pallial commissures in reptiles and mammals. *J. Comp. Neurol.* **23**: 371-478, 1913.

JOHNSTON, J. B. Further contributions to the study of the forebrain. *J. Comp. Neurol.* **35**: 337-481, 1923.

JUNG, R. & R. HASSLER. The extrapyramidal motor system. *In:* Handbook of Physiology, Section I Neurophysiology Vol. II (H. W. Magoun, ed.), pp. 863-928. Baltimore: Williams & Wilkins, 1960.

KOIKEGAMI, H. Die Kerne und Verbindungsbahnen des Corpus mamillare der Säugetiere. *Z. mikr. Anat.* **44**: 131-162, 1938.

KRIEG, W. J. S. The hypothalamus of the albino rat. *J. Comp. Neurol.* **55**: 19-89, 1932.

KRIEG, W. J. S. The medial region of the thalamus of the albino rat. *J. Comp. Neurol.* **80**: 381-415, 1944.

KUHLENBECK, H. The Human Diencephalon, 230 pp. S. Karger, Basel and New York: 1954a.

KUHLENBECK, H. Some histologic age changes in the rat's brain and their relationship to comparable changes in the human brain. *Confin. Neurol.* **14**: 329-342, 1954b.

LASHLEY, K. S. The mechanism of vision. VII. The projection of the retina upon the primary optic centers in the rat. *J. Comp. Neurol.* **59**: 341-373, 1934.

LASHLEY, K. S. Thalamo-cortical connections of the rat's brain. *J. Comp. Neurol.* **75**: 67-121, 1941.

LOCKE, S., J. B. ANGEVINE, JR. & P. I. YAKOVLEV. Limbic nuclei of thalamus and connections of limbic cortex. *Arch. Neurol.* **4**: 355-364, 1961.

LOO, Y. T. The nucleus geniculatus medialis in mammalian brains. *Monogr. Nat. Res. Inst. Psychol. Nanking* **11**: 38 pp. 1937.

MACLEAN, P. D. The limbic system with respect to self-preservation and the preservation of the species. *J. Nerv. Mental Dis.* **127**: 1-11, 1958.

MARÍN-GIRÓN, F. Topografía estereotáxica del hipotálamo-hipófisis de la rata por el procedimiento de unidades relativas. *Anales Anat.* **8**: 75-84, 1959.

MARÍN-GIRÓN, F. Transformaciones del substrato anatomico de algunas glándulas endocrinas en relación con la topografía de estereotaxis hipotalámicas parciales. *Anales Anat.* **14**: 231-252, 1962.

MASSOPUST, L. C., JR. Stereotaxic atlas of the diencephalon of the rat. *In*: Electrical Stimulation of the Brain (D. E. Sheer, ed.), pp. 182-202. Austin: Univ. of Texas Press, 1961.

MASSOPUST, L. C., JR. & R. THOMPSON. A new interpedunculo-diencephalic pathway in rats and cats. *J. Comp. Neurol.* **118**: 97-106, 1962.

MEYER, D. R., W. ISAAC & B. MAHER. The role of stimulation in spontaneous reorganization of visual habits. *J. Comp. Physiol. Psychol.* **51**: 546-548, 1958.

NAUTA, W. J. H. An experimental study of the fornix system in the rat. *J. Comp. Neurol.* **104**: 247-271, 1956.

NAUTA, W. J. H. Fibre degeneration following lesions of the amygdaloid complex in the monkey. *J. Anat. (London)* **93**: 515-531, 1961.

NAUTA, W. J. H. & V. M. BUCHER. Efferent connections of the striate cortex in the albino rat. *J. Comp. Neurol.* **100**: 257-285, 1954.

PAPEZ, J. W. The mammillary peduncle, Marchi method. *Anat. Rec.* **25**: 146, 1923a.

PAPEZ, J. W. Comparative Neurology. 518 pp. New York: Crowell, 1929. (Reprinted by Hafner, New York, 1961.)

PAPEZ, J. W. A proposed mechanism of emotion. *Arch. Neurol. & Psychiat.* **38**: 725-743, 1937.

PAPEZ, J. W. Central reticular path to intralaminar and reticular nuclei of thalamus for activating EEG related to consciousness. *EEG Clin. Neurophysiol.* **8**: 117-128, 1956.

PILLERI, G. Zur Frage der Projektion des Nucleus anterior thalami. *Acta Anat.* **37**: 335-351, 1959a.

PILLERI, G. Beiträge zur vergleichenden Morphologie des Nagetiergehirnes. *Acta Anat.* **39**: (Suppl.) 38, 1959b.

POLYAK, S. L. The Vertebrate Visual System, 1390 pp. Chicago: Univ. of Chicago Press, 1957.

POWELL, T. P. S. The organization and connexions of the hippocampal and intralaminar systems. *Recent Progr. Psychiat.* **3**: 54-74, 1958.

POWELL, T. P. S. & W. M. COWAN. The connexions of the midline and intralaminar nuclei of the thalamus of the rat. *J. Anat. (London)* **88**: 307-319, 1954.

POWELL, T. P. S., R. W. GUILLERY & W. M. COWAN. A quantitative study of the fornix-mamillo-thalamic system. *J. Anat. (London)* **91**: 419-437, 1957.

RILEY, H. A. An Atlas of the Basal Ganglia, Brain Stem and Spinal Cord. New York: Hafner, 1960.

RIOCH, D. M., G. B. WISLOCKI & J. L. O'LEARY. A precis of preoptic hypothalamic and hypophysial terminology with atlas. *In*: The Hypothalamus and Central Levels of Autonomic Function (J. F. Fulton, S. W. Ranson & A. M. Frantz, eds.), pp. 3-30. Baltimore: Williams & Wilkins, 1940.

ROSE, J. E., D. D. GREENWOOD, J. M. GOLDBERG & J. E. HIND. Some discharge characteristics of single neurons in the inferior colliculus of the cat. *J. Neurophysiol.* **26**: 294-320; 321-341, 1963.

STRÖER, W. F. H. Studies on the diencephalon. I. The embryology of the diencephalon of the rat. *J. Comp. Neurol.* **105**, 1-24, 1956.

TONUTTI, E. Über die Einflussnahme des Hypothalamus auf die corticotrophe Partialfunktion der Adenohypophyse. *In:* Hormone und Psyche die Endokrinologie des alternden Menschen. 5. Symposion der Deutschen Gesellschaft für Endokrinologie, Freiburg, 7. bis 9. März 1957, pp. 238-244. Berlin-Göttingen-Heidelberg: Springer, 1958.

TORRES DEL RÍO, A. Aportaciones a la técnica estereotáxica hipotálamo-hipofisaria en la rata para contribuir al problema del crecimiento. *Anales Anat.* **14**: 409-414, 1962.

TSANG, Y. C. The blood supply of the lateral geniculate body in the rat. *J. Comp. Neurol.* **61**: 553-562, 1935.

TSANG, Y. C. Visual centres in blinded rats. *J. Comp. Neurol.* **66**: 211-261, 1937a.

TSANG, Y. C. Visual sensitivity in rats deprived of visual cortex in infancy. *J. Comp. Psychol.* **24**: 255-262, 1937b.

TSANG, Y. C. Supra- and post-optic commissures in the brain of the rat. *J. Comp. Neurol.* **72**: 535-567, 1940.

WALLER, W. H. Topographical relations of cortical lesions to thalamic nuclei in the albino rat. *J. Comp. Neurol.* **60**: 237-269, 1934.

WURTMAN, R. L. J. & E. W. CHU. Melatonin, a pineal substance: Effect on the ovary. *Science* **141**: 277-278, 1963.

YOUNG, M. W. The nuclear pattern and fiber connections of non-cortical centers of the telencephalon of the rabbit (Lepus cuniculus). *J. Comp. Neurol.* **64-65**: 295-401, 1936.

B. TELENCEPHALON (ENDBRAIN)

The telencephalon can be conveniently viewed as a symmetrical pair of bulbs representing the two telencephalic hemispheres, which are divided by the interhemispheric fissure. The telencephalic hemispheres are connected with each other by the preoptic area and by the corpus callosum and are attached to the diencephalon by the *corona radiata*. Like the cerebellum, but unlike all other parts of the central nervous system, the mammalian telencephalon contains most of its nerve cell bodies (perikarya) in its superficial layers. This layer of gray substance is called the *cortex*; in it the perikarya are arranged in concentric layers. The nerve fibers that connect with the cortical nerve cells and that emerge from the latter, form the subcortical white matter (*album cerebri*) which is essentially devoid of nerve cells. Cortex and subcortical white matter together are called the *pallium*, which literally translated means "cloak" or "mantle." From the basal parts of the prosencephalon develop masses of nerve cells which are not arranged in laminae, but rather form characteristic accumulations of nerve cells, usually called subcortical nuclei.

The laminated arrangement of the cortical perikarya is not uniform. In general, that part of the telencephalic cortex which extends over the convex aspects of the hemispheres shows the highest degree of organization and displays six more or less distinct layers of perikarya. In contradistinction, the cortex over the base and over the medial surface contains fewer laminae. There are also local differences in the development of the various layers. Some are very prominent in one particular cortical region while others are better developed in another part of the cortex. These observations have prompted the development of a specific approach to neuroanatomy, primarily concerned with the spatial arrangement of cortical perikarya, the study of which is termed cytoarchitectonics.

For many years, it has been believed that the cytoarchitectonic parcellation of the telencephalic cortex has functional implications in the sense that a cytoarchitectonically uniform cortical field harbors a specific function. It has also been proposed that cytoarchitectonically homologous areas react uniformly to a pathogenic stimulus (*topistic* vulnerability or *pathoklisis**). Although these assumptions have been supported by observations on the functional activity of such cytoarchitectonically uniform areas as motor and visual cortex, and certain regions of the hippocampus, the original hopes attached to the cytoarchitectonic approach have generally not been borne out by the facts. Thus, the cortical fields depicted in Fig. 38, which are the result of a tedious study by Krieg (1946), do not in the opinion of Kuhlenbeck *et al.* represent a "functional map" of the telencephalic cortex.

Nonetheless, in a phylogenetic and ontogenetic perspective, cytoarchitectonics is a useful tool which has provided considerable insight into the pro-

* See footnote page 4 for explanation.

gressive development of the telencephalon with ascending phylogeny as well as during its organogenesis. In general, one can state that the six-layered cortex is phylogenetically and ontologically the most recent acquisition of the telencephalon, and therefore shows its greatest development in primates, above all in man. In recognition of its phylogenetically "recent" nature, the six-layered cortex is called the *neocortex* and, together with its underlying white matter, forms the *neopallium*. A cortical area with a slightly lesser degree of differentiation is the *mesocortex*, extending over the medial surfaces of the murine hemispheres. This term is derived from its intermediate position both in respect to topography and degree of organization between the neocortex on the one hand and the paleocortex on the other. The *paleocortex* is less differentiated than the mesocortex. It forms the cortex of the pyriform lobe. The cortex with the simplest organizational pattern, which has only three laminae of nerve cells is called the archicortex. It constitutes the hippocampus (Ammon's horn). The terminology neo-, paleo-, and archicortex was originally devised in order to express the phylogenetic age of the respective structures. Subsequent studies, however, have not corroborated this assumption, and these terms should therefore be considered misnomers. In spite of this fact, this terminology enjoys worldwide usage; for this reason it is retained in the present account. In all mammals, regardless of the degree of phyletic development, neocortex, mesocortex, paleocortex, and archicortex form distinct cortical fields. The neocortex is essentially nonolfactory, whereas the other three comprise what is commonly called the rhinencephalic cortex. Unfortunately, the terminology in respect to these various cortical structures is inconsistent and various classifications will be found in the literature.

1. Rhinencephalon (Olfactory Brain)

The telencephalic structures ventral to the rhinal fissure and surrounding the diencephalon belong to the olfactory brain (smell brain). In lower mammals, the rhinencephalon represents a relatively large part of the entire telencephalon, but with ascending phylogeny the ratio becomes increasingly smaller. Concomitantly, most rhinencephalic structures become more and more buried by the mushrooming neopallium which expands in all dimensions.

In 1929, the late James W. Papez stated that the olfactory system consisted of eight parts: (1) the olfactory mucous membrane in the nasal cavity, (2) the olfactory bulb, (3) the ventral olfactory area (*tuberculum olfactorium*), (4) the motor olfactory striatum at the anterior plane of the *corpus striatum* (comprising the *nuc. striae terminalis* and *nuc. accumbens septi*), (5) the pyriform cortex, (6) the hippocampus, (7) the mamillary bodies, and (8) the head of the caudate nucleus and the putamen, as well as the amygdala, together with their connecting pathways. Papez pointed out that the pyriform area and the hippocampal gyrus are generally conceded to be the regions of olfactory sensation although this had been disputed by Cajal and by Herrick, whereas the olfactory mucosa, the olfactory bulbs, and the ventral olfactory area serve as a relay mechanism for olfactory impulses. Mamillary bodies and *corpus striatum,* according to this interpretation, are involved in the motor responses resulting from olfactory stimulation.

In 1937, free from the bias of his own teachings, Papez proposed that the "olfactory brain," with the exception of the structures between the nasal mucosa and the olfactory tubercle, has little to do with olfaction. Instead, hippocampus, amygdala, septum, cingulate and pyriform cortex, together with certain thalamic and hypothalamic centers, must be considered as an anatomical mechanism for emotion. It took a decade until the full impact of this hypothesis became appreciated by other scientists, but from then on a flood of scientific publications has confirmed Papez' proposal, at least in principle. In retrospect, it is interesting to note that the application of the term olfactory brain, or rhinencephalon, to those parts which are now considered to represent a mechanism of emotion, was rejected by Pierre Paul Broca (1824–1890). This great French surgeon and anthropologist suggested the term "limbic lobe" rather than rhinencephalon because the former does not imply any theory in regard to function. The term "limbic" is derived from the Latin word *limbus* (border) describing the topographic position between neopallium and diencephalon. The limbic lobe shows a high degree of homology in all mammals, where it invariably surrounds the diencephalon in approximately the same topographic relationship. The intimate fiber connections of the limbic lobe with primary and secondary olfactory pathways provide the anatomical basis for the well-known influence of olfactory impressions upon emotional behavior. It might be pointed out that esthetic or foul smells, derived from perfumes, food, or unsanitary conditions, are often determining factors for human reactions. Thus, one should not depreciate the old neuroanatomists who may have overlooked the functional significance of the limbic system.

Because of the functional dichotomy presented above, the olfactory brain is considered in this book as divided into a primary olfactory part and the limbic lobe.

a. *Primary Olfactory Part.* In macrosmatic animals, i.e., animals with a highly developed sense of smell, the primary olfactory centers are massively developed in contrast to those in microsmatic animals and to those in primates.

In the macrosmatic rat, the olfactory bulb (*bulbus olfactorius*) is a club-shaped enlargement at the rostral end of the telencephalon. It is connected with the latter by the olfactory peduncle (*pedunculus olfactorius*). This structure, sometimes referred to as *crus olfactorii* blends caudally with the *tuberculum olfactorium* and the pyriform lobe. The peduncle contains not only all the connecting fiber tracts, but also gray matter, in the form of the anterior olfactory nucleus (*nuc. olfactorius anterior*). The olfactory bulb is separated from the telencephalon by the semicircular fissure. The bulb presents seven layers, four of which contain nerve cells and the remaining three consist of nerve fiber plexus (Fig. 33). It receives afferent fibers from the olfactory nerve

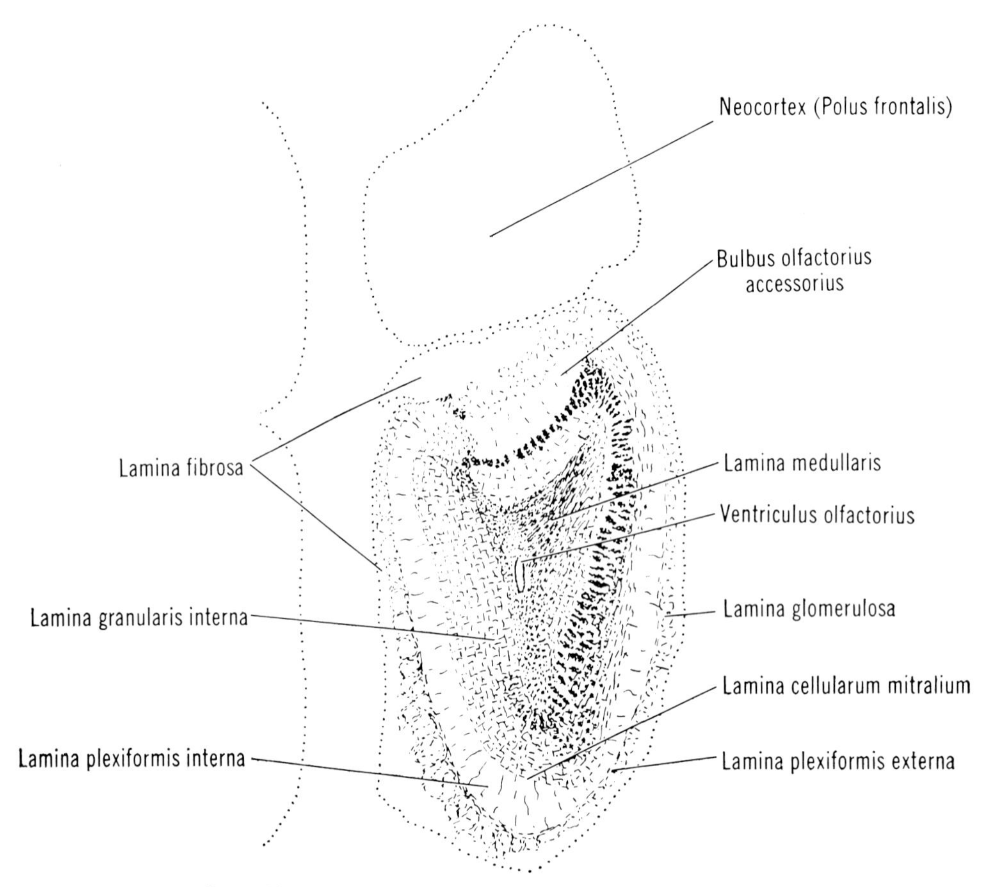

FIG. 33. Bulbus olfactorius. × 15. (This drawing is part of the Craigie series; see Fig. A2.)

cells lying in the nasal mucosa, which are part of the peripheral olfactory system. These fibers form the superficial first layer, the *lamina fibrosa* or *stratum fibrosum*. Penetrating the anterior and ventral surface of the bulb, these unmyelinated fibers terminate in the second layer, the *lamina glomerulosa*, where they participate in the formation of the olfactory glomeruli. These are little tufts of nerve endings (telodendra) of the olfactory axons mingled with the dendrites of medium-sized mitral cells of the third layer (*lamina plexiformis externa*), as well as of the large mitral cells of the fourth layer (*lamina cellularum mitralium*). The axons of the mitral cells pass through the *lamina plexiformis interna*, where collaterals of the smaller mitral cells synapse with fibers of the anterior commissure (*commissura anterior*), into the sixth layer, the inner granular layer (*lamina granularis interna*), and there converge to form the seventh layer or *lamina medullaris*.

In general, the granule cells have short axons which synapse mostly within the bulb proper. The outer granule cells of the second layer, for instance, send their dendrites into neighboring glomeruli while their axons extend to farther remote glomeruli, thus uniting several of these structures into larger groups. Axon collaterals of the mitral cells synapse with the granule cells of the sixth layer, which in turn connect again with the mitral cells. This circuit suggests an ingenious mechanism for the amplification of olfactory stimuli.

In the dorsal side of the olfactory bulb is a small lens-shaped structure, the accessory olfactory bulb (*bulbus olfactorius accessorius*) (Fig. 33). It receives the vomeronasal nerves (*nn. vomeronasales*). Its structure is similar to that of the olfactory bulb. Its significance in the rat is unknown and Papez (1929) suggested that the whole structure is vestigial, resembling the olfactory bulb of lower vertebrates. In primates it is not present, a fact which supports Papez' view.

The efferent olfactory fiber systems form the olfactory tracts and originate mostly in the mitral and some of the large granule cells. Three separate bundles, known respectively as the medial, intermediate, and lateral olfactory tract (*tr. olfactorius medialis, intermedius et lateralis*) form the olfactory fiber systems. The largest and most conspicuous is the lateral olfactory tract, or simply olfactory tract, which extends in a ventrolateral position over the anterior half of the surface of the hemispheres. It occupies a shallow depression of the cortex, the *sulcus entorhinalis.* After its emergence from the olfactory bulb, its size enlarges rapidly as it runs caudad, owing to a constant addition of fibers from the internal medullary lamina. This tract contributes fibers to the anterior olfactory nucleus, the lateral olfactory or prepyriform area, and the *tuberculum olfactorium,* or anterolateral part of the basal olfactory area. It terminates massively in the corticomedial amygdaloid complex, more specifically in the *nuc. tr. olfactorii,* the anterior amygdaloid area (*area amygdaloidea anterior*), and the *nuc. amygdaloideus centralis* and *corticalis.* Allison states this tract does not contain afferent fibers to the bulb. Some fibers of the *tr. olfactorius* cross in the anterior commissure and terminate in the contralateral amygdala (Figs. A8, A23–A25, A37).

The *tr. olfactorius medialis* is a poorly defined small bundle of loosely scattered fascicles which spiral along the medial surface of the bulb and its caudad extension, the olfactory peduncle or *crus olfactorii.* It also originates in the mitral cells and connects, according to Young, with the precommissural hippocampus (*hippocampus pars anterior*), the medial septal nucleus (*nuc. septi medialis*), and the *tuberculum olfactorium.* This is disputed by Allison, who found that most fibers connect with the anterior olfactory nucleus (Fig. 34). This nucleus extends between the olfactory bulb and the anterior septal region. It is shaped like a tunnel with the arch pointing dorsad and the base at the horizontal plane of the ventricle. There is much controversy as to which structures should be included under the anterior olfactory nucleus, and the reader is referred to the pertinent discussion of this problem by Young.

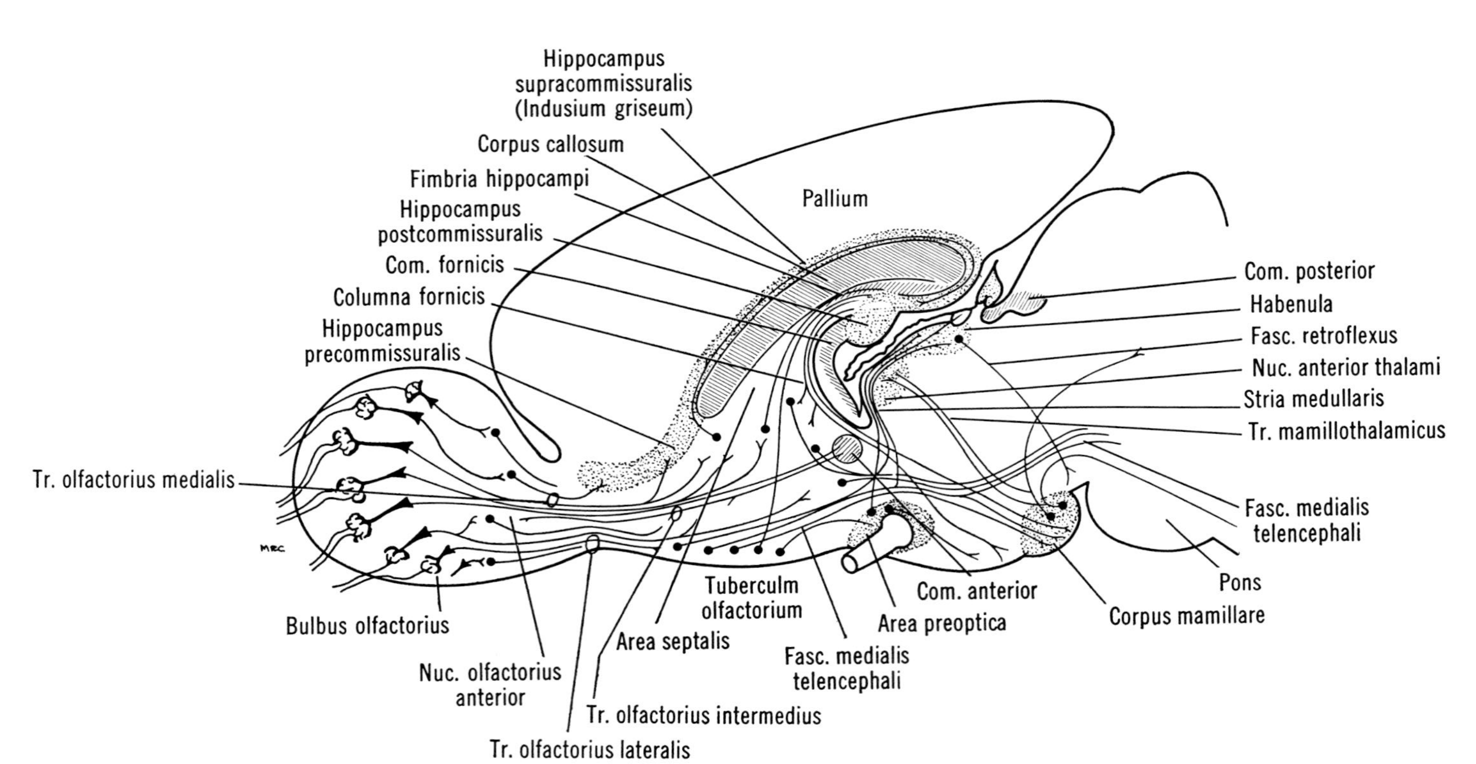

FIG. 34. Diagram of the olfactory rhincephalon, rat. (Redrawn from Herrick.)

The intermediate olfactory tract (*tr. olfactorius intermedius*) is closely related to the *pars anterior* of the anterior commissure. Its fibers run parallel and close to the surface of the olfactory ventricle (the rostral extension of the lateral ventricle) and converge caudally to form a conspicuous bundle which lies central to the anterior olfactory nucleus, in contrast to the medial and lateral olfactory tracts which are peripheral to this structure. The tract receives many fibers from the anterior olfactory nucleus and therefore increases in size as it continues caudad. Eventually it comes to lie ventral to the head of the caudate nucleus and gradually approaches the midline to cross as the most rostral component of the anterior commissure (*com. anterior pars anterior*). In its course through the forebrain, it is joined by fibers from the pyriform lobe and from the anterior part of the internal capsule, and sends fibers to the *nuc. striae terminalis* and the central amygdaloid nucleus. The fibers of this tract are both afferent and efferent and connect topographically similar regions of the two bulbs.

At its caudal end, the anterior olfactory nucleus is bounded by several distinct nuclear masses. The lateral part is continuous with the prepyriform cortex, the medial part blends into the precommissural hippocampus and the septum, and the ventral part is bounded by the *tuberculum olfactorium.* The latter consists of an outer plexiform layer of nerve fibers in which the olfactory tract axons arborize, followed by a middle layer of medium-sized pyramidal cells concentrated in clusters, the islands of Calleja, and a very thick layer of polymorphous nerve cells interspersed with myelinated fibers. The cellular arrangement gives this region a characteristic corrugated appearance in microscopic sections stained for nerve cells (Figs. A30, A31, and A33). Efferent fibers other than those of the olfactory tracts, originating in the anterior olfactory nucleus have been described, which are said to terminate in the neocortex of the frontal lobe and form the olfactocortical fascicles. Young did not find such connections in the rabbit brain.

In summary, the olfactory portion of the nervous system consists of the following nerve cell centers and their connecting fiber tracts: (1) the peripheral olfactory system located in the nasal mucosa, which connects through primary olfactory pathways with (2) the olfactory bulb. From there, two secondary olfactory pathways convey impulses to basal forebrain areas by way of the superficial lateral olfactory tract, and a more diffuse, deep system, represented by the medial and the intermediate tracts. They connect with (3) the central olfactory centers. Complex olfactory discrimination is probably dependent on the cortical areas of the olfactory tubercle and the prepyriform area, where many fibers of the lateral tract terminate. Simple olfactory discrimination can be carried out at the level of the *nuc. striae terminalis,* in which fibers of the intermediate olfactory tract terminate (Allison).

It may be added that this theory is supported by observations in man. A sensation of strong odors—in the absence of odiferous substances—is often experienced by patients with irritating lesions in the *uncus.* This does not occur in similar lesions affecting other regions of the rhinencephalon. Consequently, the uncus, the homologue of which is the prepyriform area in the rat brain, appears to represent the cortical center for olfactory discrimination in man.

The functional significance of secondary olfactory systems which connect with gray masses not involved in olfactory discrimination (such as the anterior part of the amygdala and of the tertiary olfactory connections between prepyriform cortex and insular mesocortex and the preoptic region of the hypothalamus) is not precisely known. Yet, it is an everyday experience that smells can produce a host of responses, emotional feelings, and modifications of behavior, and it is safe to assume that such reactions are based upon the mechanisms provided by these secondary and tertiary olfactory connections. Part of the latter olfactory connections, perhaps those of the olfactory-cortical fascicles, the *stria terminalis*, the fibers from the internal capsule, and their cortical and subcortical rhinencephalic and hypothalamic centers, represent a mechanism for the "oral sense." This function requires a correlation of smell, touch, taste, and motor activity of the snout region, and is important in feeding reflexes (Fig. 34).

In view of Papez' theory of a "mechanism for emotion" located largely in the olfactory brain, it is interesting to note that Allison found the entorhinal area, the hippocampus, the septum, and the cingulate cortex to receive few, if any, secondary olfactory fibers. This is essentially in agreement with electrophysiologic observations, which indicate that these structures play no significant part in olfaction.

b. *Limbic Lobe.* In contrast to the rapid evolution of the neopallium, the development of the limbic lobe is relatively constant throughout the phylogeny of mammals. This constancy is also contrary to the development of the primary olfactory system, which is extensive in macrosmates, but poorly represented in microsmatic mammals, irrespective of phyletic position.

The limbic lobe can be divided into three structurally different parts, the cortex, the subcortical nuclei, and their connecting fiber systems. It will be seen, that the limbic centers, unlike those of the nonolfactory telencephalon, possess extremely rich and complex connections with the hypothalamus. The functional implication of these links has only recently been understood and will be discussed in more detail in Chapter VIII.

The cortical areas of the limbic lobe may be subdivided into three cytoarchitectonically different types. The archicortex, so named by Ariëns Kappers, is represented by the hippocampus. During phylogeny the hippocampus becomes largely buried through the process of folding, and in higher mammals it undergoes so much displacement by the corpus callosum that it comes to lie in the inferomedial part of the temporal lobe. The arrangement of the hippocampus (*cornu ammonis,* Ammon's horn) is best understood by studying its phylogenetic history.

The hippocampus is derived from what was originally the medial wall of the cerebral hemisphere. Dorsally, it came into contact with the precursor of the dorsal pallium, which in turn was bounded by the lateral wall of the hemisphere, the *primordium pyriforme.* As the dorsal pallium developed into the neopallium and grew in extent longitudinally as well as transversely, it pushed the posterior parts of the hemisphere downward, so that the originally straight primordium of the hippocampus was bent down posteriorly, curving around until its posterior

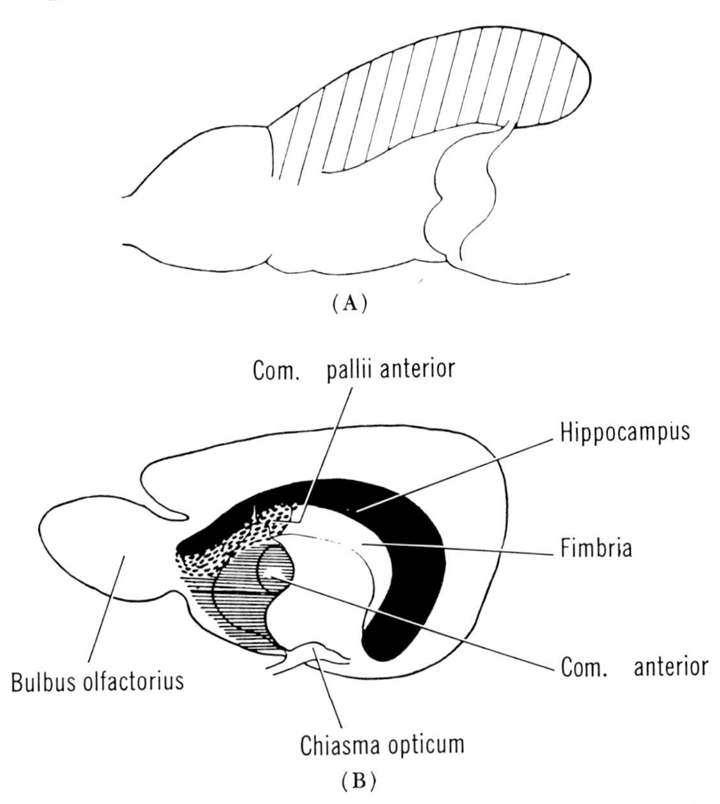

FIG. 35. (A) Diagram of medial surface of cerebral hemisphere of the frog with primordium hippocampi shaded. (Redrawn from Johnston, 1923.) (B) Diagram of medial surface of cerebral hemisphere of marsupial (opossum). (Redrawn and relabeled from Johnston.)

end pointed anteroventrally in the temporal region of the hemisphere (Figs. 35 and 36). At the same time, the transverse growth of the neopallium forced the primordium of the pyriform lobe down laterally until it reached the ventral position where we have seen it in the rat and finally the anterior ventromedial location which it occupies in man. The hippocampal area, however, could not be thus displaced and consequently became folded inward so that most of it lay at the bottom of a deep groove, the hippocampal fissure. It appears in this condition in the marsupials, but in the placental mammals the increasing pressure of the neopallium and the development of the corpus callosum have caused the anterior and dorsal part to become vestigial, so that only the posterior part which curves down into the temporal lobe is well developed (Fig. 34). The remainder is represented only by a very thin band of gray matter, the indusium (*indusium griseum, gyrus supracallosus,* supracallosal or supracommissural hippocampus), accompanied by a few white fibers (*striae longitudinales Lancisii*), which run

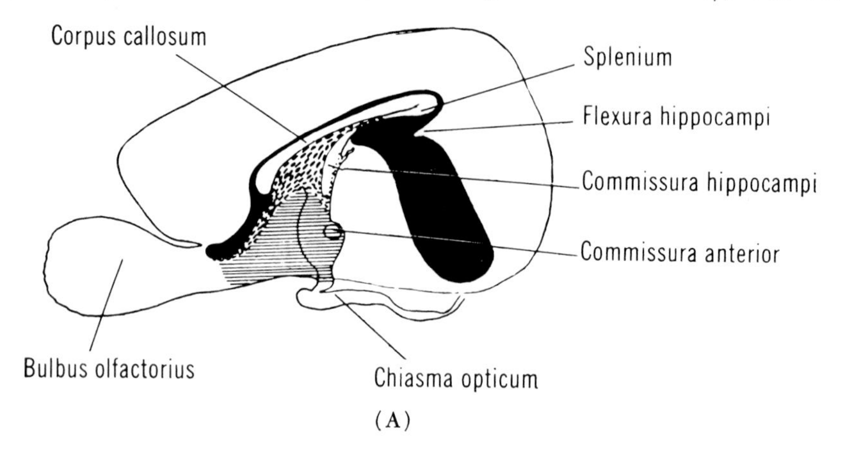

(A)

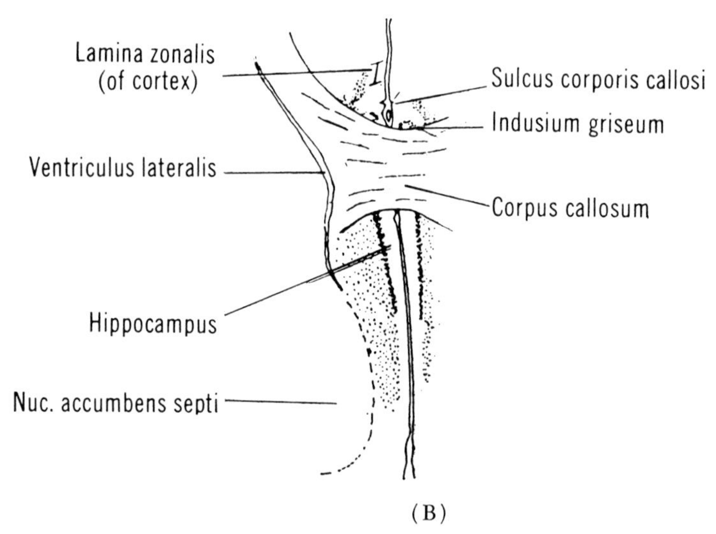

(B)

Fig. 36. (A) Diagram of medial surface of cerebral hemisphere of the rat. (Redrawn from Johnston, 1923.) (B) Middle part of transverse section of the brain of a rat immediately behind the genu of the corpus callosum. (Redrawn from Craigie, 1925a.)

along the dorsal surface of the corpus callosum under the edge of the outermost layer of the cerebral cortex. The indusium is less reduced in the rat than in man. In front of the corpus callosum in the rat is an unusually large remnant of the hippocampus, which reaches to the caudal end of the anterior olfactory nucleus. This is the precommissural hippocampus. At the genu of the corpus callosum, part of the hippocampal formation extends back ventral to it for a short distance, while the rest curves around it and becomes continuous with the indusium. Only the postcommissural hippocampus—usually called hippocampus, i.e., the portion behind and below the corpus callosum—is large and well developed.

The hippocampal formation is divided into two parts, the hippocampus proper and the *fascia dentata* or *gyrus dentatus.* The hippocampus proper is the larger part, which is folded in at the hippocampal fissure and forms a prominent ridge in the ventricle. The ventricular surface is covered with a layer of white fibers, the *alveus,* composed of hippocampal projection fibers, and these join a large tract which runs along the side of the hippocampal ridge and is known as the fimbria. The *stria medialis Lancisii* is the reduced fimbria of the degenerated supracallosal part of the hippocampus. The *fornix* is the direct continuation of the fimbria (Fig. 10, p. 25).

The hippocampus is composed of three layers of cells, the molecular, pyramidal, and polymorphic, of which the pyramidal layer stands out clearly on account of the rather crowded arrangement of its perikarya. The dentate gyrus is likewise composed of three layers, in this case molecular, granular, and polymorphic. It runs along the edge of the hippocampus and is folded around it, the two portions overlapping considerably. The cells of the granular layer are very closely crowded, making it a conspicuous object in sections where they are stained.

The paleocortex in all mammals occupies the base of the telencephalon. In primates it has an anteromedial position because of the mushrooming neocortex, but in the rat it comprises practically the entire telencephalic base and even parts of the lateral surface, where it is separated from the neocortex by the rhinal fissure (*fissura rhinica,* limbic fissure, *sulcus rhinalis*). The paleocortex can be subdivided into a number of fields, but this has been done differently by various authors. A simple classification is provided by Allison, in which the paleocortex lateral to the olfactory tract is termed *area prepyriformis* (*gyrus olfactorius lateralis*) and is divided into an anterior frontal and a posterior temporal field. Medial to the olfactory tract extends the *tuberculum olfactorium,* which is caudally bordered by the *cortex basalis* (*nuc. amygdaloideus corticalis*) of the amygdalar complex (Kuhlenbeck *et al.*). The remainder of the paleocortex, i.e., caudal to the temporal prepyriform area and its medial bordering region, the basal cortex, is occupied by the entorhinal area (*area entorhinalis*).

The third cortical division of the limbic lobe is frequently called mesocortex, as it is intermediate in differentiation and in its topographical localization between the hippocampal archicortex and the entorhinal paleocortex on the one hand and the neocortex on the other. For similar considerations, Kuhlenbeck *et al.* proposed the term parahippocampal cortex. It extends over the medial surface of the telencephalic hemispheres, comprising the cingulate cortex (*g. cinguli*) and the retrosplenial region (*area retrosplenialis*). In higher mammals, certain parts of the fronto-orbital cortex and of the insular cortex belong functionally to the limbic lobe. By now, it will not be too difficult for the reader to recognize the close ontogenetic relationship of these two structures to the frontal and temporal prepyriform regions, respectively.

The subcortical gray masses of the limbic lobe form three more or less distinct complexes. Ventral to the anterior half of the corpus callosum extends the septal area (*area septalis,* or the paraterminal body of Johnston). This region is very prominent in all lower animals, but in primates it is displaced rostrad and ventrad owing to the massive development of the neopallium and has thus become relatively inconspicuous. Anteriorly, the septal area is bounded by the precommissural hippocampus, which is included by some authors among the septal structures. Posteriorly, the septum borders the hippocampal or fornical commissure. The entire septum lies dorsal to a horizontal plane which follows the roof of the anterior part of the third ventricle, while laterally, it forms the medial walls of the ventricles and dorsally it is attached to the corpus callosum (Figs. A25–A31, A35, A37, A38).

In the rostral end of the septum there is the medial septal nucleus (*nuc. medialis septi*), which at this level blends imperceptibly with the *area parolfactoria medialis.* The latter structure is probably an extension of the cortex of the olfactory tubercle which has turned mediad and caudad and thus become buried by the cortex. Young does not describe this structure, and he considers it identical with the *nuc. tr. olfactorii medialis* of Livini, and perhaps also as a part of the medial septal nucleus. Immediately ventral to the *genu corporis callosi* and lateral to the precommissural hippocampus and the medial septal nucleus is the head of the lateral septal nucleus (*nuc. lateralis septi*), which extends caudad over the entire length of the septum. As the medial nucleus becomes smaller and disappears, approximately at the level of the anterior commissure, the lateral septal nuclei join in the midline. In the rabbit brain, Young has described a septohippocampal nucleus, but this structure is not distinct in the rat brain, where it would be represented by the dorsal layers of the lateral nuclei. At the caudal end of the medial nucleus is the *nuc. triangularis septi* which, farther caudad, comes to lie between the two *fornices obliqui* as they emerge from the ventral hippocampal commissure (*com. hippocampi ventralis, com. fornicis, psalterium ventrale*). Immediately lateral to the triangular nucleus, largely obscured by the fornix fibers, are two small but discrete nuclei, the *nuc. tr. corticohabenularis* in a dorsal position and ventral to it the *nuc. fimbrialis septi.* In the center of the ventral surface of the fornix commissure is a small mass with peculiar neuroectodermal cells which contains many capillaries and thin-walled sinusoids. Originally described by Johnston as "*nodulus marginalis*" it was rediscovered by Spiegel and designated *ganglion psalterii.* This *corpus subfornicale* (subfornical organ or intercolumnar tubercle) (Figs. 12, A26) is similar in structure to the *area postrema* and could perhaps discharge special components into the ventricular fluid (Wislocki and Leduc; see also p. 113). It was extensively studied by Cohrs (1936).

The second subcortical nuclear mass of the limbic lobe lies ventral to the septal area. It has not been named and is often included with the septal area. Anterior is the nucleus of the diagonal band of Broca, extending underneath the cortex of the *tuberculum olfactorium,* the contour of which it follows closely. Laterally and caudally it is bordered by the large *nuc. accumbens septi,* which surrounds the pars anterior of the anterior commissure and which is dorsally bounded by the caudate-putamen complex and the lateral septal nucleus. Farther caudad the nucleus of the diagonal band and the *nuc. accumbens* are separated by the medial preoptic area. Surrounding the dorsal and anterior aspects of the anterior commissure is the bed nucleus of the anterior commissure (*nuc. proprius commissurae anterioris*). Between this structure, the medial and lateral septal nuclei and the *nuc. accumbens,* extends the bed nucleus of the stria terminalis (*nuc. proprius striae terminalis*). It will be recalled that this structure together with the *nuc. accumbens septi* has also been termed the motor olfactory striatum or olfactostriatum, names which are now obsolete.

The third subcortical nuclear mass of the limbic lobe is the amygdaloid complex. This extends between the pyriform cortex (which is its lateral border) and the hypothalamus (forming the anterior medial border). Optic tract and *fissura chorioidea* represent the posterior medial boundary. At its caudal end the amygdaloid complex is medially, dorsally, and posteriorly bounded by the hippocampus while its anterior roof is provided by the caudate-putamen complex and partly by the globus pallidus. At the level of the *chiasma opticum,* lies the anterior amygdaloid area (*area amygdaloidea anterior*), which farther caudad is bounded ventrally by the nucleus of the olfactory tract (*nuc. tr. olfactorii*), and dorsally by the intercalated mass (*nuc. amygdaloideus intercalatus*). At the beginning of the *fissura chorioidea,* the anterior amygdaloid area and the nucleus of the olfactory tract are medially replaced by the *nuc. amygdaloideus medialis* and laterally by the *nuc. amygdaloideus corticalis,* bordered dorsally by the *nuc. amygdaloideus centralis,* the *nuc. amygdaloideus basalis partes lateralis* and *medialis,* and, farther dorsally, the *nuc. amygdaloideus lateralis* which is in close proximity to the putamen. The cortical nucleus of the amygdaloid complex is identical with the *cortex basalis.* It is separated from the pyriform cortex by the *zona transitionalis* (Figs. A20, A22, A23, A26).

The major limbic pathways are conspicuous structures which are easily distinguished and traced on the plates (see Figs. 34, 37, and A20–A23, A31, A35, A37, A38). They can be enumerated as follows:

1. *The fornix.* This pathway is formed by the converging fibers of the *alveus* and the *fimbria hippocampi* and, as it runs rostrad, increases in size as

it receives fibers from the septum and the cingulate gyrus. The fornix runs first cephalad and then ventrad and caudad in a semicircle to the base of the diencephalon, where many of its fibers connect with the mamillary bodies. The rostral continuation of the *fimbria hippocampi* is called *crus fornicis posterior* (*fornix obliquus*) and forms the ventral hippocampal commissure. That part of the fornix which runs parallel and ventral to the corpus callosum in a midline position is termed the *fornix longus*. Where the fornix fibers sweep in a dorsoventral curve through the septal area, the *fornix longus* splits into three parts, one unpaired precommissural fornix which passes rostral to the anterior commissure and two symmetrical postcommissural fornices which curve caudad and ventrad and pass on the caudal side of the anterior commissure to form the *columnae fornicis*. As shown by Nauta, and contrary to statements in some texts, those fibers of the fornix systems which terminate in the septal area, *area parolfactoria*, preoptic region, hypothalamus, and thalamus originate in the ipsilateral hippocampus. The hippocampal commissures which are part of the fornix system are a pathway for commissural hippocampal and entorhinal fibers.

2. *Stria medullaris.* This fiber bundle, which is formed at the anterior plane of the thalamus by fibers converging at a frontal plane has already been discussed together with the epithalamus (see p. 117).

3. *Stria terminalis.* Like the fornix, the *stria terminalis* forms a sweeping, bilaterally symmetrical arch, a fact which has been expressed by the now obsolete term "taenia semicircularis." The *stria terminalis* can be traced as a distinct bundle collecting in the dorsal region of the amygdaloid complex, swinging dorsad around the caudal end of the internal capsule following roughly the course of the optic tracts, and then lying medial to the *fimbria hippocampi;* turns cephalad at the base of the lateral ventricle and then again ventrad and slightly mediad, lateral to the fornix column. At this point, in the region of the bed nucleus of the *stria terminalis,* the tract loses its compactness and splits up into several bundles.

4. *Anterior commissure.* The anterior commissure is a very conspicuous fiber tract running horizontally in a frontal plane between the lateral septal nucleus and the preoptic area. Only its middle portion, the *pars transversalis* follows a straight course, whereas the *pars anterior* bends rostrad and the *pars posterior* caudad in the form of horseshoes. This commissure also contains decussational fibers.

5. *Medial forebrain bundle* (*Fasciculus medialis telencephali*). This important longitudinal associational system of the hypothalamus has already been discussed (see p. 120). It extends in an almost straight parasagittal course from the olfactory tubercle through the mamillary bodies into the mesencephalon, traversing the lateral regions of the hypothalamus. In its most anterior part it is laterally accompanied by the tuberculopyriform tract (Fig. A31).

6. *The diagonal band of Broca* (*gyrus diagonalis*). This mass of fibers together with its nucleus extend in an oblique dorsoventral direction underneath

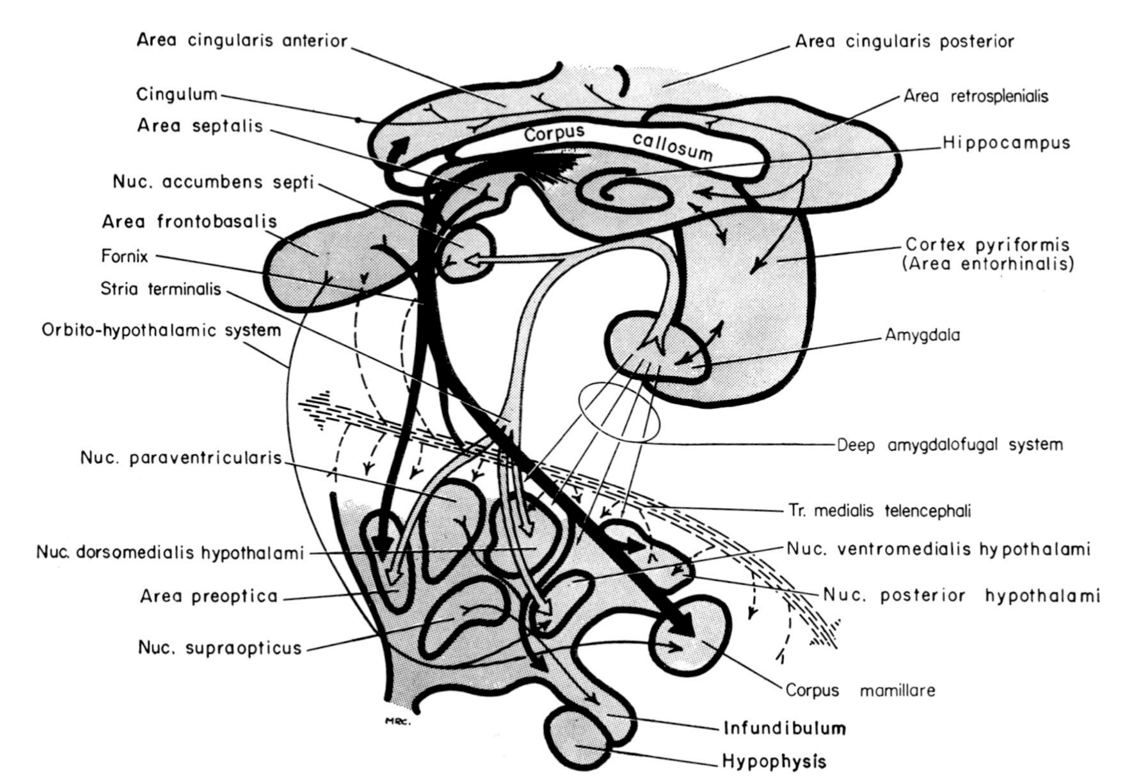

FIG. 37. Diagrammatic representation of the limbic-hypothalamic pathways. (Modified from Gloor, 1956.)

the cortex of the olfactory tubercle from the medial parolfactory area to the preoptic area of the hypothalamus, where the bundle loses its compactness. Its fibers, however, continue and can be traced to the anterior amygdaloid area and the nucleus of the lateral olfactory tract, where they apparently end. Another component joins the medial forebrain bundle.

7. *Cingulum.* This tract extends underneath the cortex of the cingulate gyrus. It picks up fibers from the frontal neocortex and is continuously being enlarged as it runs caudad by fibers from the cingulate gyrus and the retrosplenial area. It spreads diffusely into the entorhinal area and the hippocampus.

All these conspicuous systems carry fibers which conduct impulses in both directions. They are made up of many different components connecting various limbic and other centers of the central nervous system. For this reason, the fiber connections of the cortical and subcortical gray areas of the limbic lobe are described with respect to their points of connection rather than to the fiber systems in which they run.

Afferent systems to the limbic lobe have already been discussed as far as they concern the mesencephalon, diencephalon, and the olfactory part of the rhinencephalon (see p. 139). From the mesencephalon ascend fibers which originate in the dorsal and ventral tegmental nuclei and which run in the mamillary peduncle to the medial forebrain bundle. They connect with the medial nucleus of the septum. The latter projects to the hippocampus via the fornix and thus a two-neuron circuit from the mesencephalic reticular formation to the hippocampus is provided. Another ascending system connects the periaqueductal gray with the hippocampus, and these fibers also travel in the fornix. The same systems incorporate shorter neurons connecting the hypothalamus with the septal nuclei and the hippocampus. The ascending fibers from the intralaminar and the anterior thalamic nuclei have been mentioned previously (p. 123). These nuclei project to the mesocortex of the cingulate gyrus and the retrosplenial area (Fig. 32).

Afferent secondary fibers from the primary olfactory centers, in the form of the olfactory tract (*tr. olfactorius lateralis*) distribute widely through the pyriform lobe and to the anterior amygdaloid area, more specifically the *nuc. amygdaloideus corticalis* and *basalis* and to the nucleus of the olfactory tract. Tertiary olfactory fibers, originating in the pyriform cortex and connecting with the hippocampus and the entorhinal area are very few, according to Allison. There is, however, a distinct connection between the tuberculum and the medial septal nucleus, clearly identified by Brodal. This tuberculoseptal tract provides an afferent system to the hippocampus by the septohippocampal component of the fornix. Other tertiary olfactory connections from the olfactory tubercle reach the preoptic region and the hypothalamus through the diagonal band of Broca and the medial forebrain bundle by way of the olfactohypothalamic component of the latter (Fig. A24). In the cingulum, the limbic system has a well-developed afferent system from the frontal neocortex, but, as shown by Krieg (1947), there are also numerous, diffuse, short connections between neocortex and the various limbic structures. Most of these pass through the *corona radiata* of the corpus callosum.

Practically all limbic structures are connected with their contralateral, or opposite, counterpart through commissural fiber systems. Some of these cross through the anterior commissure. In the *pars anterior* cross those fibers which connect the anterior olfactory nucleus (*pars dorsalis*) and the olfactory tubercles. Practically every part of the prepyriform cortex is connected with its opposite counterpart by this commissure. Extensive bilateral connections also exist for the nucleus of the *stria terminalis* which, together with commissural connections for the corticomedial amygdaloid complex (Brodal), are carried in the posterior limb. Only the lateral and basal amygdaloid nuclei do not possess commissural connections. The transverse, or medial, limb of the anterior commissure connects the posterior and ventral neocortex, possibly the claustra, but not the corpora striata. As regards the commissural systems of the amygdaloid complex, it is noteworthy that some of these fibers take the circuitous route over the stria terminalis bilaterally (commissural component of stria medullaris), but Gurdjian has left doubt as to the existence of this bundle in the rat. Most fibers make the shorter connection via the posterior part of the commissure, constituting the ventral commissural system of the amygdala.

As shown by Blackstad, the hippocampi are connected by an extremely rich commissural system. These fibers cross largely by way of the ventral hippocampal commissure (*com. fornicis*). On the other hand, commissural fibers connecting the entorhinal area, the subiculum, and a minor part of the hippocampus pass through the dorsal hippocampal commissure (dorsal psalterium) (Fig. 35). The complexity of these connections may be appreciated after a study of Blackstad's diligent work.

The fiber tracts which connect limbic structures within the same hemisphere may be called associational systems. In this category fall many of the fornix components, such as the septohippocampal and hippocamposeptal tracts. Fibers of the precommissural fornix connect the medial parolfactory and the medial preoptic area with the hippocampus, septum, and the nucleus of the diagonal band of Broca. Other precommissural fibers extend into hypothalamus and midbrain. Postcommissural fornix fibers project almost exclusively to the diencephalon. There are extensive and widespread connections between the entorhinal area and the hippocampus on the one hand and the amygdaloid complex on the other. The amygdala is also connected with the anterior ventral gray masses of the limbic lobe through the stria terminalis. Its supracommissural component links basal and cortical amygdaloid nuclei with the septal area and the *nucleus accumbens*. The intracommissural bundle or preoptic component connect these amygdaloid nuclei with the preoptic area. Both components carry fibers which join the medial forebrain bundle to the hypothalamus.

Fibers from the *com. fornicis,* possibly originating in the hippocampus, form the origin of the tract of the diagonal band of Broca which swings rostral to the precommissural fornix in a curve toward the *tuberculum olfactorium.* It picks up fibers from the septum, the parolfactory area, and the nucleus of the diagonal band and terminates in the anterior amygdaloid area and in the *nuc. tr. olfactorii,* thus providing hippocamposepto-amygdaloid connections. A number of fibers terminate in the pyriform cortex.

Of greatest importance, and probably best understood, are the numerous efferent pathways of the limbic lobe. Impulses from the amygdala to the tegmentum are conducted over the *stria terminalis-stria medullaris-fasciculus retroflexus* and pedunculotegmental tracts, or over a shortcut from the habenular nuclei directly to the tegmentum via the habenulotegmental tract. Extensive efferent hippocampal pathways are provided by the fornix which, through its postcommissural component, connects with numerous ipsilateral regions of diencephalon and mesencephalon. Direct hippocampohypothalamic connections terminate in the preoptic region and the dorsal hypothalamus, whereas fornix fibers from the septum terminate in the lateral nuclei of the preoptic region and the lateral hypothalamic area. Another component of the efferent hippocampal fibers which originates in the caudal third of the hippocampus terminates in the *nucleus arcuatus hypothalami* (Nauta). The remainder of the fornix fibers from the hippocampus project partly to the anterior midline and intralaminar nuclei of the thalamus. Approximately 50 per cent of them, most of which originate in the hippocampus, terminate in the mamillary nuclei and the supramamillary region. From the mamillary complex impulses are mediated through the mamillothalamic tract to the anterior thalamic nuclei, and from there relayed to the cingulate cortex, which via the cingulum discharges again into the hippocampus, thus providing a complete neuronal circuit. Fornix fibers originating in the septum run to the medial habenular nucleus via the stria medullaris, but most of these fibers terminate in the paramedian region of midbrain and pontine tegmentum (Nauta). Thus, an efferent impulse from the hippocampus can reach the tegmentum in a number of different ways. The most direct route is the hippocampal-septal-tegmental relay. Other impulses travel from the septal region to the habenular complex to the interpeduncular nucleus, or might bypass the latter on their way to the same general terminal in the caudal midbrain tegmentum. Still other impulses are shunted from the mamillary nuclei over the mamillotegmental tracts. These various connections give some idea as to the tremendous complexity of such pathways.

The limbic-hypothalamic pathways (Fig. 37) involve the above-mentioned fornix connections and, in addition, other parts of the fornix which join the medial forebrain bundle. Again, this bundle is very complex with respect to its various components. It picks up fibers from the *nuc. accumbens* (the strio-hypothalamic component), from the hippocampus-fornix system (lateral cortico-hypothalamic component), from the septal area (septohypothalamic component), from the medial parolfactory area (parolfactohypothalamic component), and finally an olfactohypothalamic component from the anterior *tuberculum olfactorium* (medial olfactory area) (Gurdjian). In the opossum, this fascicle contains also olfactomamillary fibers, but Gurdjian (1925) was unable to demonstrate those in the rat brain. Efferent impulses from the amygdaloid complex to the hypothalamus are either conducted via that part of the stria terminalis that does not cross in the anterior commissure, the postcommissural stria, or by way of a more direct, so-called ventral amygdalocortical or amygdalofugal pathway. Some of its fibers travel with the diagonal band, others with the medial forebrain bundle, and still others form a rather diffuse system (Gloor). Finally, an orbitohypothalamic system has been described, the anatomy of which, however, is not known in the rat brain. This system connects the orbitofrontal mesocortex with the hypothalamus.

From this brief exposition, it is obvious that the limbic lobe is intimately connected with the hypothalamus and with the reticular formation of the brainstem, but to a much lesser extent with the nonrhinencephalic telencephalon. That these anatomical connections have most important functional implications will be demonstrated in Chapter VIII.

2. Nonolfactory Telencephalon

The nonolfactory telencephalon represents the most recent acquisition of the phylogenetic series. It is poorly developed in the lower vertebrates, but in the mammals it assumes conspicuous proportions. The nonolfactory telencephalon is conventionally divided into the basal ganglia and the neopallium.

a. *Basal Ganglia.* The basal ganglia form distinct, bilaterally symmetrical masses of gray matter having a ventral position in the nonolfactory telencephalon in mammals. They are derived from the ventral wall of the telencephalic anlage. These gray structures have a characteristic striped appearance because they are traversed by numerous fascicles of myelinated fibers. For this reason, the descriptive term *corpus striatum* has been widely used as a synonym for basal ganglia. Unfortunately, its definition is lacking preciseness, and for reason of clarification, terminology is discussed in more detail. In most texts, the *corpus striatum* is divided into the following structures:

(1) *Nucleus caudatus*
(2) *Nucleus lentiformis*
  (a) *Putamen*
  (b) *Globus pallidus*

but many authors would indicate also the

(3) *Claustrum*
(4) *Amygdala*

This classification does not seem to be ontogenetic, phylogenetic, or morphologic, nor does it have functional implications. Ontogenetically, both the *nucleus cau-*

*datus** and the *putamen* are derived from the ventrolateral part of the pallium. Both are similar in histologic appearance as they are populated by a few very large and numerous rather small perikarya in a ratio of 1:20. In addition, both react uniformly, at least in the human, to certain pathogens. For instance, in hypoxemic states caudate nucleus and putamen are similarly affected and in Huntington's chorea they exhibit the same histopathomorphologic reaction. In the rat brain, there is no clear-cut anatomical division between these two nuclei, which in the primate are separated by the internal capsule. Consequently, C. and O. Vogt have termed the nucleus caudatus-putamen complex the "striatum," or, in recognition of its close association with the neopallium, Ariëns Kappers and others call it the *neostriatum.* In contradistinction, the *globus pallidus* is derived from the lateral part of the basal wall of the prosencephalon and is therefore ontogenetically related to the diencephalon. Anatomically, it is separated from the diencephalic thalamus by the internal capsule which, as we have seen, contains fibers of both diencephalic and telencephalic origin. The *globus pallidus* is phylogenetically "older" than the striatum and is therefore called *paleostriatum,* or in keeping with the Vogts' classification, simply the *pallidum.* The term *pallidus* means pale and describes the light appearance of the pallidum in comparison to the dark gray of the putamen. This paleness, as revealed from histologic preparations, is the result of an exceedingly sparse population of the *globus pallidus* by large perikarya and the presence of numerous white fibers. The pallidum has a homotypical structure in the form of the entopeduncular nucleus (*nuc. entopeduncularis,* Figs. A22, A23) which is conspicuous in the rat brain and in that of other lower vertebrates.

Putamen and pallidum are not only histologically different, but also their chemical organization and their pattern of vulnerability are entirely discordant. For example, the pallidum has an extremely high content of iron, largely in the form of ferritin. In the light of these facts, the term *nucleus lentiformis,* comprising both putamen and pallidum, should be abandoned.

The amygdaloid complex, representing a subcortical formation of the limbic lobe structures, is in part phylogenetically even older than the pallidum and it is therefore called archistriatum. Ontogenetically, it can be divided into an older corticomedial, and a more recent basolateral complex.

Lateral to the putamen and separated from the latter by the *capsula externa,* which is a sheet of white fibers, lies the *claustrum,* a thin plate of gray matter (Figs. A24–A30). Most authors consider this to be an infolded portion of the neocortex and therefore ontogenetically belonging to the latter. The functional significance of the claustrum and its fiber connections are practically unknown, but Wood *et al.* suggested recently a functional relation to the lateral

---

* In the rat brain, the term *nucleus caudatus* is actually a misnomer, because this nucleus does not extend back on the medial and dorsal aspects of the internal capsule as it is seen in primates. Instead it ends rather abruptly and flat, so that only the "head" or caput of the caudate appears to be present.

amygdala. There is some evidence that both claustra are connected with each other by commissural fibers which cross through the transverse limb of the anterior commissure (Brodal, 1948). Afferent fibers from the amygdala were found in the monkey brain by Nauta (1961).

Taking into account the preceding considerations, the following revised terminology of the telencephalic basal ganglia emerges.

Nuc. caudatus or *caudatum* *Putamen*		=	*Corpus striatum* or *Neostriatum* or *Striatum*	together form Basal ganglia
Globus pallidus or *pallidum*		=	*Paleostriatum*	
Claustrum	(Part of neocortex)			
Nuc. amygdalae		=	*Archistriatum*	(subcortical limbic cell station)

The striatum forms the lateral walls of the lateral ventricles over practically their entire anterior-posterior extension. Rostrally, dorsally, and laterally it is surrounded by the *album cerebri* represented in the rat brain chiefly by the callosal radiation (*corona radiata corporis callosi*). Its caudal border is represented by the hippocampus. Proceeding caudad the pallidum appears at the level of the ventral hippocampal commissure, where it forms the ventral part of the medial border of the striatum, and in turn is bordered medially over its entire extent by the internal capsule. In the rat brain, the pallidum is not as distinct a structure as it is in the primate brain. Anteriorly, the ventral border of the striatum is formed by the *nucleus accumbens septi.* At the caudal end of this nucleus, the striatum comes to lie immediately dorsal to the anterior commissure, and farther caudad the ventral border becomes indistinct owing to the close approximation of the central and lateral nuclei of the amygdala.

The fiber connections of the basal ganglia are highly complex, and in many instances difficult to trace. In general, the basal ganglia are connected with rhinencephalic, more correctly, limbic centers, as well as with the diencephalon, mesencephalon, and rhombencephalon. Whether direct connections with the neopallium exist, is still a matter of controversy. Afferent fibers from the frontal neocortex were described by Cajal, but they have not been confirmed. For the rat, Krieg (1946) states that the neocortex does not send myelinated fibers to the corpus striatum, but most neuroanatomists agree that unmyelinated collaterals of the neocortical pyramidal fibers terminate in the putamen, at least in primates (Crosby *et al.*, 1962).

The fiber systems of the basal ganglia will be discussed according to their connections. The most important afferent system originates in the nucleus of the *centrum medianum* (*nuc. centre médian,* centromedial nucleus of the thalamus) and runs through the entire striatum in a caudorostral direction in small bundles. The centromedial nucleus receives afferent fibers through the superior cerebellar peduncle from the *nuc. emboliformis* of the cerebellum and from the reticular formation. This fiber system is often called the striatal system.

The efferent pathways of the basal ganglia form the striopallidoreticular, the striopallidocortical, and the strionigral systems. The first two pass through the *ansa lenticularis,* where they form a compact tract of myelinated fibers, at least in primates. Fibers of the striopallidoreticular system terminate largely in the pallidum, synapsing with perikarya which receive impulses from the intralaminar nuclei of the thalamus. These cells, in turn, send their axons to the *nuc. ruber* and to the reticular formation of the mesencephalon, whence the rubrospinal and reticulospinal tracts originate. In addition, the pallidum has strong reciprocal connections with the subthalamic nucleus, which receives afferent fibers from the motor cortex. Fibers from the pallidum break through the internal capsule and terminate in the *nuc. ventromedialis hypothalami.* The striopallidocortical system provides a further link between basal ganglia and neocortex. These connections are made between the pallidum and the ventrolateral thalamic nuclei, which in turn project to various neocortical areas. Thus the pallidum, receiving strong afferents from the striatum, projects via the ventral thalamus to the neocortex, particularly to those regions from which the corticofugal motor pathways arise. The third efferent pathway, the strionigral system, sends its fibers mostly through the internal capsule, bypassing the pallidum. From the substantia nigra originate descending spinal tracts, but also ascending fibers to the pallidum.

From these fiber connections, it is apparent that striatum and pallidum belong to a system which also includes the red nucleus, the substantia nigra, the reticular formation, thalamus, subthalamus, premotor neocortex, as well as cerebellar motor nuclei. Functionally this system has been referred to as the extrapyramidal motor system, which is believed to subserve stereotyped and "experienced" movements, in contradistinction to the exploratory and discriminatory movements said to have their mechanisms in the neocortical pyramidal motor system.

There is mounting evidence that these functional considerations may in a broad sense apply to the human being and to simian primates, but that they do not fully represent the situation existing in lower mammals. Actually, in lower vertebrates, the striatum comprises a relatively large part of the nonolfactory telencephalon and thus may harbor a much greater variety of mechanisms. In such animals the anterior parts of the striatum have a close relationship to the olfactory brain. With ascending phylogeny, however, the striatum appears to lose some of its autonomy and to become restricted in its functions so that it is chiefly motor in the human being. It is therefore not surprising that Harrison and Lyon (1957) working with rats and Mettler (1948) working with cats observed behavioral disturbances following destruction of the anterior neostriatum. An anatomical basis of this observation may be found in the strong fiber connections between the intralaminar thalamic nuclei and the basal ganglia, which may not all be extrapyramidal in function.

In summary, the fiber connections of the basal ganglia in the rat brain are in line with their functional significance, i.e., a relay center for the motor expression of behavioral mechanisms. This area of activity appears to be somewhat narrowed with ascending phylogeny. It should, however, be pointed out that the studies of C. and O. Vogt (1952) on the human striatum have tended to incriminate the basal ganglia as a site of pathologic changes resulting in psychologic disturbances.

b. *Neopallium.* The neopallium of the rat brain extends over the dorsomedial, the dorsal, and most of the lateral surfaces of the telencephalic hemispheres. It is this part of the brain which in the course of evolution expands to tremendous proportions, so that in the human brain it accounts for almost three-fourths of the weight of the entire central nervous system. Commensurate with this structural evolution intellectual functions and capabilities increase, so that the neocortex is generally considered to be the site of intellectual function and of consciousness. This is, however, not entirely correct, though it is probably true that the neopallium provides an encoding and amplification mechanism for integrating functions of the limbic system and other lower brain mechanisms, and also for memory.

The neopallium consists of the neocortex, which with the inclusion of the claustrum contains all the perikarya, and of the subcortical white matter (*album cerebri*) made up exclusively of axons and supporting tissue. Owing to the meager development of the neocortex in the rat brain, the surface of the neopallium is smooth or lissencephalic. The neocortex, in contrast to the limbic cortex, consists of six layers of nerve cells (Chart I), but in the separation of the second and third layers it is somewhat indistinct. From the surface toward the white matter these layers are named

(1) *lamina zonalis* (plexiform or molecular layer)
(2) *lamina granularis externa* (outer granular layer)
(3) *lamina pyramidalis* (layer of medium-sized pyramidal cells)
(4) *lamina granularis interna* (internal granular layer)
(5) *lamina ganglionaris* (layer of large pyramidal cells)
(6) *lamina multiformis* (layer of polyhedral nerve cells)

Certain differences in the development of these layers, and the occurrence of sublayers, form the basis of cytoarchitectonics as discussed above. No attempt is being made here to dwell further on the principles of cytoarchitectonics, and the reader interested in more detail is referred to the pertinent literature. Figures 38 and 39 represent cortical maps depicting the results of cytoarchtectonic and of functional considerations, respectively. It will be noted from these maps that the complete lack of sulci in the rat brain does not permit a proper separation of the various neocortical areas into the respective lobes as is possible in higher mammals, especially in primates. Conventionally, the areas constituting the homologies to the lobated neocortex are referred to as *regiones frontalis, insularis, parietalis, temporalis,* and *occipitalis,* respectively.

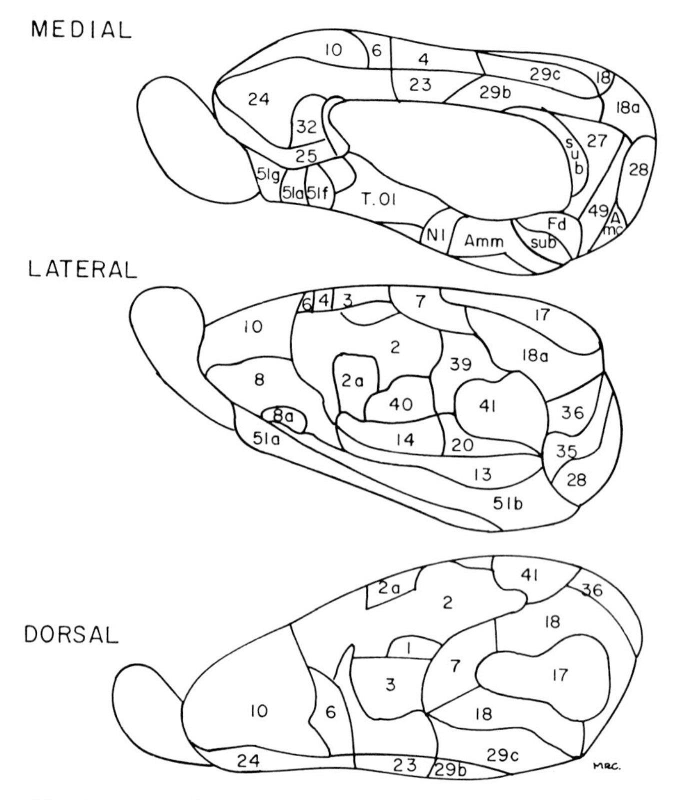

FIG. 38. Telencephalic cortex parcellated by Krieg (1946) (redrawn).

Electrical stimulation of the frontal area produces coordinated movements of the opposite side of the body. This area has been extensively studied by Woolsey *et al.*, who gave a detailed functional map of the frontal region of the rat neocortex. Anatomical studies permit identification of the parietal region as the terminal of projection systems originating largely in the ventral thalamic nuclei and concerned with somatosensory function. The cortical projection area for taste is located in the insular neocortex, as recently demonstrated by Benjamin and Akert. Temporal area 41 represents the primary auditory cortex and occipital area 17 the primary visual cortex.

The nerve fibers of the neocortex, with few exceptions, are not arranged in conspicuous tracts as is the case for the lower telencephalic centers. Instead, they form a three-dimensional feltwork, the neopallial white matter. There are, in addition, loosely arranged bundles which extend through the cortex parallel to the surface. Functionally and anatomically one can differentiate (1) association systems which connect various neocortical areas situated in the same hemisphere with each other, (2) commissural systems connecting the two opposite hemi-

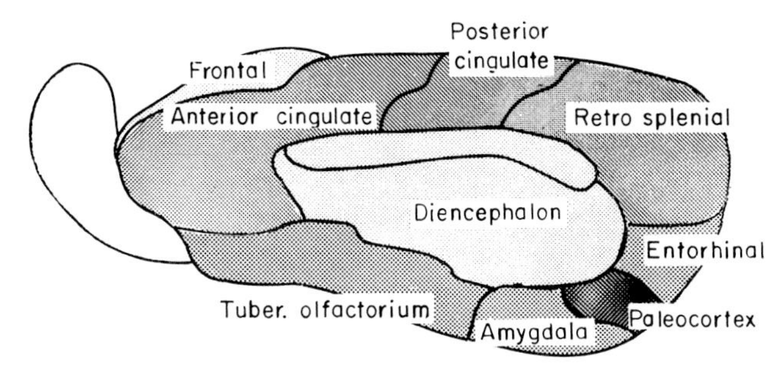

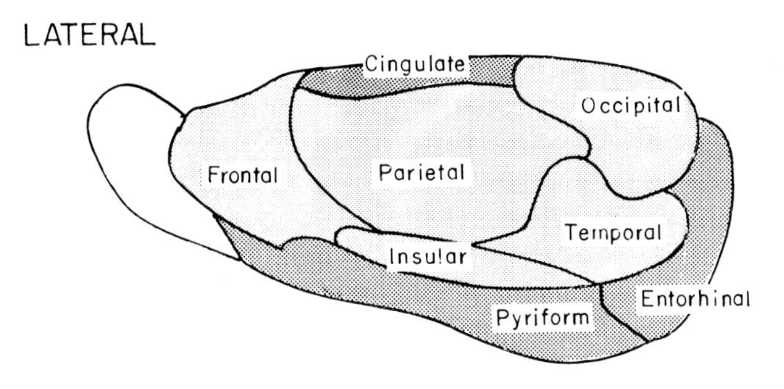

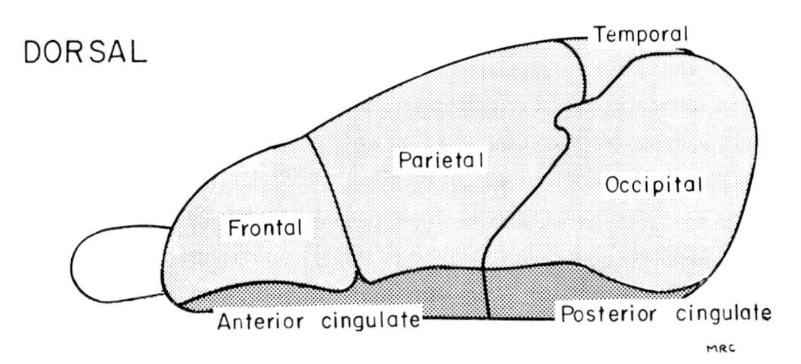

Fig. 39. Telencephalic cortex parcellated roughly by Kuhlenbeck *et al.* (1960) (redrawn, with permission from S. Karger, Basel and New York).

sphere cortices, and (3) projection systems connecting the cortex with subcortical structures.

The association systems either run within the cortex, where they form tangential laminae of white matter, often separating two adjacent cell layers from each other, or they extend immediately underneath the cortex, where they give rise to the so-called U-fibers in the convoluted or gyrencephalic brain of higher mammals. According to Krieg (1946), association fibers of all sorts are relatively few in the rat and those present are mostly intracortical throughout their course. This is in contrast to the human brain, which contains massive association tracts deep in the *album cerebri* connecting quite distant cortical areas.

All commissural fibers of the neocortex run through the corpus callosum, and these are apparently the only types of fibers found in that structure. All corticofugal neurons which send fibers to the internal capsule send collaterals to the corpus callosum. Krieg (1962) has studied the architecture of these fibers and found that they are arranged in such a way as to reach the corpus callosum in the shortest possible course but to sweep smoothly into the callosum. The capsular collaterals branch off as nearly at a right angle as possible and drop into the internal capsule. Krieg (1946) reported that commissural fibers connect bilaterally symmetrical areas (homotopic fibers), but in the visual cortex (area 17) and the closely associated area 18 Nauta and Bucher observed a considerable overlap (heterotopic fibers). Termination of commissural fibers is most profuse in layer VI, less in layers V and IV, while only few reach layers III and II. In view of the conspicuous development of the corpus callosum, it comes perhaps as a surprise that very little is known about the functional significance of this system. In human medicine, it is almost axiomatic that complete surgical transection of the corpus callosum produces little, if any, demonstrable deficit. There are, however, human observations in which congenital absence or underdevelopment of this structure may be associated with mirror movements. Recent experimental data obtained on monkeys with a transected corpus callosum (split brain preparation) suggest that in these animals transfer of acquired skills and of conditioned reflexes from one hemisphere to the other is impossible. Innes and Saunders (1962) quote cases of agenesis of the corpus callosum in many species and some of these were asymptomatic.

The neocortical projection systems are both ascending and descending. All are mediated through the internal capsule and the thalamic radiation. These fibers penetrate the bundles of the callosal system at right angles and radiate into the cortex perpendicularly to the surface, forming the cortical radiation. Krieg (1946) stated for the rat that all neocortical areas have descending fibers which reach at least as far as the *pes pedunculi* of the midbrain. Others extend further caudad to the pons, the medulla oblongata, and the cervical spinal cord, forming the corticopontine and corticospinal tracts. Of all parts of the central nervous system, the hypothalamus is the only one which receives few, if any, fibers from the neocortex, neither does it project to the latter. In this respect the neocortex is similar to the thalamus, projections of which to the hypothalamus are not in evidence (Krieg, 1944). As a comprehensive designation, descending projection systems are called corticofugal pathways in contradistinction to the corticopetal projection systems. By far the greatest majority of the latter ascend from the diencephalon, more specifically from the sensory and motor relay centers of the ventral and lateral thalamic nuclei, the pretectal nuclei, subthalamus, and metathalamus. Again these fibers are diffusely spread and, in the rat brain, do not form any compact tracts as they do in the primate brain. In reference to origin and termination of these systems, we speak of (1) the geniculo-occipital or geniculostriate system, designating the optic projection to area 17; (2) the geniculoparietal system conveying auditory impulses to area 41; and (3) the thalamoparietal projection system involved in the mediation of somatic sensory impulses, to name but a few. These corticopetal projection systems are sometimes reciprocal or nearly so. For instance, area 17 receives strong projections from the dorsal nucleus of the lateral geniculate body and sends many efferent fibers to the ventral nucleus, but few to the dorsal. Other corticofugal fibers from area 17 in the rat reach the posterior part of the lateral thalamic nucleus, the pretectal area, the anterior colliculi, zona incerta, and even the pons (Nauta and Bucher).

In summary, the neocortex represents a sheet of perikarya arranged in six laminae. Most of these cortical neurons are connected with each other by an infinitely complex and rich meshwork of fibers, the associational and commissural systems. Along with the projection fibers these form the white matter. Connections with other parts of the central nervous system are established by the corticofugal systems and by the ascending projection systems. Most of the corticofugal and corticopetal connections are with the diencephalon, to a lesser extent with the mesencephalon and rhombencephalon, but few if any direct connections exist with the hypothalamus.

References

ABBIE, A. A. The relations of the fascia dentata, hippocampus and neocortex and the nature of the subiculum. *J. Comp. Neurol.* **68**: 307-323, 1938.

ABBIE, A. A. The origin of the corpus callosum and the fate of the structures related to it. *J. Comp. Neurol.* **70**: 9-44, 1939.

ADELMANN, H. B. The development of the neural folds and cranial ganglia of the rat. *J. Comp. Neurol.* **39**: 19-169, 1925.

ADEY, W. R., C. W. DUNLOP & S. SUNDERLAND. A survey of rhinencephalic interconnections with the brain stem. *J. Comp. Neurol.* **110**: 173-203, 1958.

ALLISON, A. C. The structure of olfactory bulb and its relationship to olfactory pathways in the rabbit and rat. *J. Comp. Neurol.* **98**: 309-353, 1953.

ALLISON, A. C. The morphology of the olfactory system in the vertebrates. *Biol. Revs. Cambridge phil. Soc.* **28**: 195-244, 1953.

ARIËNS KAPPERS, C. U., G. C. HUBER & ELIZABETH C. CROSBY. The Comparative Anatomy of the Nervous System of Vertebrates, Including Man. 2 Volumes. New York: Macmillan. 1936.

BENJAMIN, R. M. & K. AKERT. Cortical and thalamic areas involved in taste discrimination in the albino rat. *J. Comp. Neurol.* **111**: 231-259, 1959.

BENJAMIN, R. M. & C. PFAFFMANN. Cortical localization of taste in albino rats. *J. Neurophysiol.* **18**: 56-64, 1955.

BLACKSTAD, T. W. Commissural connections of the hippocampal region in the rat, with special reference to their mode of termination. *J. Comp. Neurol.* **105**: 417-537, 1956.

BRODAL, A. The amygdaloid nucleus in rat. *J. Comp. Neurol.* **87**: 1-16, 1947.

BRODAL, A. The origin of the fibers of the anterior commissure in the rat. Experimental studies. *J. Comp. Neurol.* **88**: 157-205, 1948.

BROOKS, C. M. Studies on the cerebral cortex. II. Localised representation of hopping and placing reaction in the rat. *Amer. J. Physiol.* **105**: 162-171, 1933.

CAJAL, S. RAMÓN Y. Histologie du système nerveux de l'homme et des vertébrés. Paris: Maloine, 1909-1911. (Reprinted by C.S.I.S., Madrid, 1952.)

COHRS, P. Das subfornikale Organ des 3. Ventrikels. Nach Untersuchungen bei den Haussäugetieren, einigen Nagetieren und dem Menschen. *Z. Anat. Entwickl.* **105**: 491-518, 1936.

CROSBY, ELIZABETH C., T. HUMPHREY & E. W. LAUER. Correlative Anatomy of the Nervous System. New York: Macmillan, 1962.

DAITZ, H. M. & T. P. S. POWELL. Studies of the connexions of the fornix system. *J. Neurol. Neurosurg. Psychiat.* **17**: 75-86, 1954.

DROOGLEEVER-FORTUYN, A. B. Cortical cell lamination of the hemispheres of some rodents. Mus decumanus (Pall). *Arch. Neurol. Psychiat.* (*London*) **6**: 221-354, 1914. (Rat, p. 260.)

GLOOR, P. Telencephalic Influences upon the Hypothalamus. Hypothalamic-Hypophysial Interrelationships (W. S. Fields, R. Guillemin & C. A. Carton, eds.), pp. 74-114. Springfield, Illinois: C. C Thomas, 1956.

GUILLERY, R. W. Degeneration in the postcommissural fornix and the mamillary peduncle of the rat. *J. Anat.* (*London*) **90**: 350-370, 1956.

GURDJIAN, E. S. Olfactory connections of the albino rat, with special reference to the stria medullaris and anterior commissure. *J. Comp. Neurol.* **38**: 127-163, 1925.

GURDJIAN, E. S. The corpus striatum of the albino rat. *J. Comp. Neurol.* **45**: 249-281, 1928.

GUREWITSCH, M., G. BYCHOWSKY & J. URANOWSKY. Zur vergleichenden Architektonik der Grosshirnrinde der Säugetiere. I. Mitteilung. Nager. *Z. Anat. Entwickl.* **90**: 549-596, 1929.

HARRISON, J. M. & M. LYON. The role of the septal nuclei and components of the fornix in the behaviour of the rat. *J. Comp. Neurol.* **108**: 121-138, 1957.

HASSMANNOVÁ, J. The development of orientation in the space (the importance of neopallium and visual reception in the rat). *Plzeň. lék. Sbornik*, Suppl. **3**: 135-136, 1961.

HERMANDIDES, S. R. & M. KÖPPEN. Über die Furchen und über den Bau der Grosshirnrinde bei den Lissencephalen, insbesondere über die Lokalisation des motorischen Centrums und der Sehregion. *Arch. Psychiat.* **37**: 616-634, 1903.

HERRICK, C. J. Brains of Rats and Men. A Survey of the Original and Biological Significance of the Cerebral Cortex. Chicago: Univ. of Chicago Press, 1926.

HERRICK, C. JUDSON. An Introduction to Neurology. 5th Ed. Philadelphia: Saunders, 1931.

HOLT, C. M. Studies on the olfactory bulbs of the albino rat. II. Number of cells in the bulb. *J. Comp. Neurol.* **27**: 201-259, 1917.

INNES, J. R. M. & L. Z. SAUNDERS. Comparative Neuropathology; p. 284. New York: Academic Press, 1962.

JOHNSTON, J. B. The morphology of the septum, hippocampus and pallial commissures in reptiles and mammals. *J. Comp. Neurol.* **23**: 371-478, 1913.

JOHNSTON, J. B. Further contributions to the study of the evolution of the forebrain. *J. Comp. Neurol.* **35**: 337-481, 1923.

JUNG, R. & R. HASSLER. The extrapyramidal motor system. *In:* Handbook of Physiology, Section I Neurophysiology Vol. II (H. W. Magoun, ed.), pp. 863-928. Baltimore: Williams & Wilkins, 1960.

KLOTZ, D. A. & G. CLARK. An attempt at graphic cytoarchitectonic description. *J. Comp. Neurol.* **92**: 215-225, 1950.

KOIKEGAMI, H., S. FUSE, S. YOKOYAMA, T. WATANABE & H. WATANABE. Contributions to the comparative anatomy of the amygdaloid nuclei of mammals with some experiments of their destruction or stimulation. *Folia Psychiat. et Neurol. Japon.* **8** (No. 4), 336-370, 1955.

KREINER, G. Bulbus olfactorius der weissen Ratte (Topographie und Myeloarchitektonik). *Z. Anat. Entwickl.* **102**: 232-245, 1933–1934.

KRIEG, W. J. S. The medial region of the thalamus of the albino rat. *J. Comp. Neurol.* **80**: 381-415, 1944.

KRIEG, W. J. S. Connections of the cerebral cortex. I. The albino rat. A. Topography of the cortical areas. B. Structure of the cortical areas. C. Extrinsic connections. *J. Comp. Neurol.* **84**: 221-275, 277-323, 1946; *ibid.* **86**: 267-394, 1947.

KRIEG, W. J. S. General conclusions from an experimental study of the cerebral cortex of the albino rat. *Anat. Rec.* **97**: 350-351, 1947.

KRIEG, W. J. S. Influence on fiber structure of universal bifurcation of corticofugal stalks into capsular and callosal components. *Anat. Rec.* **142**: 249, 1962.

KUHLENBECK, H. Some histologic age changes in the rat's brain and their relationship to comparable changes in the human brain. *Confin. Neurol.* **14**: 329-342, 1954.

KUHLENBECK, H., E. G. SZEKELY & H. SPULER. Some remarks on the zonal pattern of mammalian cortex cerebri as manifested in the rabbit: Its relationship with certain electrocorticographic findings. *Confin. Neurol.* **20**: 407-423, 1960.

LASHLEY, K. S. Visual discrimination of size and form in the albino rat. *J. Anim. Behavior* **2**: 310-331, 1912.

LASHLEY, K. S. Studies of cerebral function in learning. VII. The relation between cerebral mass, learning and retention. *J. Comp. Neurol.* **41**: 1-58, 1926.

LASHLEY, K. S. The mechanism of vision. I. A rapid method for the analysis of pattern vision in the rat. *J. Genet. Psychol.* **37**: 453, 1930.

LASHLEY, K. S. The mechanism of vision. IV. The cerebral areas necessary for pattern vision in the rat. *J. Comp. Neurol.* **53**: 419-478, 1931.

LASHLEY, K. S. The mechanism of vision. VII. The projection of the retina upon the primary optic centers in the rat. *J. Comp. Neurol.* **59**: 341-373, 1934.

LASHLEY, K. S. The mechanism of vision. XVI. The functioning of small remnants of the visual cortex. *J. Comp. Neurol.* **70**: 45-67, 1939.

LASHLEY, K. S., W. T. MACDONALD & H. N. PETERS. Studies of cerebral function in learning. X. The effect of dilatation of the ventricle upon maze learning. *Amer. J. Physiol.* **104**: 51-61, 1933.

LOO, Y. T. The mammalian endbrain. I. The septum. II. The strio-amygdaloid complex. *Contrib. Biol. Lab. Sci. Soc. China* **15**: 29-70, 1941; *ibid.* **16**: 1-25, 1941 (both printed in 1947).

LOO, Y. T. The paraphysis in adult mammalian brains. *Contrib. Biol. Lab. Sci. Soc. China* **15**: 71-76, 1941 (printed in 1947).

LOUCKS, R. B. The efficacy of the rat's motor cortex in delayed alternation. *J. Comp. Neurol.* **53**: 511-567, 1931.

MACLEAN, P. D. The limbic system with respect to self-preservation and the preservation of the species. *J. Nerv. Mental Dis.* **127**: 1-11, 1958.

MAIER, N. R. F. The effect of cerebral destruction on reasoning and learning in rats. *J. Comp. Neurol.* **54**: 45-75, 1932.

MAIER, N. R. F. The cortical area concerned with coordinated walking in the rat. *J. Comp. Neurol.* **61**: 395-405, 1935.

METTLER, F. A. Neuroanatomy. St. Louis, Missouri: C. V. Mosby, 1948.

MYSLIVEČEK, J., J. HASSMANNOVÁ, L. JILEK *et al.* The influence of the elimination of brain cortex on the development of higher nervous activity. *Plzeň. lék. Sbornik*, Suppl. **3**: 25-32, 1961a.

MYSLIVEČEK, J., Z. CHALOUPKA, S. REINIŠ *et al.* Consequences of the elimination of neopallium in newborn rats. *Plzeň. lék. Sbornik*, Suppl. **3**: 133-134, 1961b.

NAUTA, W. J. H. An experimental study of the fornix system in the rat. *J. Comp. Neurol.* **104**: 247-271, 1956.

NAUTA, W. J. H. Fibre degeneration following lesions of the amygdaloid complex in the monkey. *J. Anat. (London)* **95**: 515-531, 1961.

NAUTA, W. J. H. & V. M. BUCHER. Efferent connections of the striate cortex in the albino rat. *J. Comp. Neurol.* **100**: 257-285, 1954.

PAPEZ, J. W. Comparative Neurology. 518 pp. New York: Crowell, 1929. (Reprinted by Hafner, New York, 1961.)

PAPEZ, J. W. A proposed mechanism of emotion. *Arch. Neurol. & Psychiat.* **38**: 725-743, 1937.

PENNINGTON, L. A. The function of the brain in auditory localization. *J. Comp. Neurol.* **67**: 33-48, 1937.

POWELL, T. P. S., R. W. GUILLERY & W. M. COWAN. A quantitative study of the fornix-mamillo-thalamic system. *J. Anat. (London)* **91**: 419-437, 1957.

RILEY, H. A. An Atlas of the Basal Ganglia, Brain Stem and Spinal Cord. New York: Hafner, 1960.

ROSE, M. Cytoarchitektonischer Atlas der Grosshirnrinde der Maus. *J. Psychol. u. Neurol. (Leipzig)* **40**: 1-51, 1929.

SCHOLZ, W. Selective neuronal necrosis and its topistic patterns in hypoxemia and oligemia. *J. Neuropath. Exper. Neurol.* **12**: 249-261. 1953.

SCHULZ, C. Die relative Grösse cytoarchitektonischer Einheiten im Grosshirn der weissen Ratte, weissen Maus und Zwergmaus. *Zool. Jb. Abt. allg. Zool. u. Physiol. Tiere* **63**: 64-106, 1951-1953.

SMITH, C. G. Pathologic changes in olfactory nasal mucosa of albino rats with "stunted" olfactory bulbs. *Arch. Otolaryng. (Chicago)* **25**: 131-143, 1937.

SMITH, C. G. Changes in the olfactory mucosa and the olfactory nerves following intranasal treatment with one percent zinc sulphate. *Canad. Med. Ass. J.* **39**: 138-140, 1938.

STAMM, J. S. Function of median cerebral cortex in maternal behavior of rats. *J. Comp. Physiol. Psychol.* **48**: 347-356, 1955.

SUGITA, N. Comparative studies on the growth of the cerebral cortex. I. On the changes in size and shape of the cerebrum during the postnatal growth of the brain—albino rat. *J. Comp. Neurol.* **28**: 495-510, 1917.

SUGITA, N. Comparative studies on the growth of the cerebral cortex. III. On the size and shape of the cerebrum in the Norway rat (Mus norvegicus), and a comparison of these with the corresponding characters in the albino rat. *J. Comp. Neurol.* **29**: 1-9, 1918a.

SUGITA, N. Comparative studies on the growth of the cerebral cortex. VIII. General review of data for the thickness of the cerebral cortex and the size of the cortical cells in several mammals, together with some postnatal growth changes in these structures. *J. Comp. Neurol.* **29**: 241-278, 1918b.

SUITSU, N. Comparative studies on the growth of the corpus callosum. I. On the area of the corpus callosum, measured on the sagittal section of the albino rat brain. *J. Comp. Neurol.* **32**: 35-60, 1920.

TSUNEDA, N. Zur Cytoarchitektonik des Neocortex des Mäusegehirns. *Okajimas Folia Anat. Japon.* **15**: 1-47, 1937.

UCHIDA, Y. A contribution to the comparative anatomy of the amygdaloid nuclei in mammals, especially in rodents. Part I. Rat and mouse. *Folia. Psychiat. Neurol. Japon.* **4**: 25-42, 1950.

VALENSTEIN, E. S. & W. J. H. NAUTA. A comparison of the distribution of the fornix system in the rat, guinea pig, cat, and monkey. *J. Comp. Neurol.* **113**: 337-363, 1959.

VAZ FERREIRA, A. Cortical areas of albino rat studied by silver impregnation. *J. Comp. Neurol.* **95**: 177-243, 1951.

VOGT, CECILE & O. VOGT. Altérations anatomiques de la schizophrénie et d'autres psychoses dites fonctionelles. *Proc. 1st Internatl. Congr. Neuropathology* **1**: 514-532, 1952.

VON MILLISER, R. Cortical lesions and projection fibers in the brain of the rat. *Anat. Rec.* **52**: 1-81, 1932.

VON VOLKMANN. Vergleichende Untersuchungen an der Rinde der "motorischen" und "Sehregion" von Nagetieren. *Anat. Anz.* **61**: 234-243, 1926.

WEBER, A. & M. BARBEY-GAMPERT. La Fascia dentata dans le cerveau du rat adulte. *Schweiz. med. Wschr.* **80**: 1242, 1950.

WHITE, L. E. J. Ipsilateral afferents to the hippocampal formation in the albino rat. *J. Comp. Neurol.* **113**: 1-43, 1959.

WOOD, C. D., B. SCHOTTELIUS, L. L. FROST & M. BALDWIN. Localization within the amygdaloid complex of anesthetized animals. *Neurology* **8**: 477-480, 1958.

WOODBURNE, R. T. Certain phylogenetic anatomical relations of localizing significance for the mammalian central nervous system. *J. Comp. Neurol.* **71**: 215-257, 1939.

WOOLSEY, C. N., P. H. SETTLAGE, D. R. MEYER, W. SENCER, T. P. HAMUY & A. M. TRAVIS. Patterns of localization in precentral and "supplementary" motor areas and their relation to the concept of a premotor area. *Res. Publ. Ass. Nerv. Mental Dis.* **30**: 238-264, 1952.

YOUNG, M. W. The nuclear pattern and fiber connections of non-cortical centers of the telencephalon of the rabbit (Lepus cuniculus). *J. Comp. Neurol.* **64-65**: 295-401, 1936.

CHAPTER VIII

Neural Mechanisms

In the preceding chapters we have dwelt on structures. Occasionally, the functions of certain structures were defined in a superficial way. More than any other factor, the correlation of structure with function has provided the stimulus for probing deeper and deeper into morphologic details, and a more adequate discussion of the problems involved is in order.

In reference to the correlation of structure and function, the term "neural mechanism" is often used, and a definition of this term is elucidated by the following consideration. A ventral horn cell in the spinal cord is a structure which can be seen under the microscope. We also can see that this cell connects by way of its axon with skeletal muscle fibers, but we know from physiologic observations that an impulse generated by the ventral horn cell causes the muscle fibers to contract. Therefore, we call the combination of ventral horn cell–muscle fibers a "motor unit," which designates a neural mechanism. In keeping with this terminology, the ventral horn cell is also called "motor neuron," which designates a part of a neural mechanism.

A mechanism such as the motor unit is not self-contained, at least not under normal conditions of life. It is subject to the influence of numerous other neurons synapsing with the motor neuron, and it is the combined total of afferent excitatory and inhibitory impulses on the motor neuron which determines the activity of the motor unit. The motor neuron and the nerve fibers which synapse with it then constitute another neural mechanism. This is more complex than the motor unit, and may be called a "segmental motor mechanism" since all participating structures are located in one segment of the spinal cord. The afferent neurons synapsing with the motor neuron, in turn, receive impulses from still other neurons, perhaps located in cerebrum and cerebellum. Those neurons again are influenced by yet another set of neurons. Obviously numerous, if not all, parts of the nervous system are somehow involved in causing a single motor unit to perform. The situation is even more complex if one considers that the activity of the motor neuron generates signals in other neurons, operating on the feedback principle. These impulses "report back" to the centers involved in the initiation of motor activity, as discussed above.

Hence, the ostensibly simple process of a motor neuron producing an impulse is inconceivably complex, if all determining and consequential events are considered. In other words, there are neither "simple" nor "complex" neural mechanisms. The nervous system operates as one integrated mechanism and it should be clear that the living organism, from ameba to man, acts as a single unit, not as a collection of systems. Thus, in speaking of systems and of their mechanisms, we are introducing a nonexistent parcellation, which is, at best, a didactically expedient fiction.

Generally, one can state that neural mechanisms imply neuronal pathways. Only a fraction of known neuronal pathways has been described in the present book. These restrictions are not only the result of limitations of space; they have also been purposely imposed for didactic reasons since the scope of this book is that of an introduction to neuroanatomy. On the other hand, it should not be forgotten that even detailed knowledge of the morphology of neuronal pathways permits only limited conclusions as to how they function and work together. It may, perhaps, be appropriate to point out that the total number of neurons (about ten to fourteen billion in the human brain) and their possible connections, being greater by orders of magnitude, will preclude a complete understanding of the neural mechanism probably forever.

Since the operational organization of the human nervous system is so complex, scientists have turned to simpler mechanisms and to models. This is the reason why so much research is being done on arthropods and mollusks in which anatomic and functional organization are infinitely more simple. Unfortunately, it is almost impossible to gauge the "mind" of such lower forms of life, and even if possible it would have little bearing on the more ambitious goals of the biological sciences, namely to understand the higher functions of the human nervous system. As the next best approach, biologists have broken down the nervous mechanism into a series of "simpler" mechanisms. In doing so they may have been guided by anatomic considerations; for instance, they would group several nerve cell stations closely linked by extensive fiber connections together as a "system," and then explore this system by physiologic techniques. In a different approach, nervous mechanisms are studied after parts of the nervous system have been "isolated" from suprasegmental cell stations, for instance, by severing the spinal cord from the medulla oblongata, which permits the observer to investigate "intrinsic spinal mechanisms."

The significance of the neural mechanism within the living organism might be expressed in the following way. Environmental stimuli, received by the "exteroreceptors," and stimuli from within the organism, received by "proprioceptive and interoceptive elements," are conducted by way of the peripheral nerves to the central nervous system. These stimuli are coded, encoded, amplified, or otherwise modulated; some are "stored," many probably are "lost," but others eventually initiate appropriate motor, visceral, and behavioral activities. In a nutshell then, the nervous system provides the means for the successful adaptation of an organism to its environment. The magnitude of the performance of this system may be appreciated, if one considers that a human being receives approximately five billion impulses per second, of which three billion are received by way of the visual system alone. Coding, classification, amplification, and suppression of these impulses is not only executed with speed, but also with an astonishing degree of accuracy, selection, and determination.

With the increasing size of the nervous system, the basis of activity is widened and deepened. The telencephalon reaches a particularly large size with ascending phylogeny, and progressively more and more neural mechanisms become located there, a development implied in the term "progressive encephalization of function." On the last page of "The Integrative Action of the Nervous System," Sir Charles S. Sherrington superbly epitomized this fact as follows: "We thus, from the biological standpoint, see the cerebrum, and especially the cerebral cortex, as the latest and highest expression of a nervous mechanism which may be described as the *organ of, and for, the adaptation of nervous reactions* [italics ours]. The cerebrum, built upon the distance-receptors and entrusted with reactions which fall in an anticipatory interval so as to be *precurrent*, comes, with its projicience of sensation and the psychial powers unfolded from that germ of advantage, to be the organ *par excellence* for the readjustment and the perfecting of the nervous reactions of the animal as a whole, so as to improve and extend their suitability to, and advantage over, the environment. . . . It is then around the cerebrum, its physiological and psychological attributes, that the main interest of biology must ultimately turn."

That Sherrington's advice has been heeded is amply documented on the 2000 printed pages which comprise the section on *Neurophysiology* in the Handbook of Physiology (Magoun). Here, we shall discuss but two nervous mechanisms which have been selected as *pars pro toto* from the many that psychologists and physiologists have come to distinguish. It is the goal of this discussion to familiarize the reader with the present thinking and knowledge on mechanisms and to show the fundamental and significant contributions of neuroanatomy toward this end.

A. RETICULAR ACTIVATING SYSTEM

The reticular activating system (RAS) is an example of a nervous mechanism *a fortiori*. Its function can be studied by the isolation technique referred to above; in fact, it was discovered in precisely such preparation. In addition, the RAS elucidates an important principle of higher nervous function, namely the discordance of structural and functional organization, both being highly ordered but occupying planes at different levels. The present-day concept of the RAS is probably understood best by following its history of discovery.

1. Anatomic Considerations

The anatomic basis of the RAS is the reticular formation of the brainstem (*formatio reticularis*). According to Cajal, the reticular formation extends cephalad from the medulla oblongata above the decussation of the pyramids in a central position through pons and midbrain to the thalamus. It consists of collections of perikarya which in several instances form aggregations of distinct nuclei. In an extensive study, Olszewski (1954) has described and named 98 such nuclear masses. A detailed discussion of these, however, would be pointless as these aggregations of perikarya do not appear in general to represent functional units or simple neural mechanisms. Rather, the physiologic characteristics exhibited by the reticular formation appear largely to be independent of visible structural relationships.

The anatomic pattern of the connections of these nuclei is most interesting. The size of the perikarya populating the reticular formation varies anywhere from 12 to 90 μ in greatest diameter. It is presumed that soma size is directly related to axon length in the reticular formation, and it can be demonstrated by histologic preparations that the various nuclear aggregations of the reticular formation are connected with each other in many different ways. The smallest nerve cells send their axons into the neighboring structures, whereas larger perikarya bridge over one or several nuclei before their axons terminate. Thus, any two distant nuclei of the reticular formation may be connected by a multisynaptic pathway, by a two- or three-neuron pathway, or by a direct path. Accordingly, impulses between two remote nuclei may be conducted with variable velocity. Cajal noted that the axons of the reticular formation not only often cross the midline and ramify both ipsi- and contralaterally, but also send one branch cephalad and one caudad. This pattern suggests that one single reticular cell may be capable of exerting its influence toward the brain and downward to the spinal cord, on either side of the neuraxis or both. Succinctly then, the reticular formation is morphologically precisely what the term implies, namely a multidimensional network of neurons connected intrinsically with each other by direct and/or by more or less circuitous multisynaptic routes.

The rostral end of the reticular formation is not too well delimited, and it is probably a matter of definition whether thalamic nuclei beyond the reticular formation of the thalamus should be included. Papez (1956) and others have shown that cephalic conduction from the reticular formation to the midline and intralaminar nuclei of the thalamus and to the subthalamus occurs in relatively well-marked fiber bundles—the reticulothalamic, tegmentothalamic, and tectothalamic tracts. Whether the reticular nucleus of the thalamus bears a relationship to the reticular formation, ostensibly implicit in terminology, is still a matter of conjecture. Papez (1956) states that this nucleus is functionally related to the intralaminar nuclei, from which it receives many fibers. Its cells send fibers into the internal capsule which presumably go to the occipital, temporal, parietal, and frontal regions of the neocortex. Thus, Papez suggested, although he did not specifically state so, that the reticular formation has an efferent pathway to the neocortex via midline and intralaminar thalamic nuclei and the reticular nucleus of the thalamus. Descending fibers from the reticular formation run by way of the reticulospinal tracts which send massive collaterals into the red nucleus and into other structures belonging to the extrapyramidal motor system. Another important projection system of the reticular formation is directed into the cerebellum, more specifically the anterior lobe and the vermis. Finally, fibers from the reticular formation ascend in the mamillary peduncle to reach the hypothalamus, the septum, and by synapsis also the hippocampus.

Reticulopetal connections from the spinal cord are made by collaterals branching off the spinothalamic and spinocerebellar tracts as they cross through the brainstem. Similar collaterals from the medial lemnisci are implicated by electrophysiological observations but have not been demonstrated morphologically as yet. There are also direct connections from perikarya in the spinal cord forming the spinoreticular pathways. Moreover, the reticular formation receives afferent fibers from intrinsic brainstem structures such as the trigeminal and lateral lemnisci, and motor and sensory nuclei, either directly or by collaterals. Corticoreticular fibers run in the corticospinal and corticobulbar tracts and originate in the motorsensory cortex and in the cingulate gyrus. Afferent fibers from hippocampus, septum, and hypothalamus via the fornix system, the diencephalic periventricular system, and the medial forebrain bundle, reach the reticular formation at its midbrain level.

The reticular formation by way of extensive and often reciprocal systems is connected to the spinal cord, the cerebellum, the surrounding structures of the brainstem, diencephalon, neocortex, and rhinencephalon—in short to practically all parts of the central nervous system. Curiously, the functional implications of these wide connections have not been fully understood until very recently. On account of its demonstrated fiber connections, the *formatio reticularis* has been considered to represent a third motor mechanism in addition to the pyramidal and extrapyramidal systems. Its connections with the hypothalamus by way of the diencephalic periventricular system were incriminated in the causation of visceral phenomena following destructive lesions of this formation, but its major functions remained obscure until 1949.

2. Physiologic Considerations

The true significance of the reticular formation in the neural mechanism, however, has been revealed only recently and it is on the basis of this discovery that the term reticular activating system has been coined. If the cerebrum in an animal is isolated from the hindbrain by a cut at the collicular level (*cerveau isolé*), the animal will fall into a state of sleep or coma. Bremer, who first performed this experiment, correctly suggested that this condition was the result of a deafferentiation of the neocortex. The assumption, however, that cortical deafferentiation was the result of blocking the primary sensory signals which ascend in the lemnisci, proved incorrect when Moruzzi and Magoun (1949) showed that the coma of *cerveau isolé* animals could be overcome by stimulation of the centrally located reticular formation, rather than by stimulation of the laterally located lemnisci. In other words, the electrically produced arousal from the coma of the *cerveau isolé* animal shows that before stimulation the higher structures of the cerebrum had been excluded from receiving "activating stimuli" conducted through the reticular formation rather than through the classical ascending sensory pathways.

Since this discovery, the reticular activating system has become one of the most thoroughly investigated cerebral mechanisms, and a host of data have been accumulated within a relatively short period of time. It has been shown, for instance, that evoked potentials (that is electric action current recorded in a specific area upon electric or chemical stimulation of a distant structure) can be recorded throughout the entire reticular formation as a result of excitation of somatic sensory, proprioceptive, sympathetic and parasympathetic, auditory, visual, and olfactory receptive systems. It has further been demonstrated that these impulses are projected into the sub- and hypothalamus and into the medial and intralaminar thalamic nuclei. In contrast to some other brain mechanisms, particularly sensory perception, which show a spatial organization, a single electrode placed into the reticular formation can record evoked potentials produced by stimulation of all the receptors mentioned above. This convergence or funneling of different stimuli into a circumscribed area is not absolute, since potentials may be evoked in a given area more readily from excitation of one conductive system than from another. Even more important is the observation that the sensory projection areas of the neocortex upon electrical stimulation will evoke potentials in the reticular formation which implies a direct parietoreticular pathway. This so-called efferent sensory system apparently operates on a feedback and on an anticipatory principle. That is to say, this system provides a mechanism to anticipate a sensory impulse and by doing so blocks possible lower mechanisms which are unwanted or unnecessary. Thus, if we know that we must tolerate a painful stimulus, e.g., a hypodermic injection, we can effectively block the "normal" pain reflex which would produce a withdrawal response immediately upon reception of the pain signal.

That the reticular activating system has its own specific mode of function is already suggested by its exceptional intrinsic fiber connections. For instance, if the diffuse thalamic projection system is electrically stimulated at 5 cycles per second, sleep is induced, whereas stimulation of the same region with 30–90 cycles per second pulses awakens the experimental animal. Furthermore, the arousal response in the *cerveau isolé* animal can be obtained by stimulation of practically any part of the reticular formation, but also by stimulation of its immediate projection sites in the thalamus and the septal region. The reticular activating system is an extremely flexible neuronal mechanism. As has been shown, it is capable of distinguishing impulse frequencies and it responds to different chemical stimuli. Thus, carbon dioxide, epinephrine, and acetylcholine, among numerous drugs, have been shown to exert a direct influence upon the reticular activating system. The fascinating aspect of this chemoreceptive ability is that it is not stereotyped, but modulated by the tonic potencies of the RAS under the influence of other afferent stimuli. This flexibility is borne out by innumerable experiences in daily life, but also under pathologic conditions which may often prove highly confusing to the physician. For instance, impairment of the reticular formation by a pathologic process may lead to a general agitation, yet the same condition may produce coma if only a few or even one of the other parameters of reticulopetal systems are altered.

In a greatly simplified fashion, one may envision the reticular activating system as a collection of condensers both in series and in parallel, which is continuously being charged by the billions of afferent impulses reaching it from the various receptors. This system of condensers then discharges rhythmically into all parts of the central nervous system and by doing so exerts a master control upon the latter. By discharging at higher frequencies it will "alert" the central nervous system and keep it in an excitable or responsive state making possible such "higher" functions as learning, motivation, and practically all activities of the nervous system. By discharging at low frequencies, excitability of the nervous system is reduced to the level of sleep, and a complete loss of function of the RAS means coma from which there is no awakening. On a similar principle, the reticular activating system controls visceral activity and exerts a critical degree of influence over motor functions concerned in phasic and tonic muscular control. Finally, the reticular activating system modifies reception, conduction, and integration of sensory signals to the extent that some will be preserved so as to become an "experience," whereas others will be suppressed and thus go unnoticed.

B. LIMBIC SYSTEM

The problem of emotional behavior has long occupied the attention of biological scientists. For almost 80 years, hypotheses in which the cerebral mechanisms of emotion have been deliberated have periodically appeared in the literature. These early attempts were necessarily doomed to failure, for in those days too little was known about the neural mechanism. In 1937, the clinical observations of Klüver and Bucy on monkeys with extensive bilateral temporal neocortical and paleocortical ablations incriminated limbic structures as the possible mechanism of emotive control, since such preparations displayed severe disturbances of emotional behavior. These observations coincided with Papez' speculative paper (1937) in which he expounded his ideas on a mechanism of emotion in the following words: "The central emotive process of cortical origin may then be conceived as being built up in the hippocampal formation and as being transferred to the mamillary body and thence through the anterior thalamic nuclei to the cortex of the gyrus cinguli. The cortex of the cingular gyrus may be looked on as the receptive region for the experiencing of emotion as the result of impulses coming from the hypothalamic region, in the same way as the area striata is considered the receptive cortex for photic excitations coming from the retina. Radiation of the emotive process from the gyrus cinguli to other regions in the cerebral cortex would add emotional coloring to psychic processes occurring elsewhere. This circuit would explain how emotion may arise in two ways: as a result of psychic activity and as a consequence of hypothalamic activity."

Since the structures implicated by Papez and by Klüver and Bucy in the mechanism of emotion are largely located in the limbic lobe, the entire mechanism has been designated the limbic system. A synonym for this term is visceral brain, and the intimate connections of this system with the mesencephalic part of the reticular formation has been expressed by the term limbic-midbrain circuit. Finally, in honor of Papez' contribution, the hippocampal-septal-hypothalamic-anterior thalamic-cingulate-hippocampal circuit is sometimes referred to as Papez cycle or circuit.

1. Anatomic Considerations

As described in Chapter VII (Section B,1,b; pp. 144–159), the limbic lobe of the telencephalon surrounds the brainstem and comprises meso-, paleo-, and archicortex together with their subcortical cell stations, the amygdala and septum, and their connecting fiber systems. In addition to these limbic lobe structures, the limbic system, as presently discussed, also comprises the entire hypothalamus, the rostral thalamus, the epithalamus, and parts of the fronto-orbital neocortex. The extensive fiber connections between limbic lobe and hypothalamus have been adequately described. The reciprocal connections between the latter structures and the reticular formation by way of the medial forebrain bundle, the fornix, the mamillary peduncle, and via the intralaminar and midline thalamic nuclei have also been elaborated.

2. Physiologic Considerations

Physiologic studies of the limbic system during the past 25 years have provided a wealth of data. Inspection of these immediately reveals that interest has centered around some parts of the limbic system, while others have been neglected. For instance, practically no physiologic data are available on the function of the habenular complex, which is intimately connected with limbic structures by way of the stria medullaris and the fasciculus retroflexus. Likewise, the mamillary bodies have not been systematically explored, and it is apparent that this issue has been dodged in many of the comprehensive treatises on the hypothalamus.

In contrast, the other cell stations of the limbic system have been extensively explored and some of the more important data are presented here in summary fashion.

a. *Amygdala and Adjacent Prepyriform Cortex.* In the original experiments of Klüver and Bucy, ablation of the anterior temporal lobe, including the amygdala and the pyriform cortex, produced dramatic behavioral changes in monkeys.

These animals became hypersexed, trying to copulate excessively and indiscriminately. They showed a lack of emotional responsiveness to aversive stimuli and of discrimination. For instance, they would pick up a nail and examine it for edibility and repeat this numerous times, showing no evidence of recollection or experienced judgment. In another set of experiments on cats, complete removal of the neocortex with preservation of the limbic lobe produced markedly placid and emotionally unresponsive animals. Further studies suggested that the amygdaloid complex or the cingulate gyrus, or both, might be involved in producing this placidity. Interruption of the fornix in such neodecorticated cats resulted in a significant lowering of the rage threshold. In view of these findings, it is confusing that ablation of the amygdaloid complex, together with the overlying pyriform cortex and parts of the adjacent hippocampus, with preservation of the neocortex converts notoriously wild, mean, and intractible animals such as the lynx, the wild Norway rat, the agoutis, and several types of monkeys into tame and docile individuals without any noticeable loss of motorsensory functions. These animals may still retain some ability to react with rage and excitement if properly stimulated.

The important common features of such experiments are that these behavioral effects are of limited duration, or, in other instances, may occur only after latencies up to several weeks. The contradictory nature of the results—on the one hand the amygdala appears to exert a restraint upon emotional behavior, on the other it seems to facilitate emotional expressions—has never been properly explained. Admittedly, it is practically impossible to produce lesions of precisely the same extent in two different animals so that the results from one animal to another may vary with the extent of the lesion. Species differences must also be taken into consideration. The lack of consistency in the results of temporal lobe ablations, presumably due to variations in the anatomical extent of the lesions, seems to indicate a critical degree of topographic organization of function in this part of the limbic system or a delicately balanced equilibrium between adjacent structures.

Stimulation and minute electrolytic destruction of the various amygdaloid nuclei have provided an entirely different set of data. Autonomic and motor responses have been obtained by stimulating the anteromesial amygdala, and stimulation of the lateral part of the amygdala has produced behavioral responses. The medial part of the basal nucleus is said to influence sympathetic function, whereas the cortical and medial nuclei are believed to activate parasympathetic systems. These experiments then show that stimulation of circumscribed areas of the amygdala produces responses which are similar to, but not quite identical with, those obtained after manipulation of the vegetative hypothalamus. It is well to recall the strong fiber connections between these two structures provided by the ventral amygdalofugal path, and, to a lesser extent, by the *stria terminalis* (Koikegami *et al.*, 1957, 1958; Wood *et al.*, 1958).

b. *Hippocampus.* The physiologic study of this part of the limbic system is beset with difficulties and the problem is such that Olds (1959) once stated facetiously: "The hippocampus changes function with each new experiment." Despite intensive experimentation, stimulation and ablation studies on the hippocampus have not yielded any clear-cut changes of behavior and of other nervous functions. On the other hand, it has been shown that the hippocampus has a rather stable electric activity of its own and an extremely low threshold for paroxysmal electric activity leading to seizure discharges. On account of its widespread fiber connections, seizure discharges may be induced by afferent stimulation from many limbic regions, but, more important, they spread readily into the limbic system. It is believed that this spread of the hippocampal seizure discharge accounts for the bizarre and highly variable emotional behavioral manifestations of psychomotor seizures rather than the discharge in the hippocampus itself. The intrinsic fiber connections within the hippocampal formation are believed to provide the mechanism for its stable electric rhythm and also for the buildup of paroxysmal activity, a mechanism to which the term "reverberating circuit" has been applied. It would appear from these data that the original hypothesis of Papez commands some physiologic support.

c. *Septal Area.* Destruction of the medial and lateral septal nuclei, including the precommissural fornix, has produced animals with behavioral changes summarily designated as hyperemotionality. Docile and tame laboratory rats are rendered fearful, unpredictably aggressive, and exhibit startling reactions following almost any extrinsic stimulus. The effect of such lesions, however, wears off in a few weeks despite the permanence of the lesion. It has also been shown that the sequel to the septal ablation can be prevented by prior ablation of the amygdala or eliminated by amygdalectomy following destruction of the septum (King, 1958). The results suggest an antagonism between septum and amygdala, but they are difficult to reconcile with the information presented above and also with the experiments to be discussed. Stimulation by electrodes implanted in the septum, but also in other areas of the limbic system, produces what has been termed "progressive reinforcement stimulation." The animal with such an implanted electrode is able to stimulate itself by pressing a bar. If the electrode is placed in the "right spot," the animal will work hard, very hard indeed, in order to stimulate itself, and such animals can be seen to press the bar as fast as physically and mechanically possible, perhaps 5000 times per hour and more, until exhausted. The same response can be produced by injecting minute amounts of neurohumoral agents by way of a microsyringe assembly. Extensive mapping of the points from which progressive reinforcement stimulation is obtained and of those which give negative results, has been achieved. The pattern is confusing since positive and negative points may be found in the same anatomic structure, and points giving homologous responses may be located in entirely different structures. Electric stimulation of the septal region has also elicited a variety of responses generally belonging to the category of sexual behavior and sociability considered to be directed to the purpose of preservation of the species.

d. *Fronto-orbital Cortex.* Ablation and stimulation studies of this part of the limbic system have produced evidence that this region may be concerned with the motivational behavior of food collection and consumption, and therefore subserves self-preservation (McLean, 1958).

e. *Vegetative Hypothalamus.* This part of the limbic system has been extensively studied and mapped in reference to its topographic organization of function, but only a few examples of this organization will be mentioned. The anterior zone as shown by electrolytic lesions mediates the release of growth hormone from the anterior pituitary lobe. The amygdala, likewise, exerts control on growth since bilateral ablation in young animals produces marked retardation in growth. The posterior zone of the hypothalamus is known to mediate sympathetic adrenal-medullary as well as pituitary adrenal-cortical components of the responses to stress, and again this mechanism can be influenced by stimulation of the amygdala, more specifically the medial part of the basal nucleus. Furthermore, ACTH release results also from stimulation of the mesencephalic parts of the reticular formation. Parasympathetic and sexual responses can be elicited by stimulation of the anterior hypothalamus but also by stimulation of certain regions of the septum as well as the medial and cortical amygdaloid nuclei.

3. Synthesis

These observations on the physiologic activity of the various parts of the limbic system are confusing if considered individually, but taken as a whole, they provide some insight into the limbic mechanism. There is little doubt that this system is concerned with general behavior, but not exclusively with emotion. Its organization is variable from one part to another. For example, amygdala and hypothalamus display some degree of topographic localization of function, but it appears that this is combined with a more diffuse and poorly organized mechanism subserving similar functions. The other extreme is represented by the hippocampus in which no functional localization has been discovered as yet, but which appears to operate on an entirely different nervous principle. By numerous intrinsic reverberating circuits implicit in its fine histologic organization, it seems to build up activity which is discharged into various limbic structures and into the hypothalamus, a manner of functioning somewhat similar to what has been found for the reticular formation. The significance of this intrinsic activity is unknown, but it has been speculated that it provides in part the delicate dynamic equilibrium of the entire system. There are centers which may inhibit or dampen the activity of the limbic system, such as the septal nuclei and the precommissural hippocampus, and others which activate the system, such as the amygdala.

The vegetative hypothalamus receives afferent impulses from different limbic cell stations mediating similar functions. Thus, motivational behavior can be elicited by stimulation not only of certain parts of the amygdala, but also of the fronto-orbital cortex and of the hypothalamus proper. Changes in blood pressure have been recorded after stimulation of the same regions. Sexual behavior has been altered by septal stimulation, by hypothalamic stimulation, and by stimulation of the hippocampus. This multiple representation of function may explain the limited duration of behavioral changes following permanent destruction of parts of the limbic system, thus exemplifying the law of safety intrinsic to all biologic systems. The elusiveness of functional localization in large parts of the limbic system is testimony not only to its complex organization, but also to the inadequacies of presently discussed hypotheses.

In summary, we may conceive of the limbic system as a mechanism, intercalated between the reticular activating system and the neocortex, which operates on principles still poorly understood. From experimental and clinical observation, it appears that the limbic system exerts a continuous influence upon incoming information and outgoing expressions, which under normal conditions are harmoniously balanced. While its input can be considered as being mediated through the classic afferent sensory, the efferent sensory systems, and the reticular formation, its output regulating motivational and expressive behavior flows right back into the reticular system, but also into efferent motor pathways and into the vegetative hypothalamus. Its delicately balanced activity appears to be largely provided by the hippocampus, which shows little or no topographically localized function. However, if the spontaneous electrical activity of the hippocampus is altered, radical changes of all behavioral components, as well as of emotional feelings, may become manifest as demonstrated by that unwanted but revealing experiment of nature, the psychomotor seizure.

References

BARD, P. & D. M. RIOCH. A study of four cats deprived of neocortex and additional portions of the forebrain. *Bull. Johns Hopkins Hosp.* **60**: 73-147, 1937.

BARD, P. & V. B. MOUNTCASTLE. Some forebrain mechanisms involved in expression of rage with special reference to suppression of angry behavior. *Res. Publ. Ass. Nerv. Ment. Dis.* **27**: 362, 1948.

BOVARD, E. W. A concept of hypothalamic functioning. *Perspectives in Biol. and Med.* **5**: 52-60, 1961.

BRICKNER, R. M. Telencephalisation of survival characteristics. *Res. Publ. Ass. Nerv. Mental Dis.* **27**: 658-688, 1948.

CAJAL, S. RAMØN Y. Histologie du système nerveux de l'homme et des vertébrés. Paris: Maloine, 1909-1911. (Reprinted by C.S.I.S., Madrid, 1952.)

HARRISON, J. M. & M. LYON. The role of the septal nuclei and components of the fornix in the behaviour of the rat. *J. Comp. Neurol.* **108**: 121-138, 1957.

HERRICK, C. J. An Introduction to Neurology. 5th Ed. Philadelphia: Saunders, 1931.

ISAACSON, R. L. & W. O. WICKELGREN. Hippocampal ablation and passive avoidance. *Science* **138**: 1104-1106, 1962.

JASPER, H. H., L. D. PROCTOR, R. S. KNIGHTON, W. C. NOSHAY & R. T. COSTELLO. Reticular Formation of the Brain. Boston: Little, Brown, 1958.

KING, F. A. Effects of septal and amygdaloid lesions on emotional behavior and conditioned avoidance responses in the rat. *J. Nerv. Mental Dis.* **126**: 57-63, 1958.

KLÜVER, H. & P. C. BUCY. "Psychic blindness" and other systems following bilateral temporal lobectomy in Rhesus monkeys. *Am. J. Physiol.* **119**: 352-353, 1937.

KOIKEGAMI, H., T. DODO, Y. MOCHIDA & H. TAKAHASHI. Stimulation experiments on the amygdaloid nuclear complex and related structures. Secretion, movements of the urinary bladder, blood pressure and respiratory movements. *Folia Psychiat. et Neurol. Japon.* **11** (No. 2), 157-206, 1957.

KOIKEGAMI, H., S. FUSE, S. HIROKI, T. KAZAMI & Y. KAGEYAMA. On the inhibitory effect upon the growth of infant animals or on the obesity in adult cat induced by bilateral destruction of the amygdaloid nuclear region. *Folia Psychiat. et Neurol. Japon.* **12** (No. 3), 207-223, 1958.

MACLEAN, P. D. The limbic system with respect to self-preservation and the preservation of the species. *J. Nerv. Mental Dis.* **127**: 1-11, 1958.

MAGOUN, H. W. Handbook of Physiology. Section I. Neurophysiology (3 volumes). Edit. Amer. Physiological Society, Washington, D.C., 1959–1960.

MORUZZI, G. & H. W. MAGOUN. Brain stem reticular formation and activation of the E.E.G. *EEG Clin. Neurophysiol.* **1**: 455-473, 1949.

OLDS, J. High functions of the nervous system. *Ann. Rev. Physiol.* **21**: 381-402, 1959.

OLZEWSKI, J. *In:* Brain Mechanisms and Consciousness. (E. D. Adrian, F. Bremer, H. H. Jasper & J. F. Delafresnaye, eds.), p. 54. Springfield, Illinois: C. C Thomas, 1954.

PAPEZ, J. W. A proposed mechanism of emotion. *Arch. Neurol. & Psychiat.* **38**: 725-743, 1937.

PAPEZ, J. W. Central reticular path to intralaminar and reticular nuclei of thalamus for activating EEG related to consciousness. *EEG Clin. Neurophysiol.* **8**: 117-128, 1956.

SHERRINGTON, C. S. The Integrative Action of the Nervous System. London: Constable, 1906.

TRACY, W. H. & J. M. HARRISON. Aversive behaviour following lesions of the septal region of the forebrain in the rat. *Amer. J. Psychol.* **69**: 443-447, 1956.

VALVERDE, F. A new type of cell in the lateral reticular formation of the brain stem. *J. Comp. Neurol.* **117**: 189-195, 1961b.

WINDLE, W. F. & R. E. BAXTER. Development of reflex mechanisms in the spinal cord of the albino rat embryos. Correlations between structure and function, and comparisons with the cat and the chick. *J. Comp. Neurol.* **63**: 189-209, 1936.

WOOD, C. D. Behavioral changes following discrete lesions of temporal lobe structures. *Neurology* **8**: 215-220, 1958.

WOOD, C. D., B. SCHOTTELIUS, L. L. FROST & M. BALDWIN. Localization within the amygdaloid complex of anesthetized animals. *Neurology* **8**: 477-480, 1958.

Atlas

The following plates represent an atlas of the central nervous system of the laboratory rat. The plates are arranged in a caudorostral sequence, which is the usual procedure in neuroanatomy. This approach permits the tracing of fiber tracts and of gray structures. It will be noted that not all parts of the central nervous system have received the same degree of attention. Particular emphasis has been placed on those areas which harbor the largest number of discernible structures, the functional significance of which is fairly well understood.

The atlas contains the drawings of Weigert-stained sections (Craigie, 1925), the levels being indicated in Fig. A2. Interspersed between these levels are the halftone reproductions of photographs of sections stained with luxol fast blue-cresylviolet. Since the orientation of these sections is different from those of Craigie's drawings (see Fig. A1), the levels of the drawings and halftones correspond only at a line obtained by the intersection of the cutting plane of the drawings with the cutting plane of the photographs, and this imaginary line is about in the center of the picture. As a consequence, the structures of the base of the central nervous system are relatively far apart, the drawings depicting regions which are 1.5 mm rostrad to those represented on the adjacent halftones.

Figs. A1 and A2	Orientation Diagrams
Figs. A3 to A34	Frontal Sections arranged in a caudorostral sequence
Figs. A35 and A36	Sagittal Sections
Figs. A37 and A38	Horizontal Sections

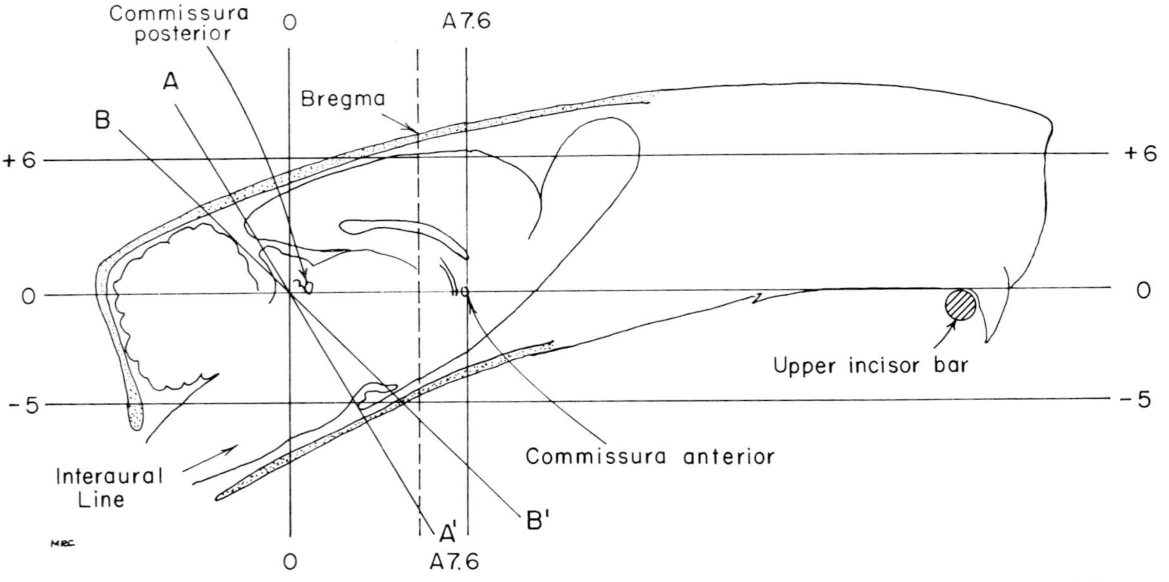

FIG. A1. Midsagittal section showing reconstruction (horizontal and vertical reference points) of the coordinate system by De Groot (1959), determined by location of upper incisor teeth and external acoustic meatus. Figures given indicate main distances in millimeters. (Redrawn by courtesy of Dr. De Groot.) *A–A′* is the axis of sections stained with luxol fast blue-cresylviolet and reproduced as halftone illustrations: *B–B′* is the axis of the black and white drawings in Craigie (1925) and indicated in Fig. A2.

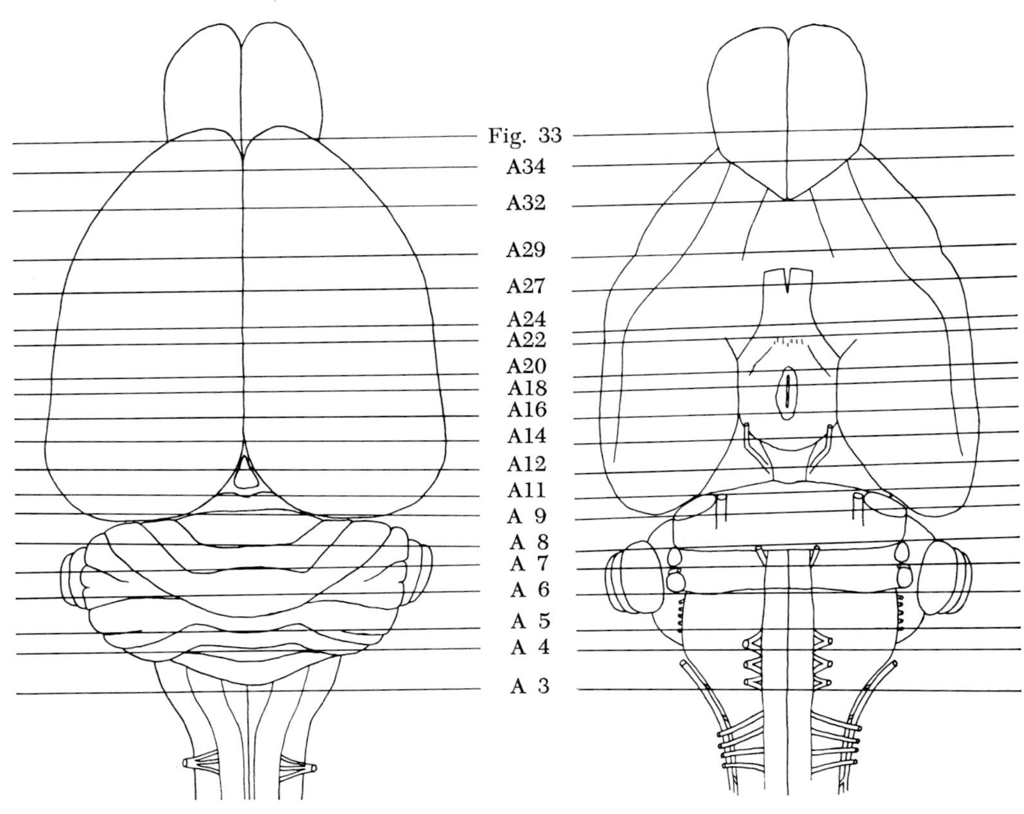

Fig. A2. Charts (Craigie, 1925). Dorsal view on left, ventral on right, indicating sections through frontal planes used for Figs. A3 to A34. The numbers of the corresponding figures are given in the middle.

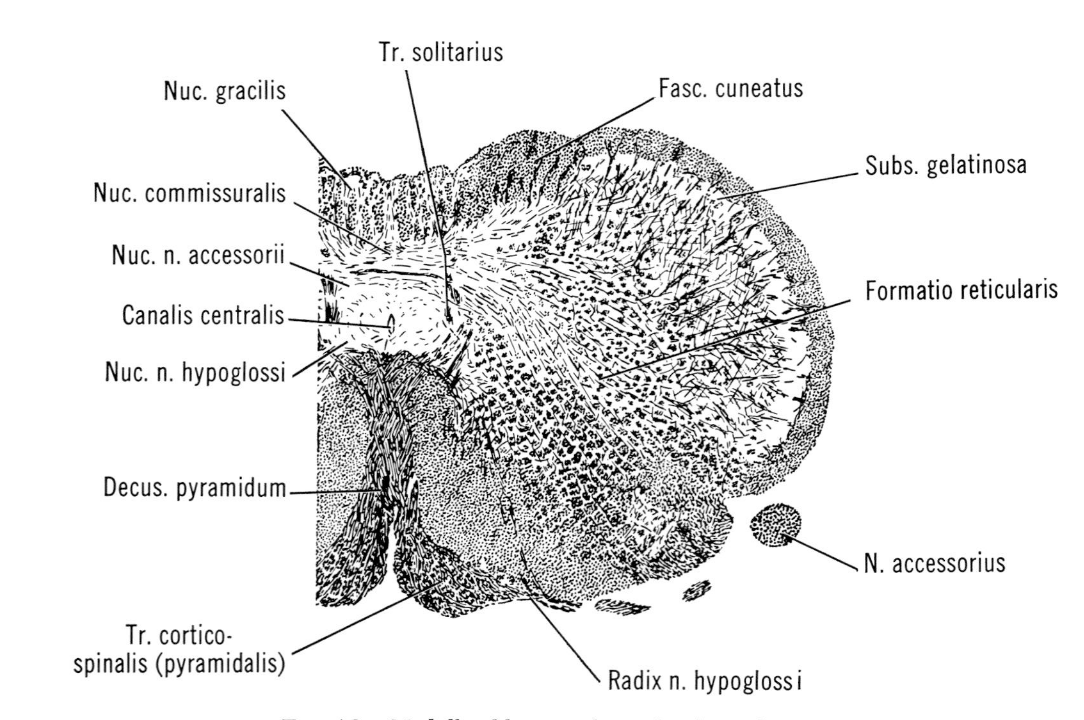

FIG. A3. Medulla oblongata, lower level. × about 17.

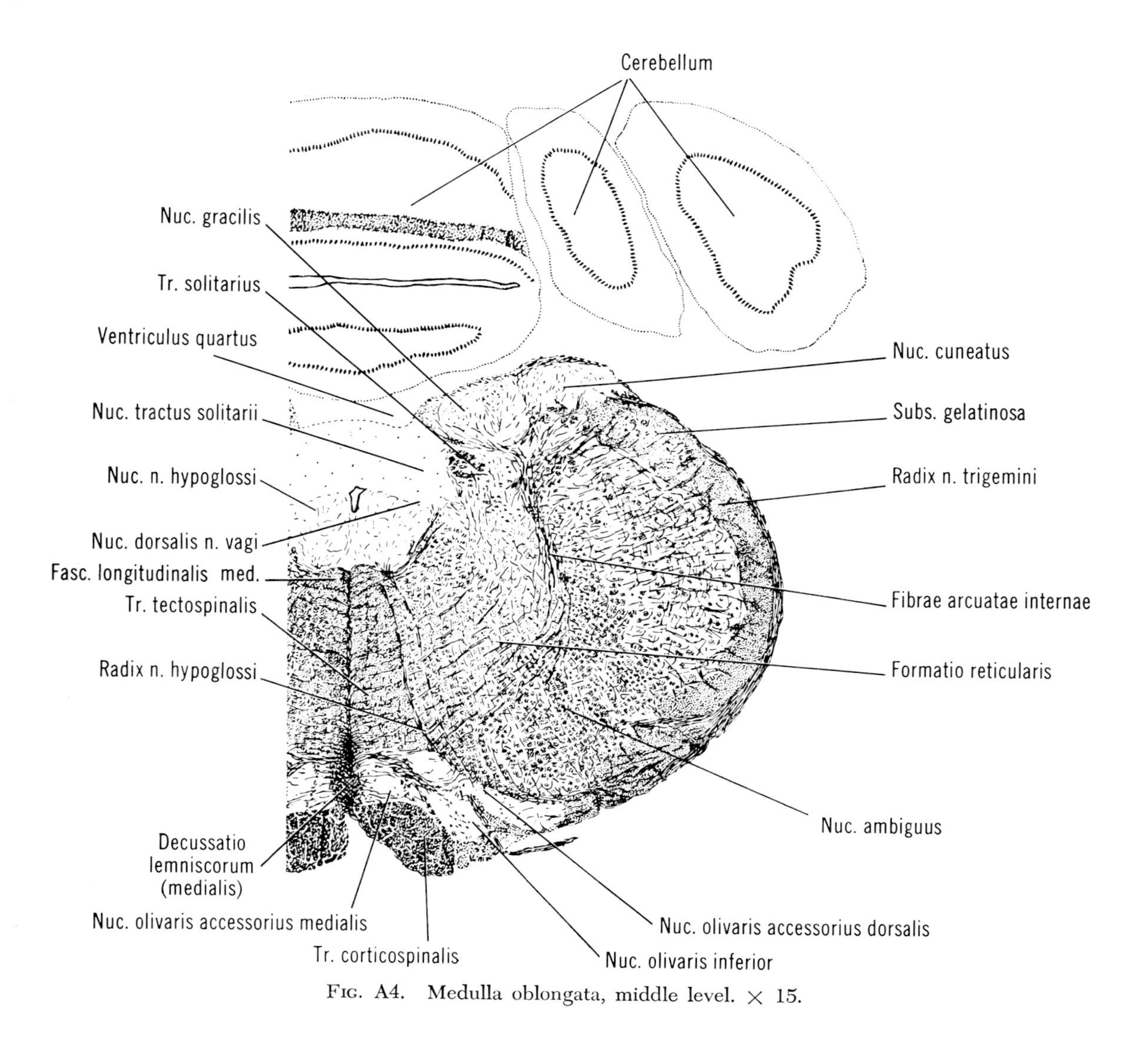

Fig. A4. Medulla oblongata, middle level. × 15.

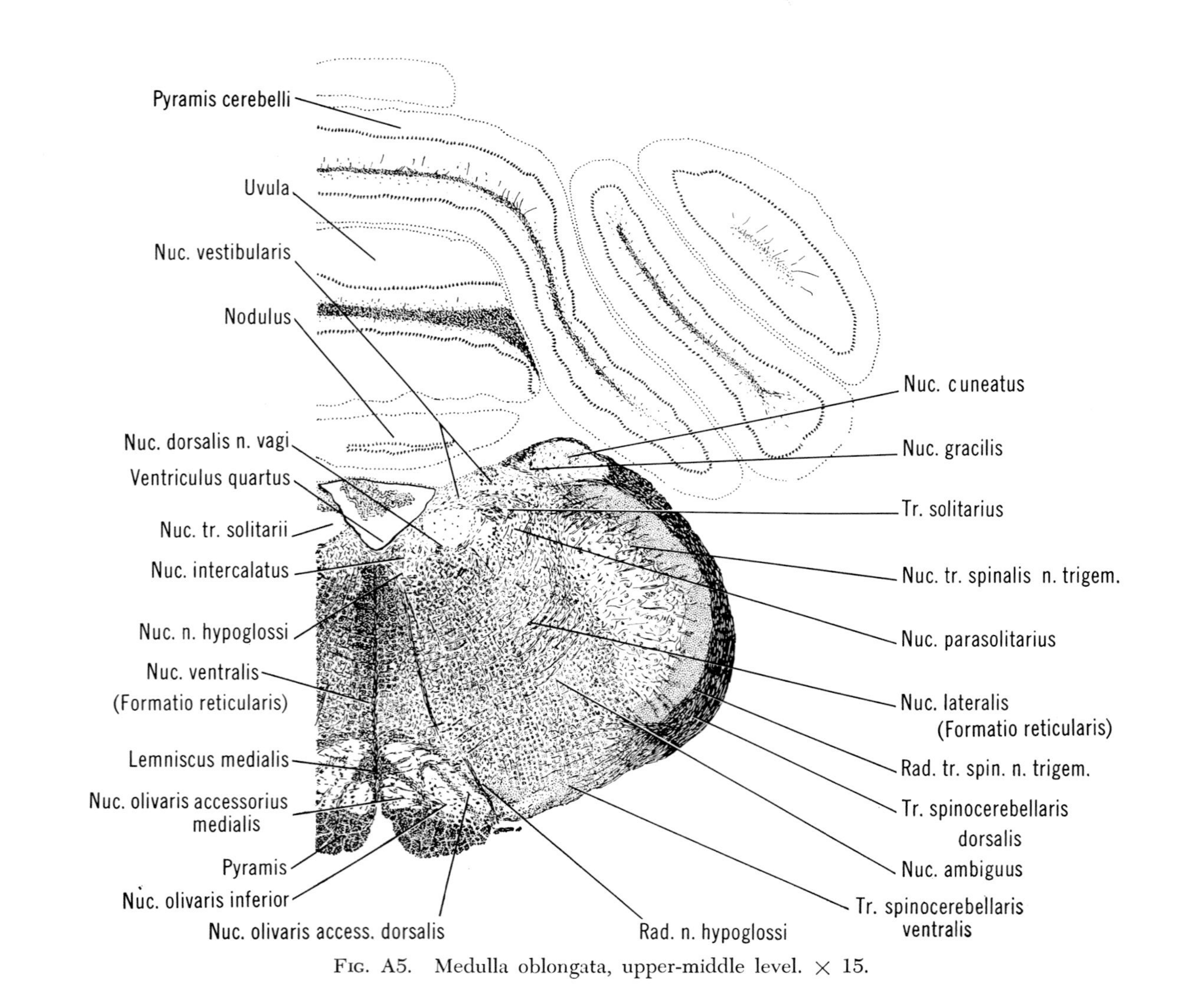

Fig. A5. Medulla oblongata, upper-middle level. × 15.

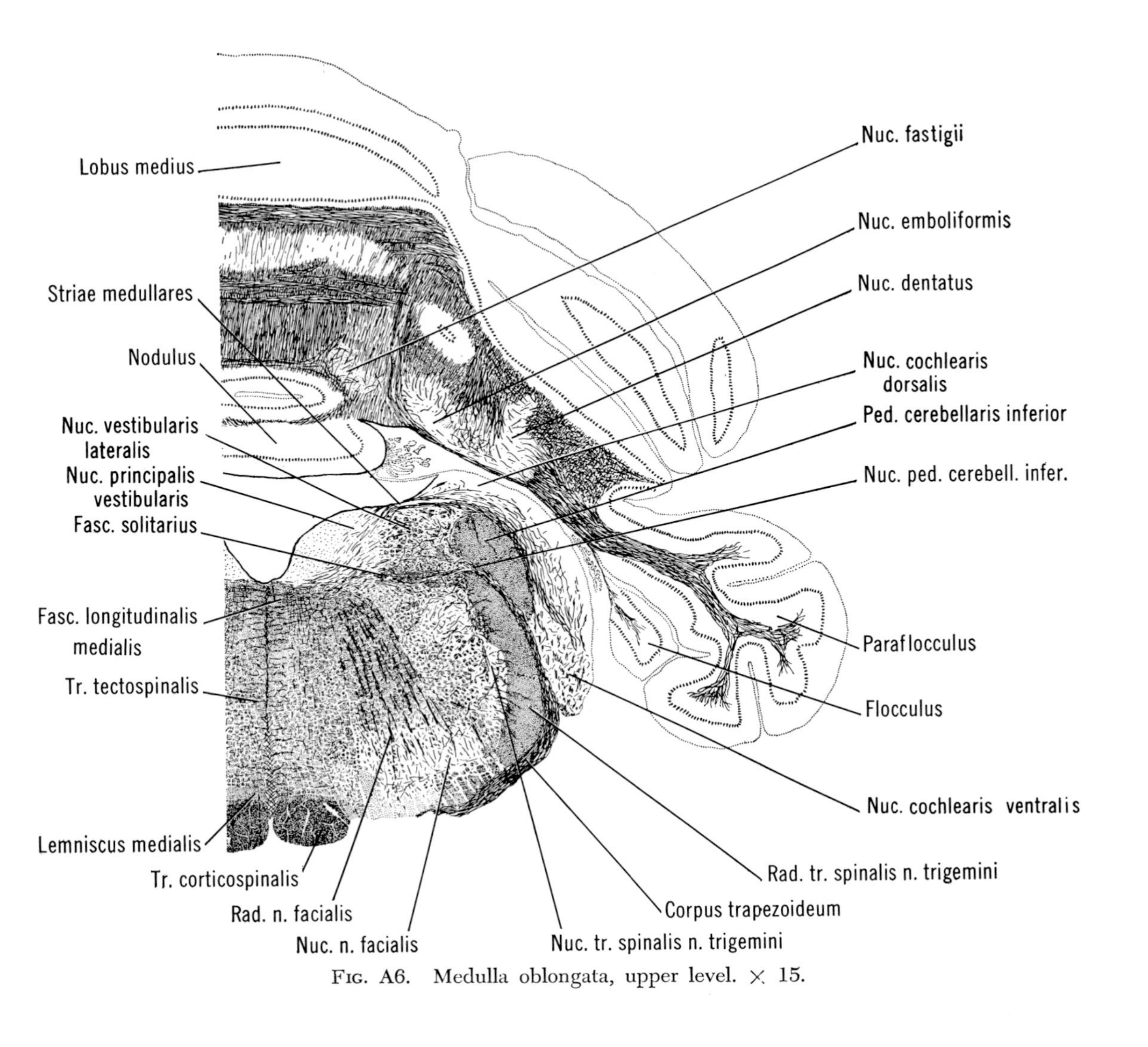

Fig. A6. Medulla oblongata, upper level. × 15.

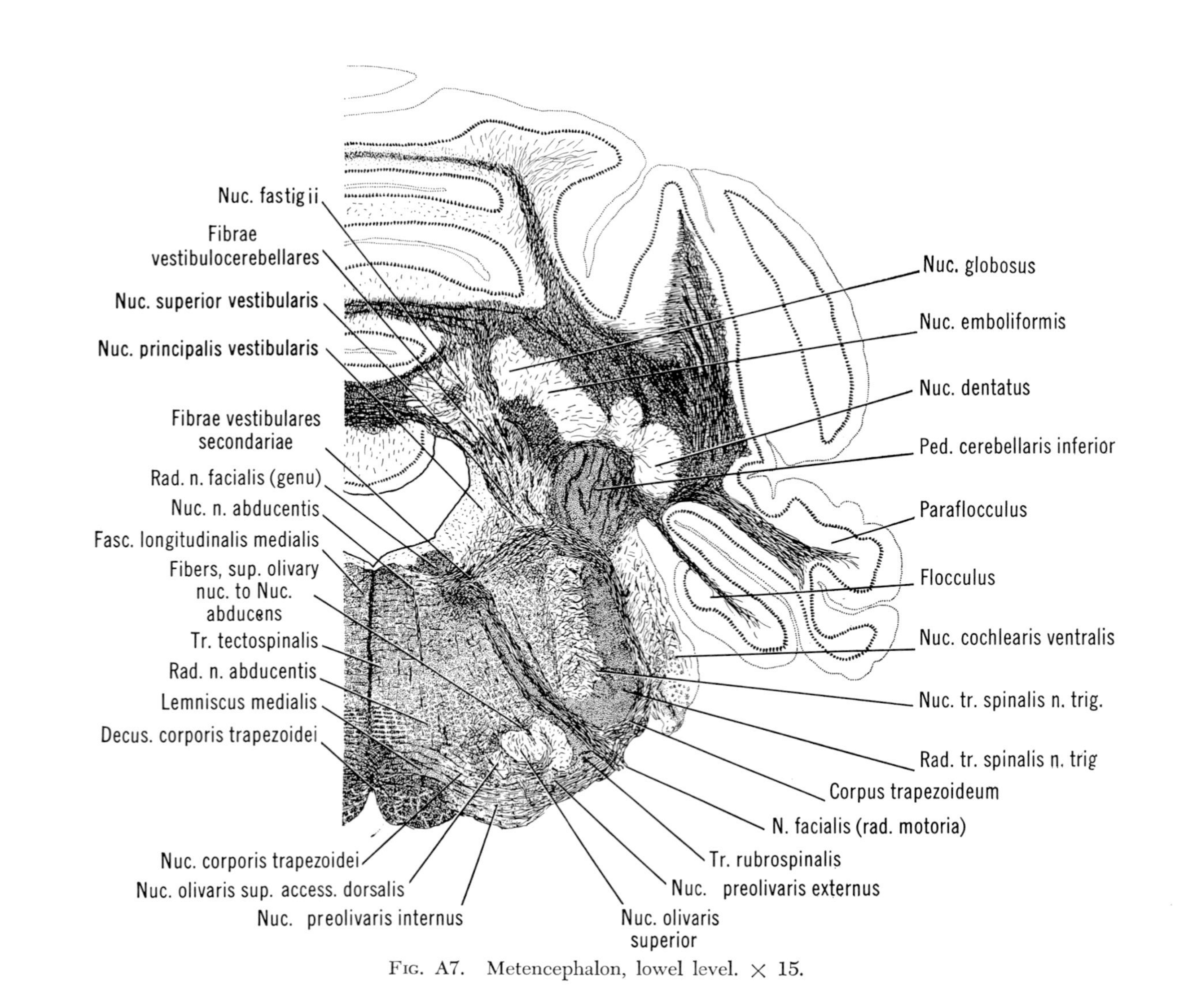

Fig. A7. Metencephalon, lowel level. × 15.

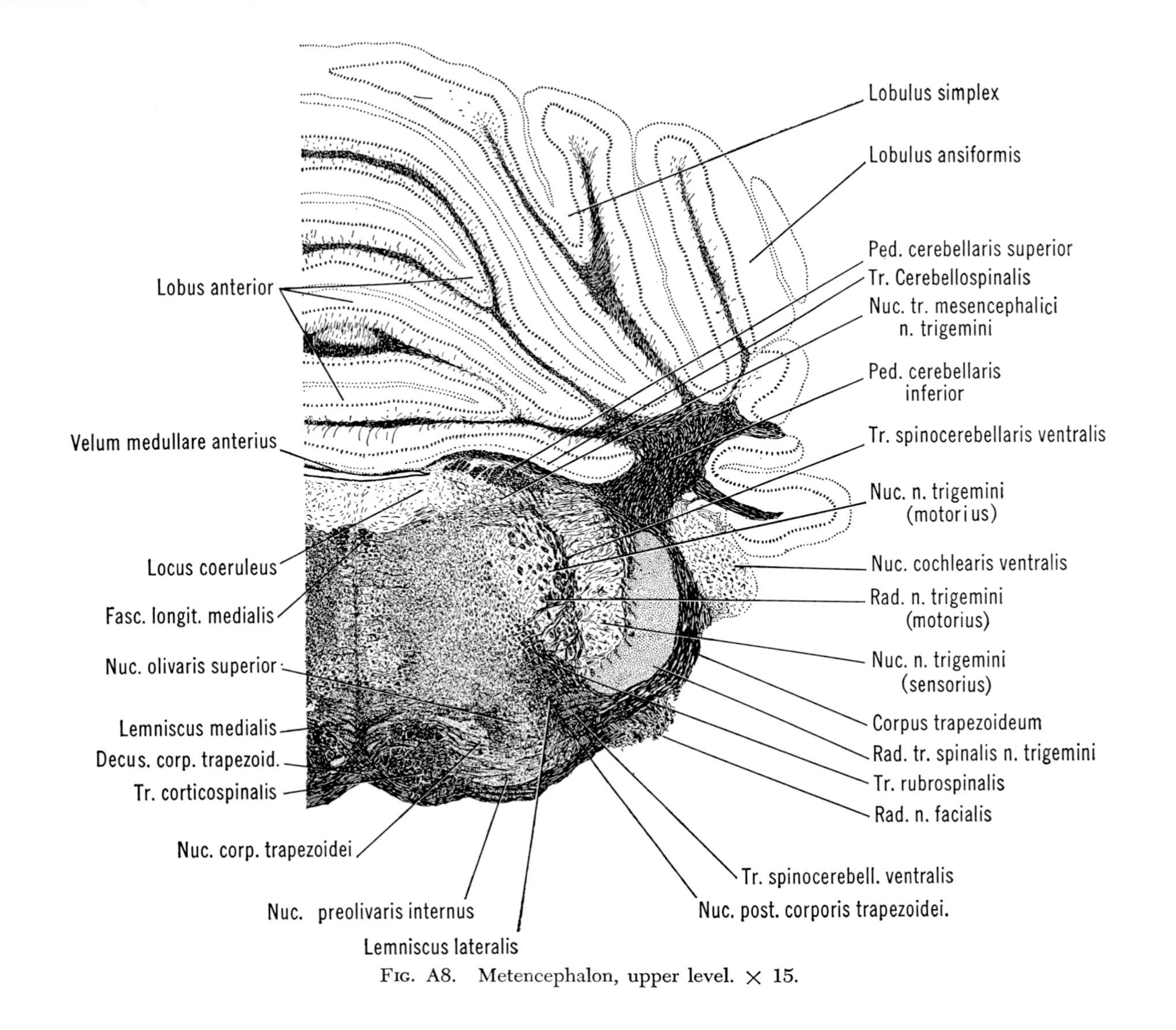

Fig. A8. Metencephalon, upper level. × 15.

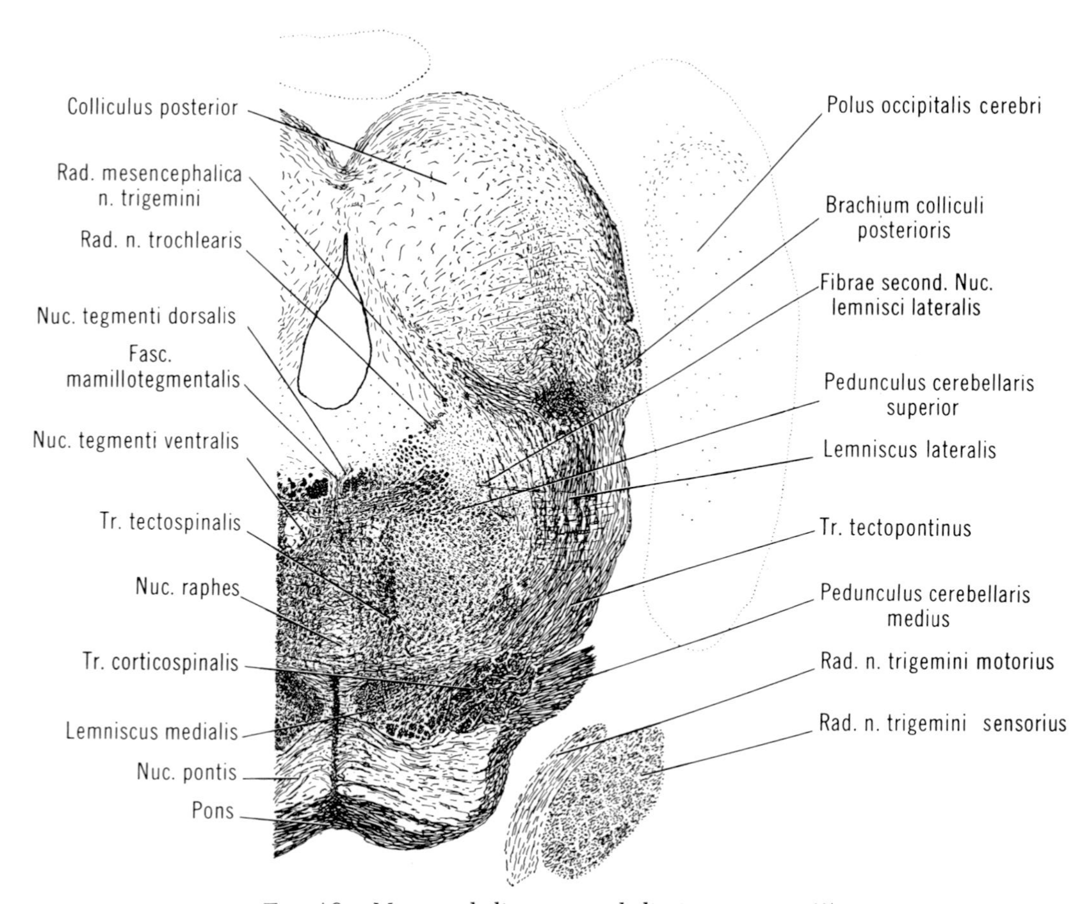

Fig. A9. Mesencephalic-metencephalic junction. × 15.

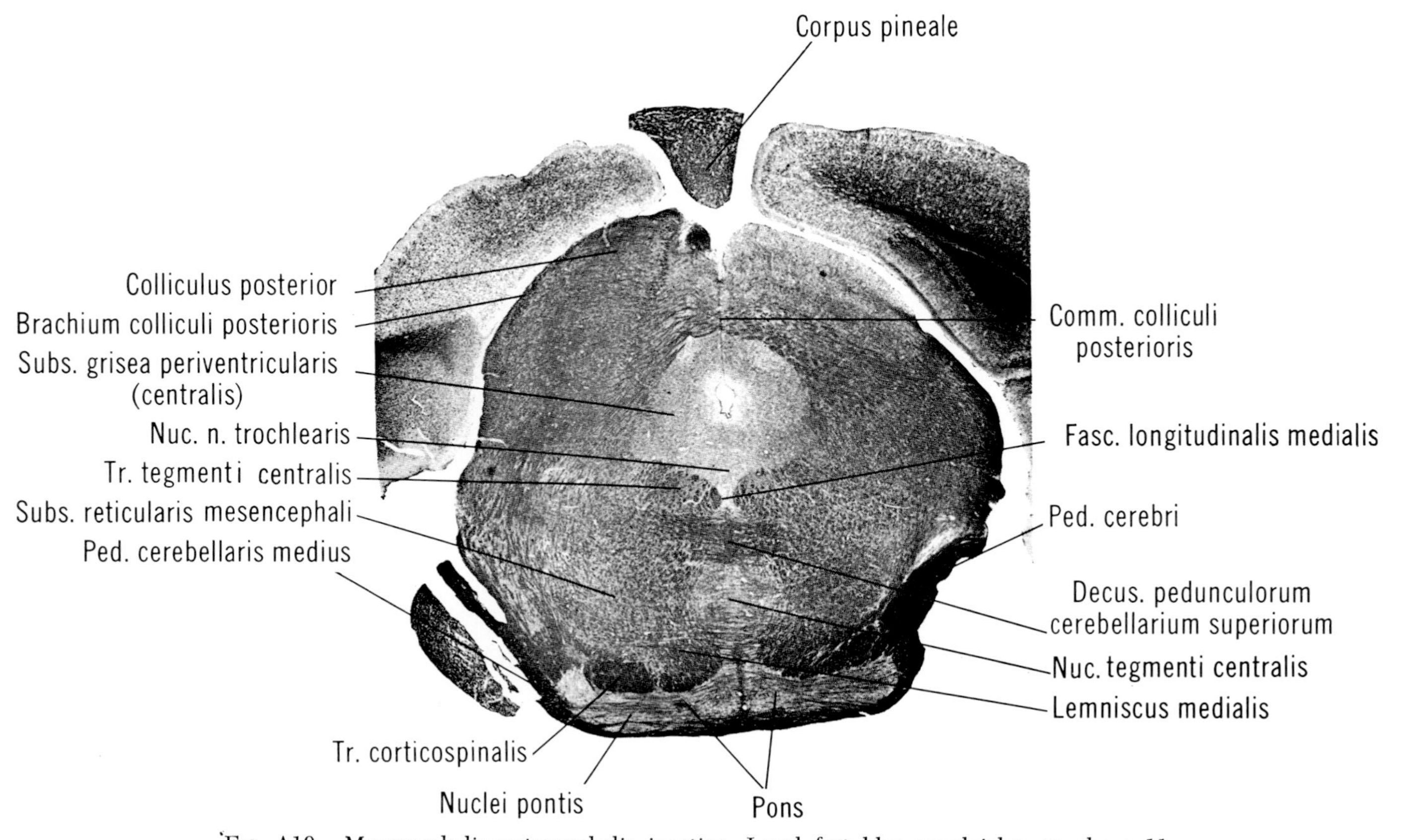

FIG. A10. Mesencephalic-metencephalic junction. Luxol fast blue-cresylviolet. × about 11.

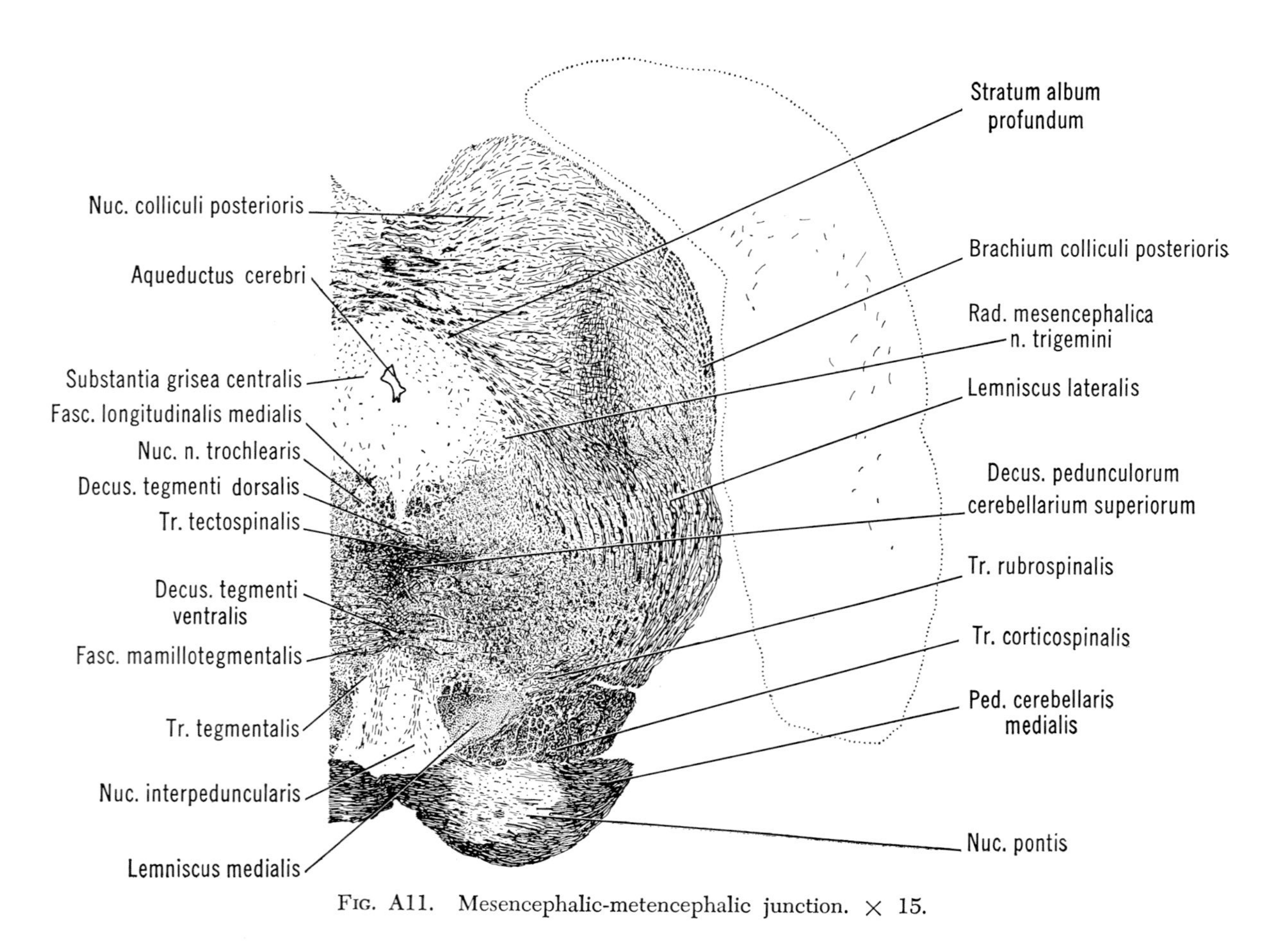

Fig. A11. Mesencephalic-metencephalic junction. × 15.

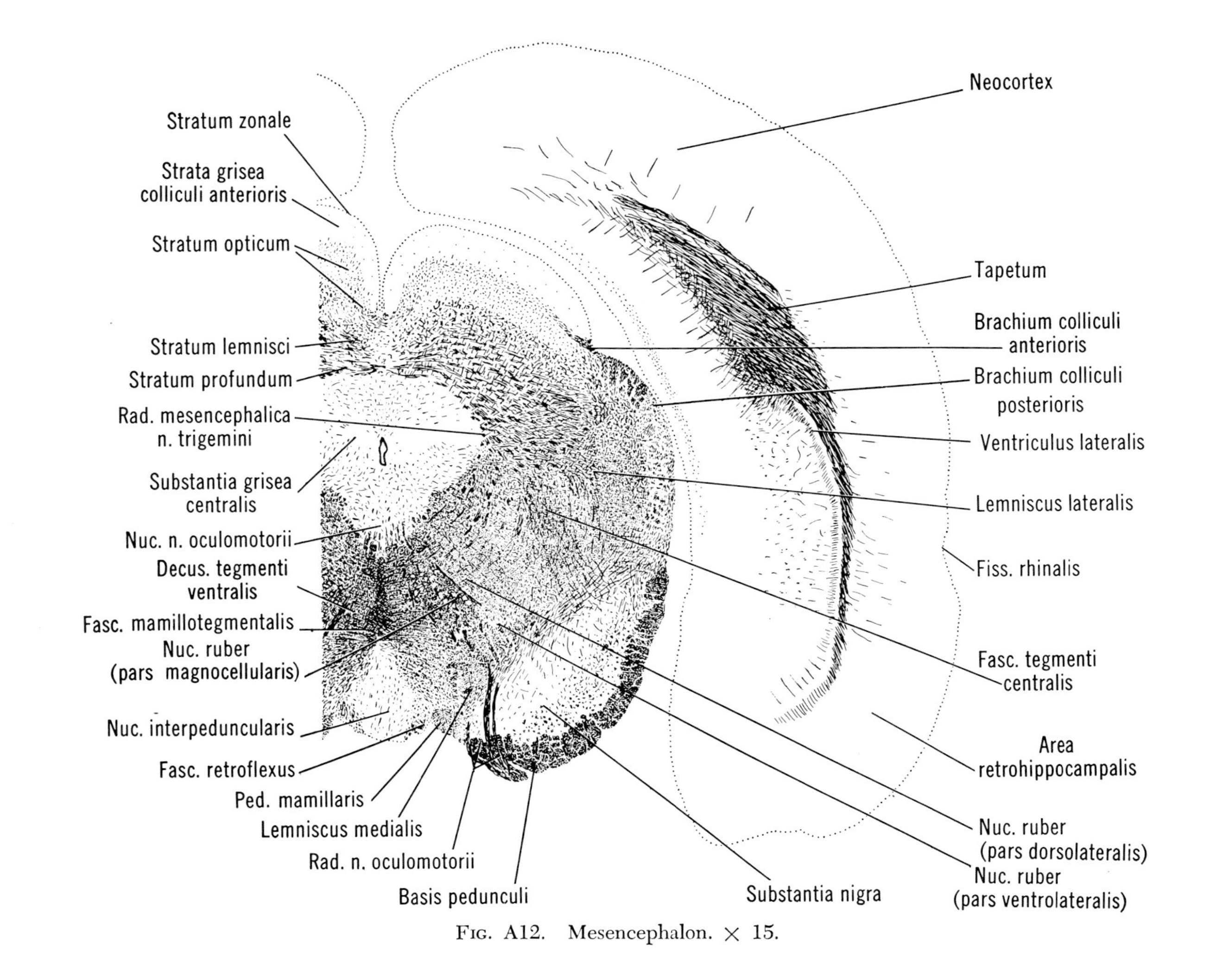

Fig. A12. Mesencephalon. × 15.

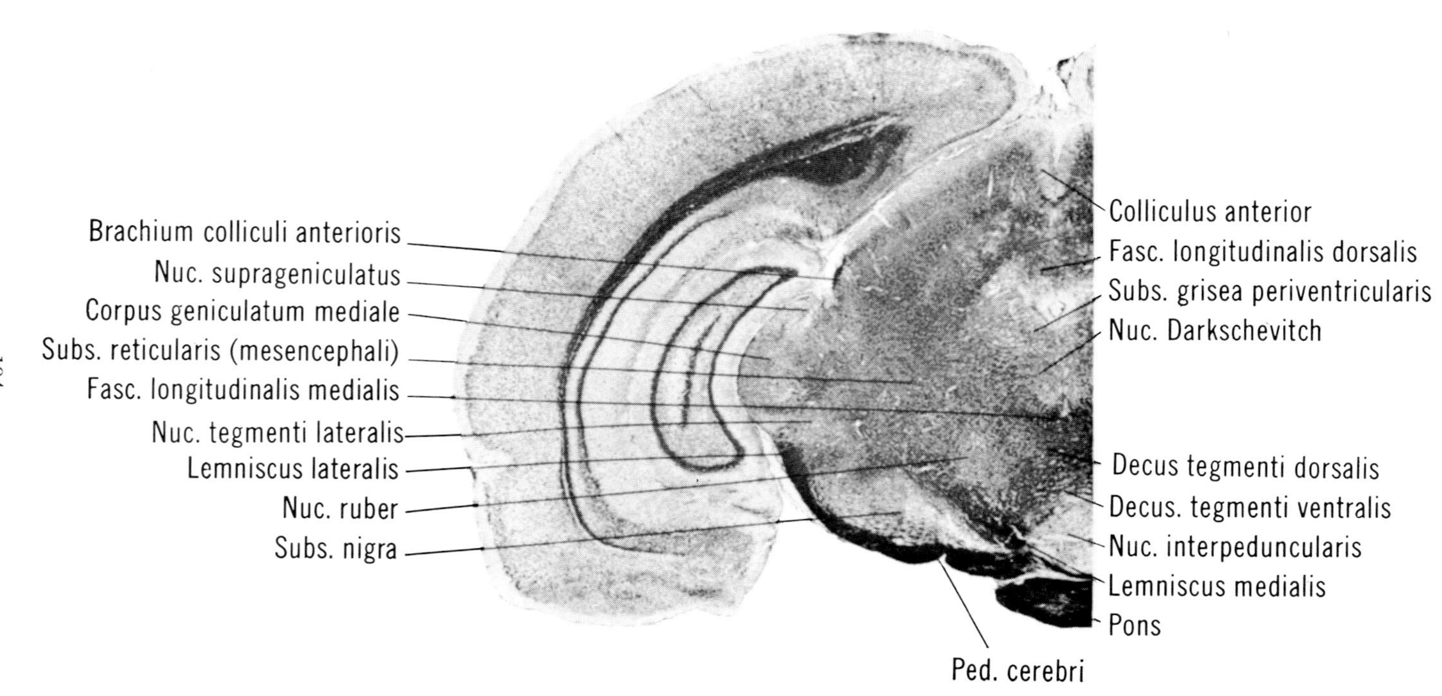

Fig. A13. Mesencephalon. Luxol fast blue-cresylviolet. × about 11.

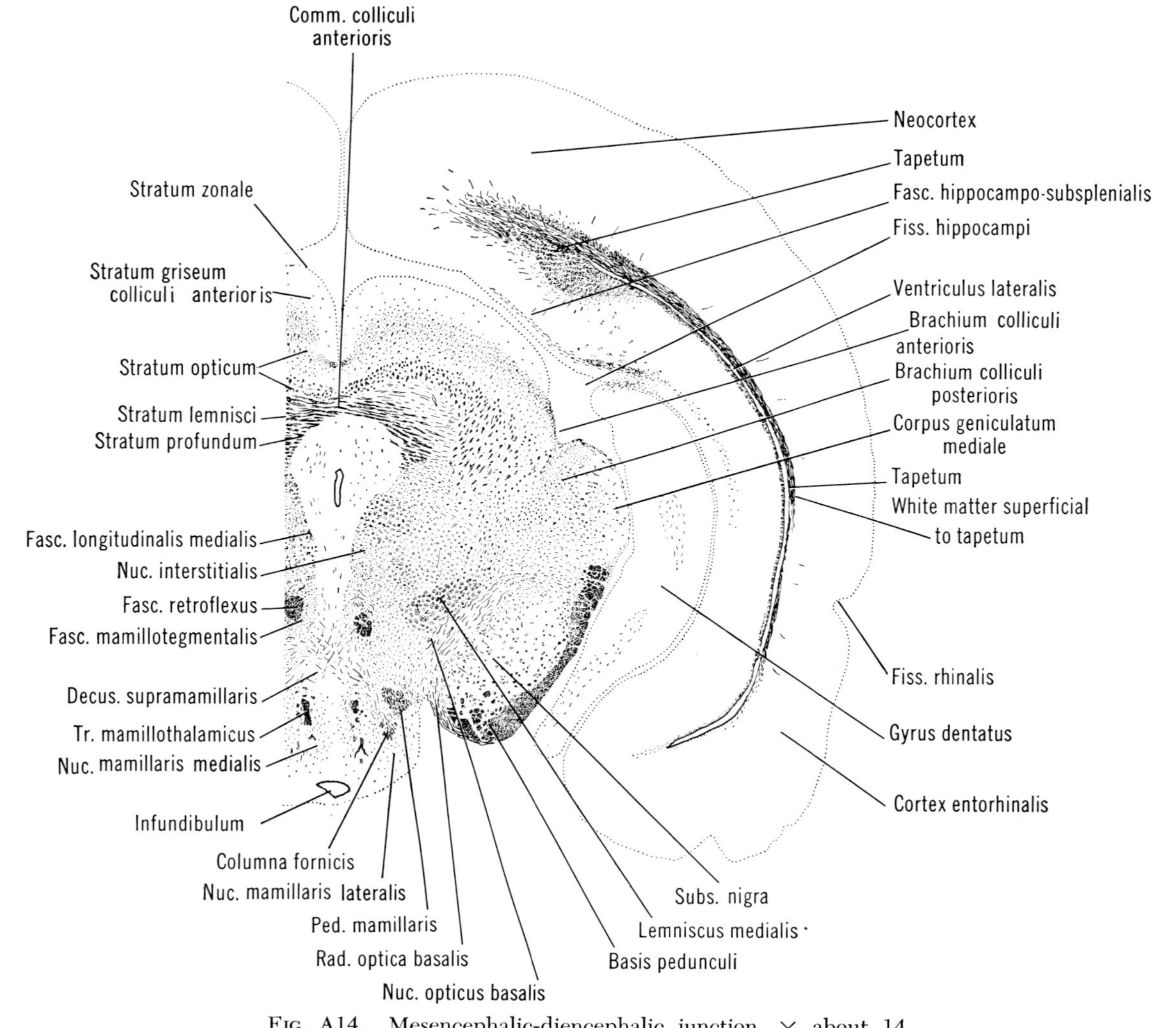

FIG. A14. Mesencephalic-diencephalic junction. × about 14.

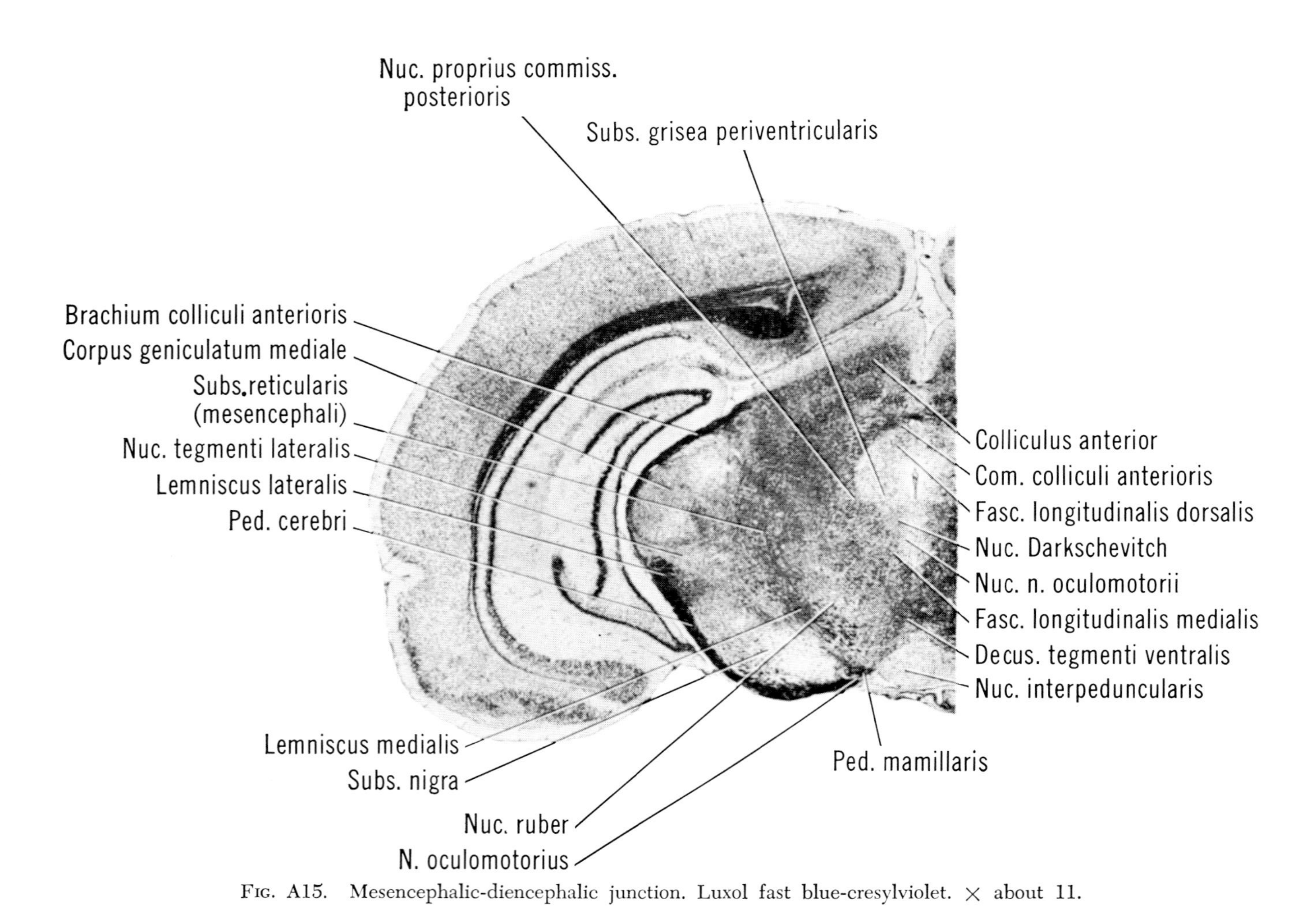

Fig. A15. Mesencephalic-diencephalic junction. Luxol fast blue-cresylviolet. × about 11.

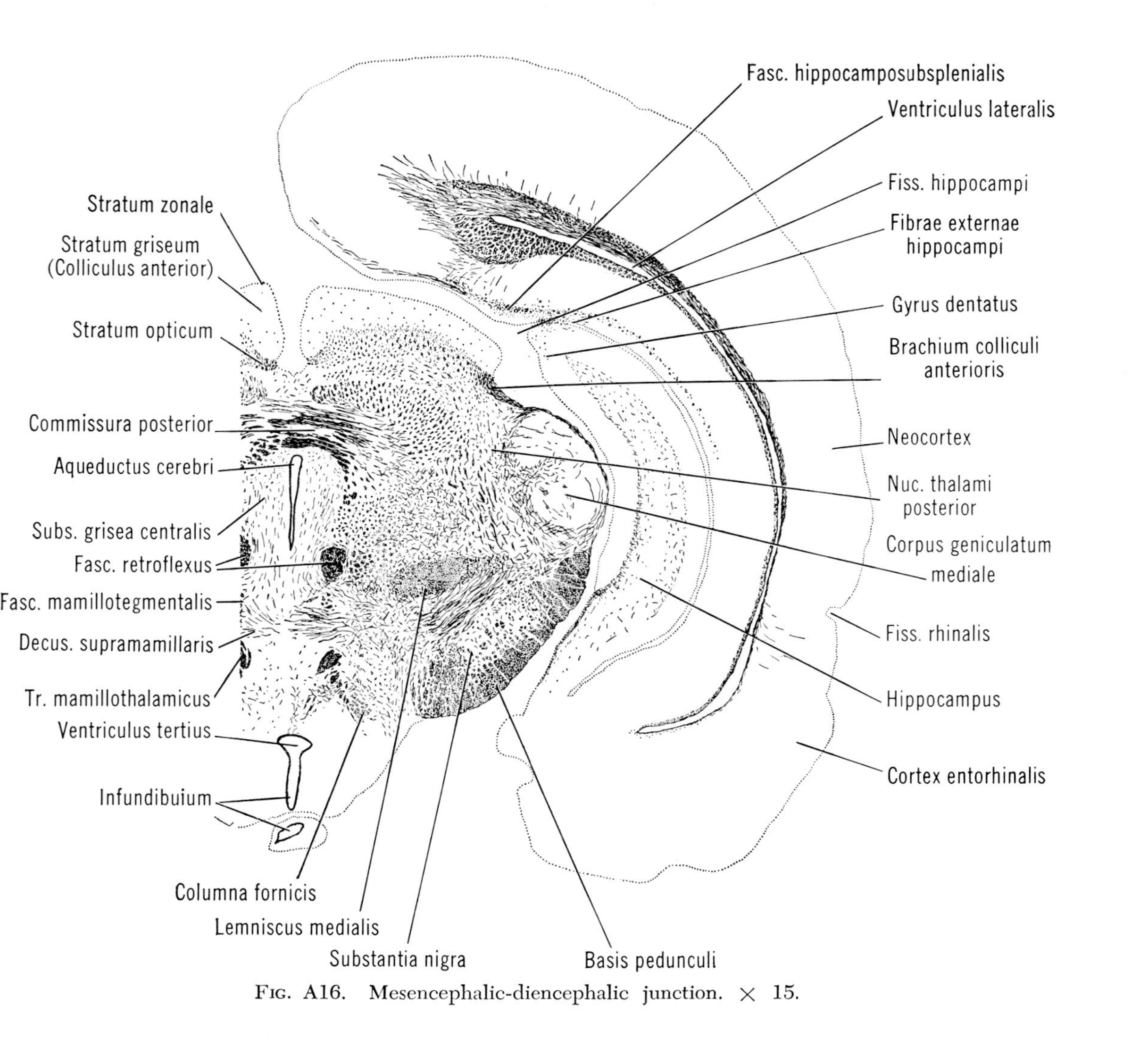

Fig. A16. Mesencephalic-diencephalic junction. × 15.

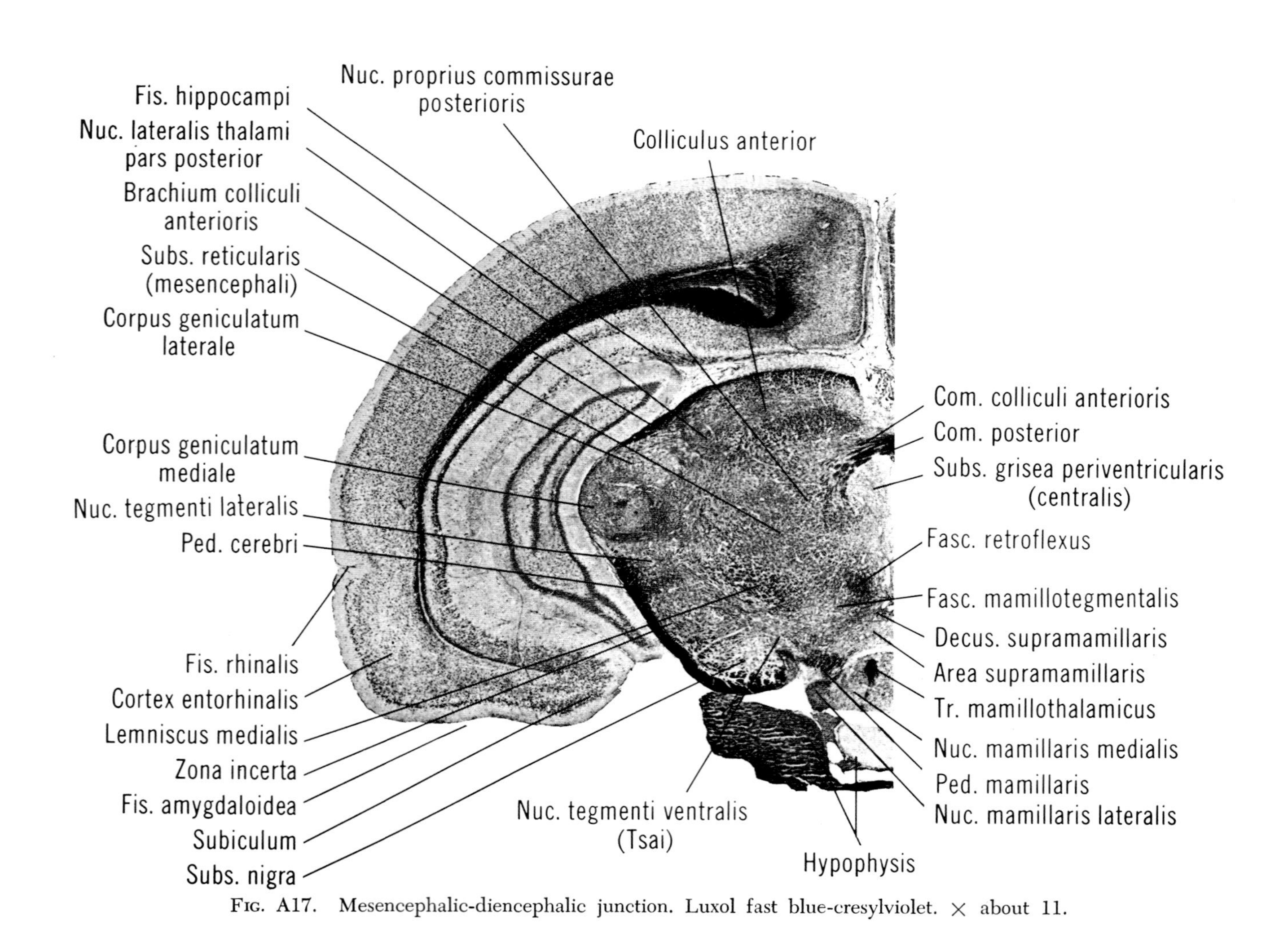

Fig. A17. Mesencephalic-diencephalic junction. Luxol fast blue-cresylviolet. × about 11.

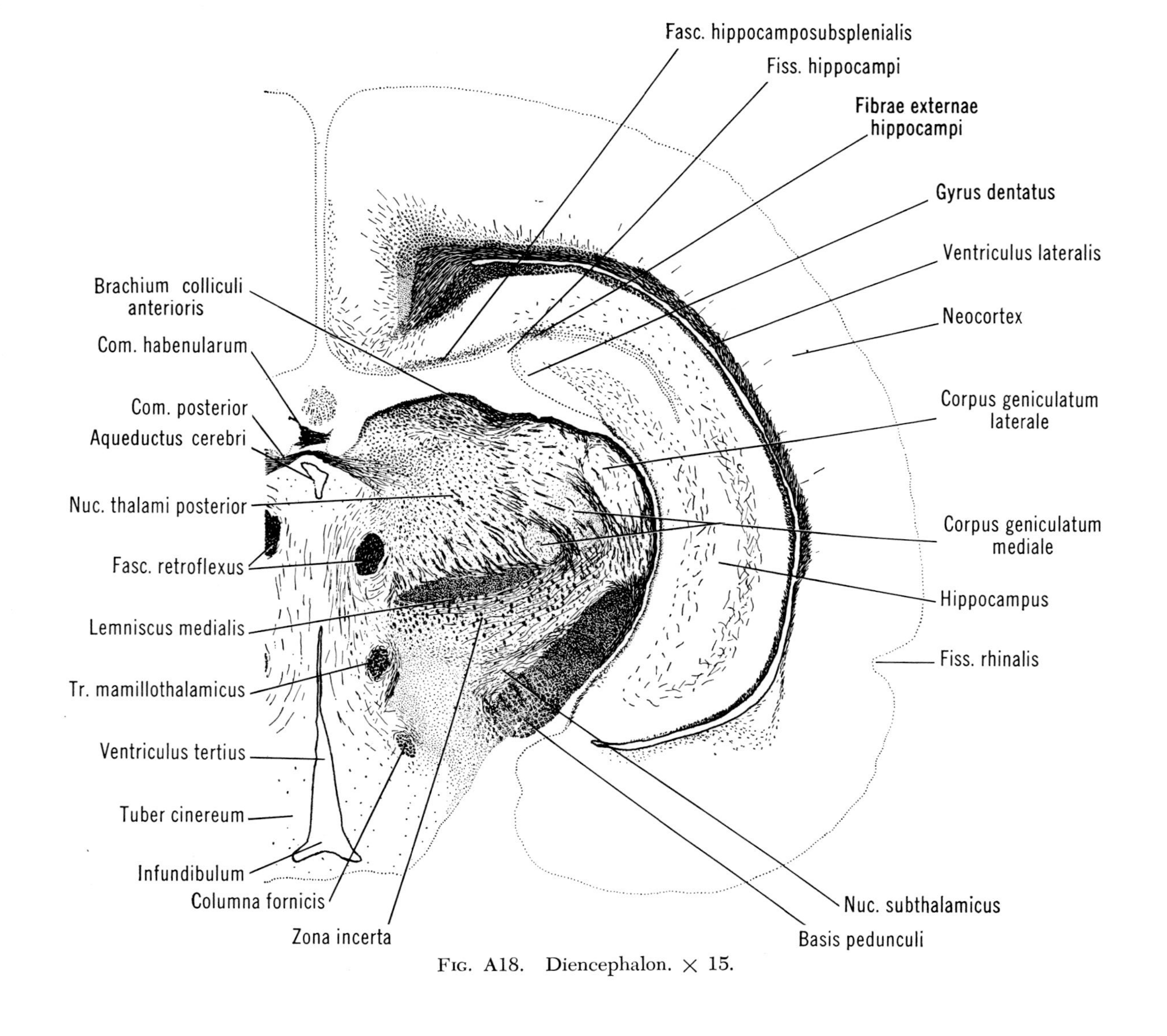

Fig. A18. Diencephalon. × 15.

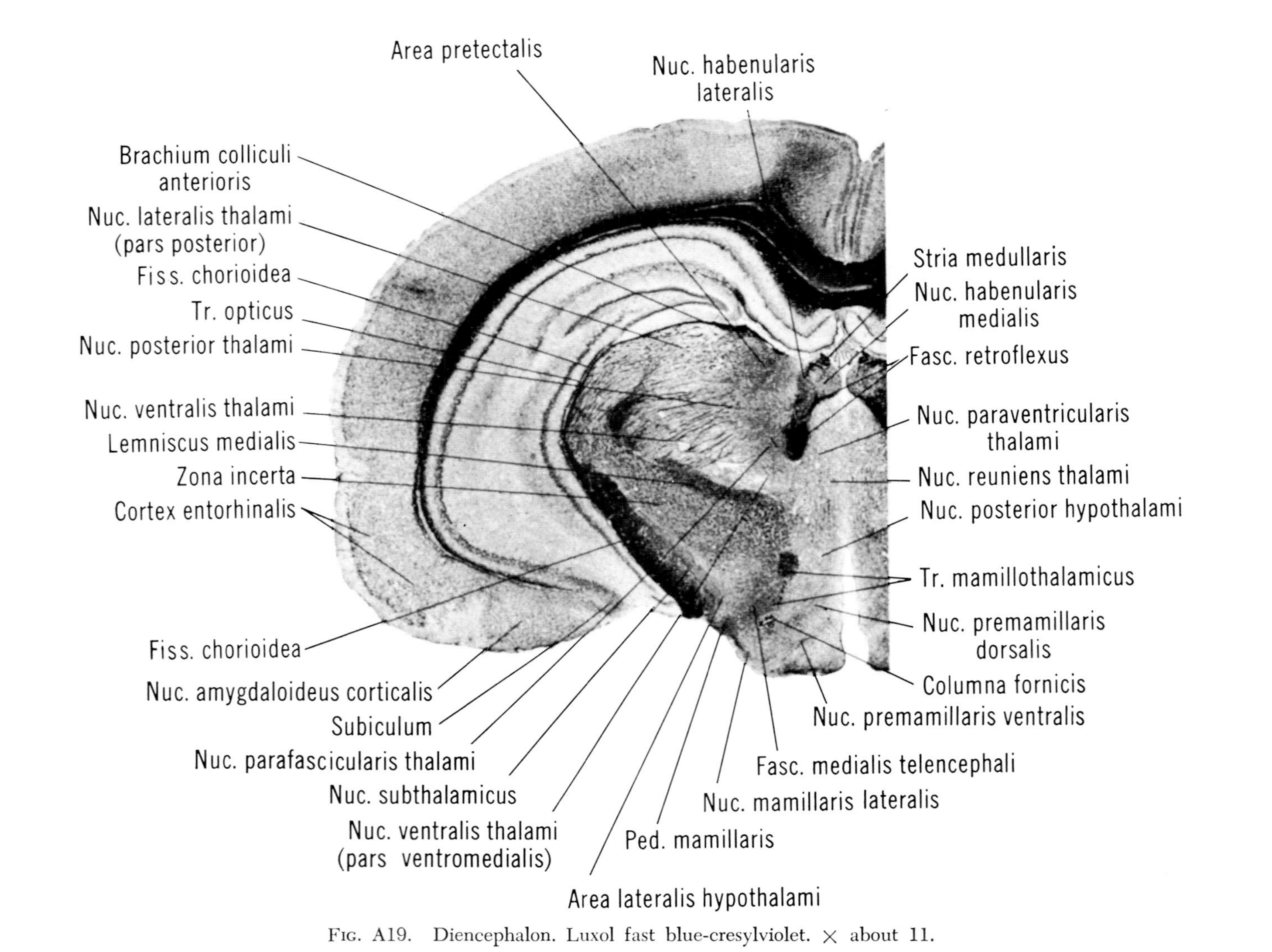

Fig. A19. Diencephalon. Luxol fast blue-cresylviolet. × about 11.

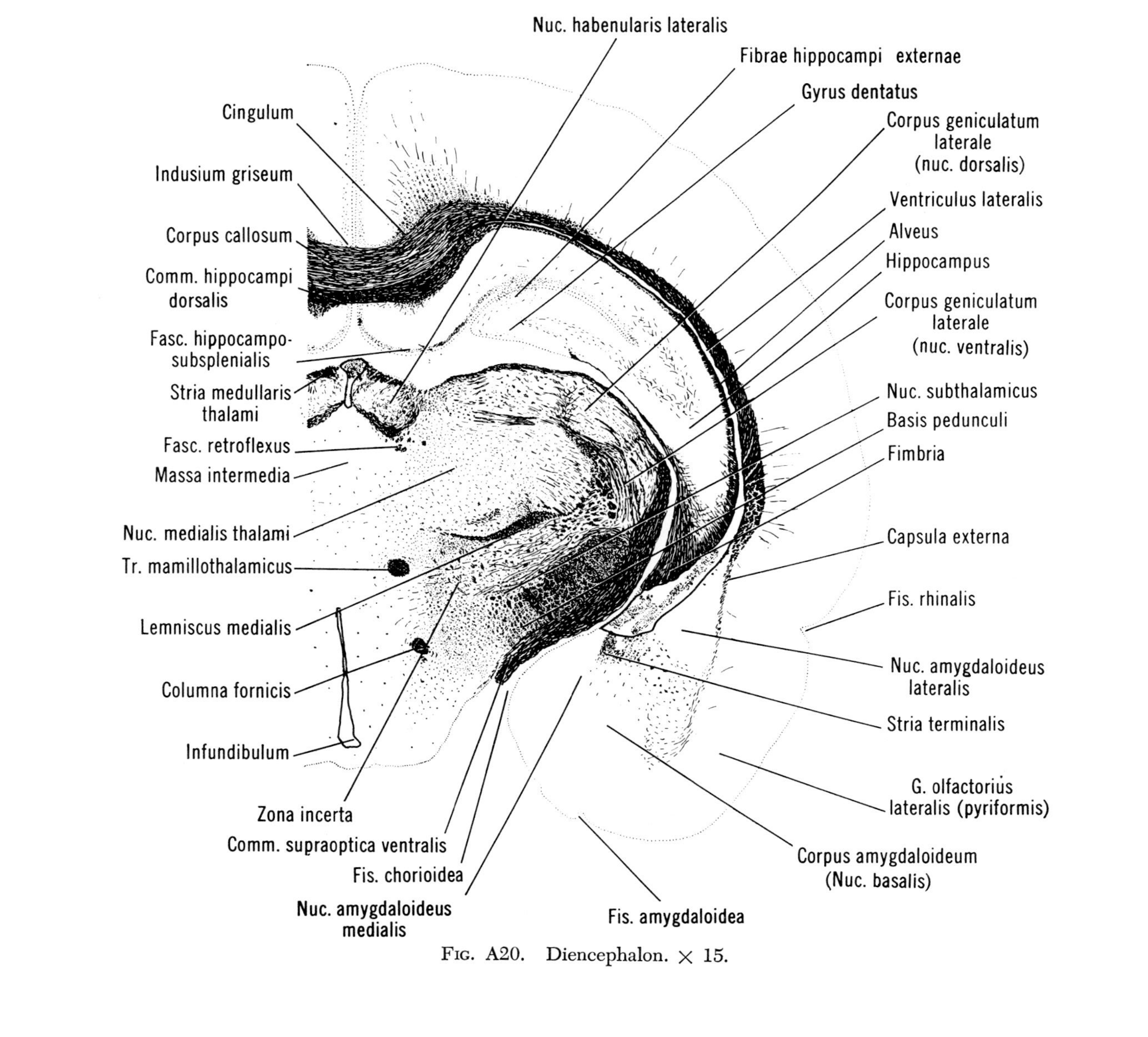

FIG. A20. Diencephalon. × 15.

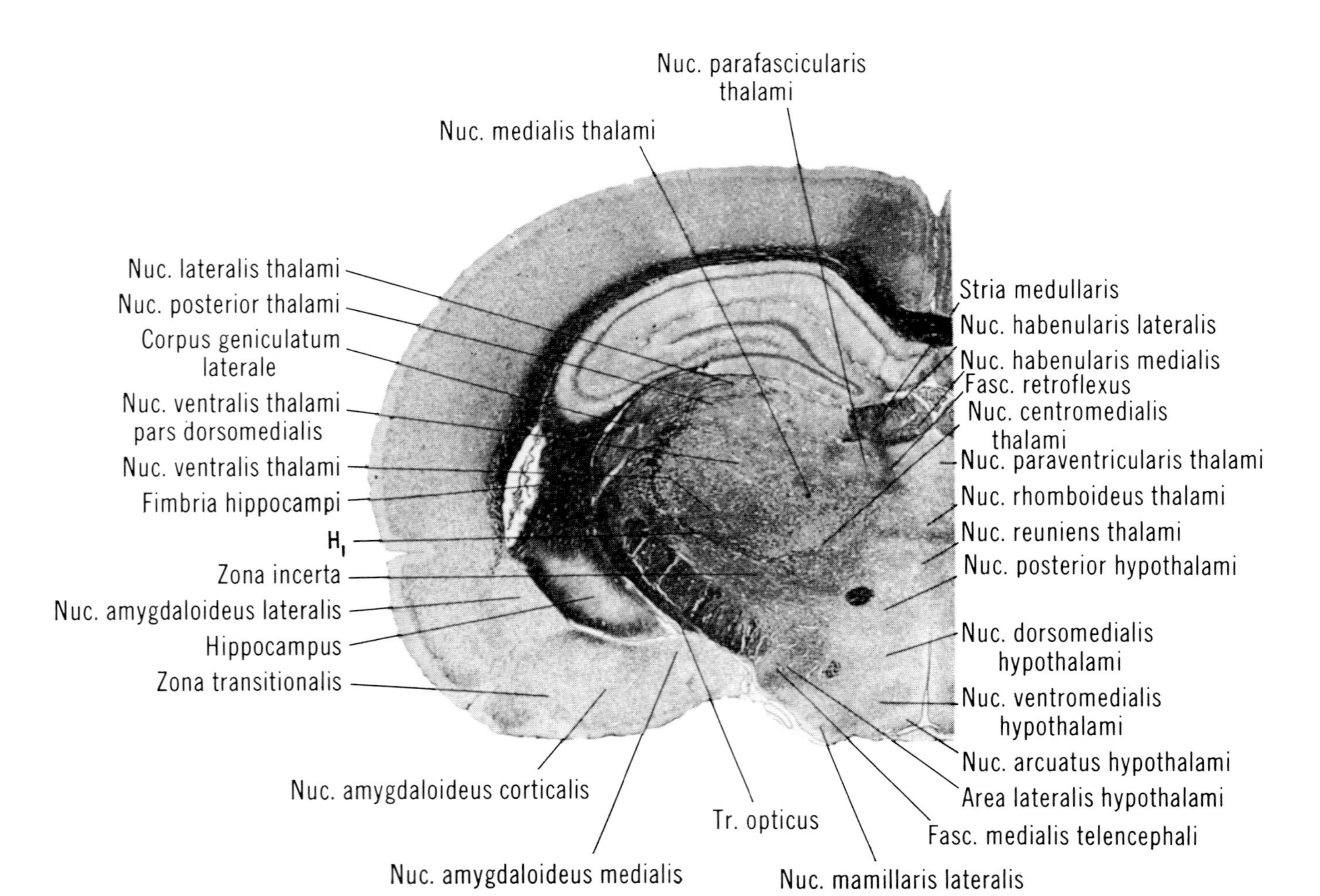

FIG. A21. Diencephalon. Luxol fast blue-cresylviolet. × about 11.

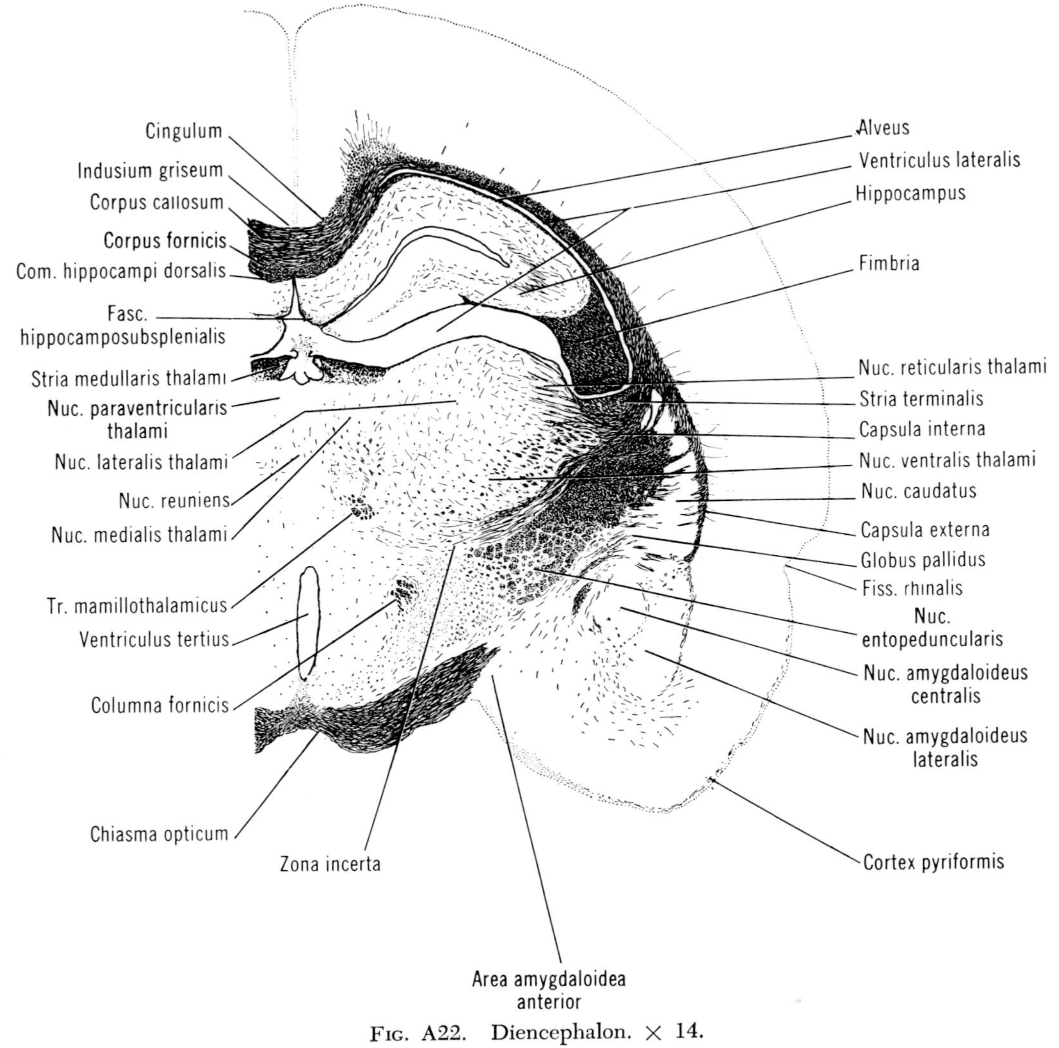

FIG. A22. Diencephalon. × 14.

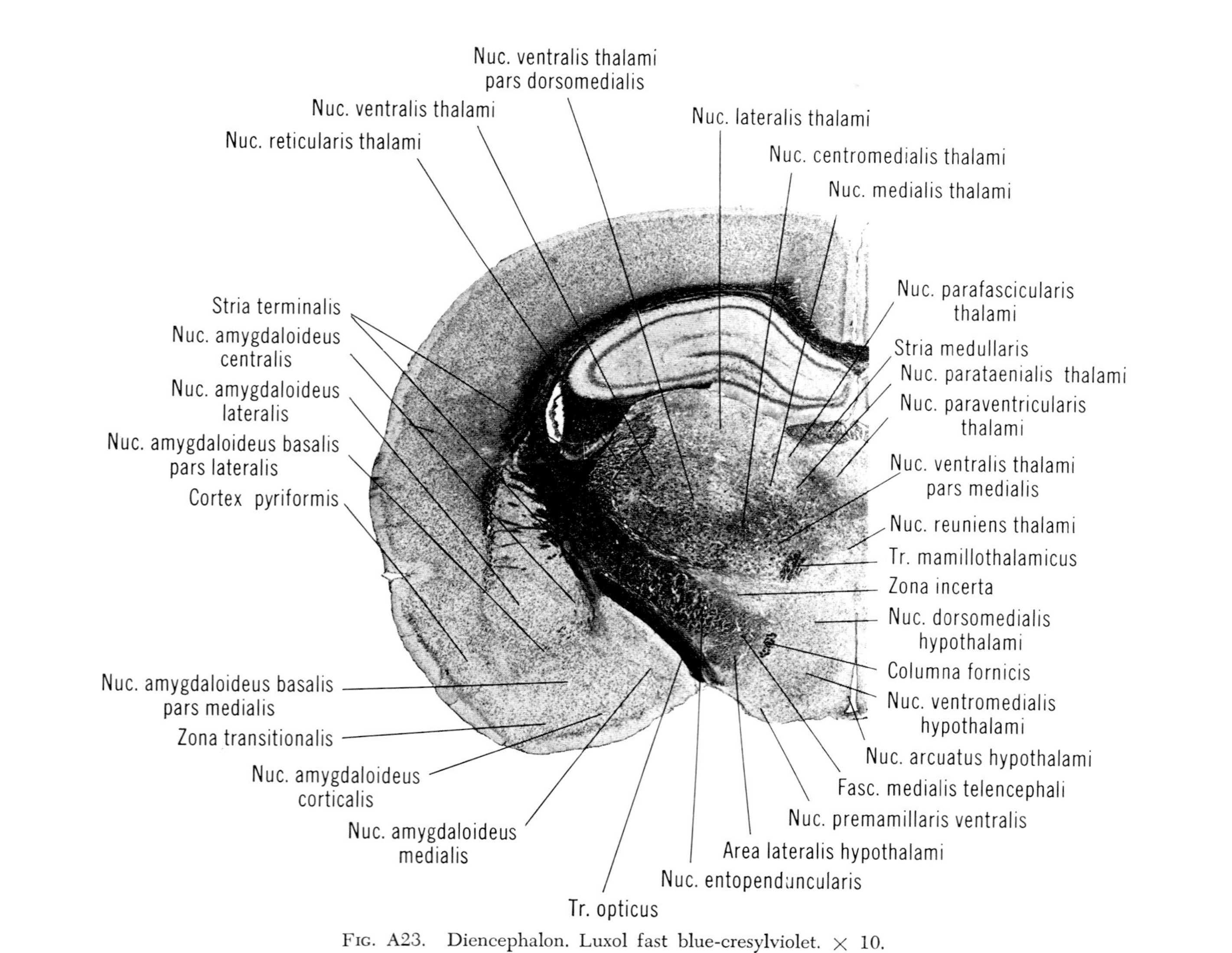

FIG. A23. Diencephalon. Luxol fast blue-cresylviolet. × 10.

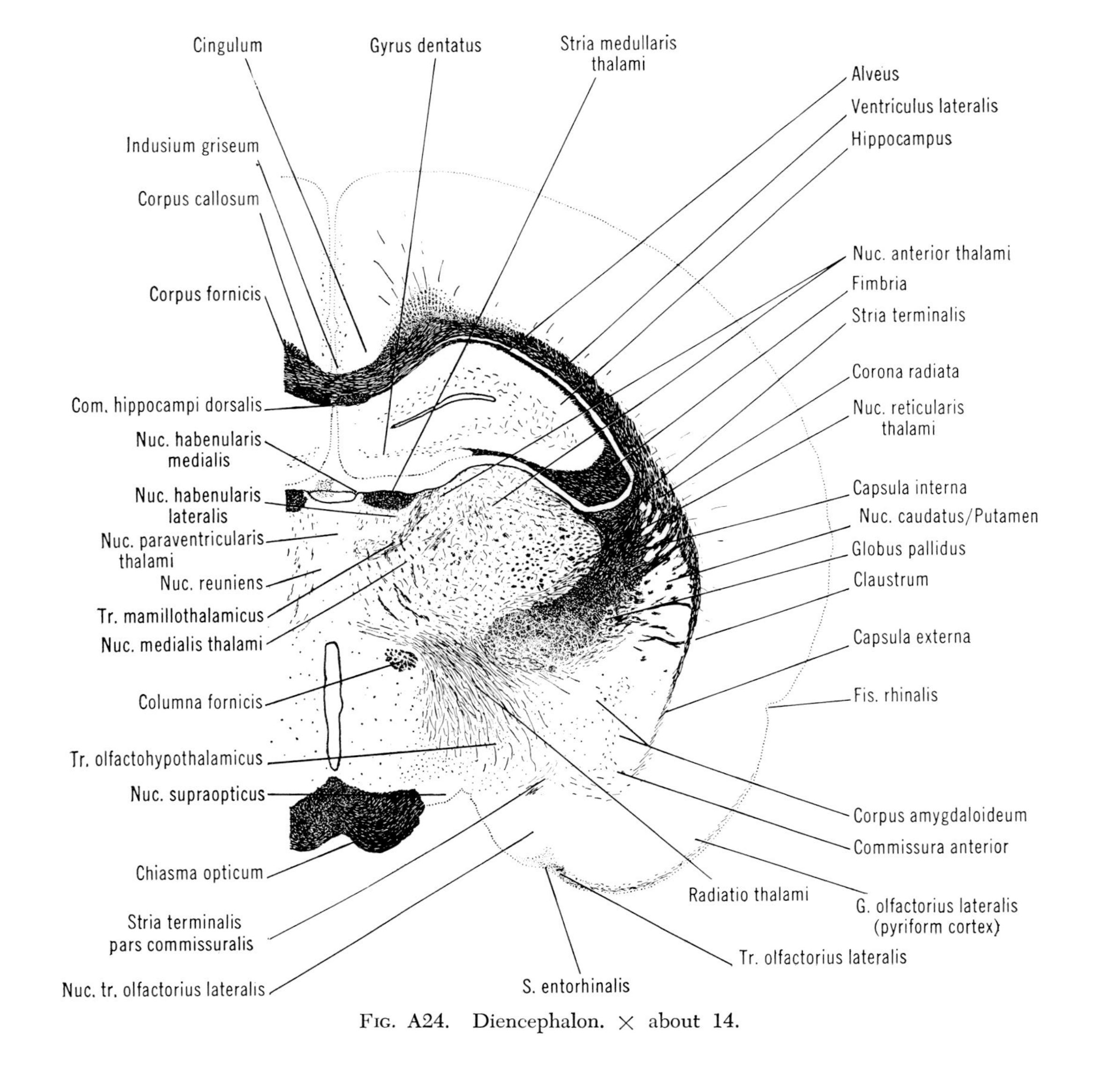

Fig. A24. Diencephalon. × about 14.

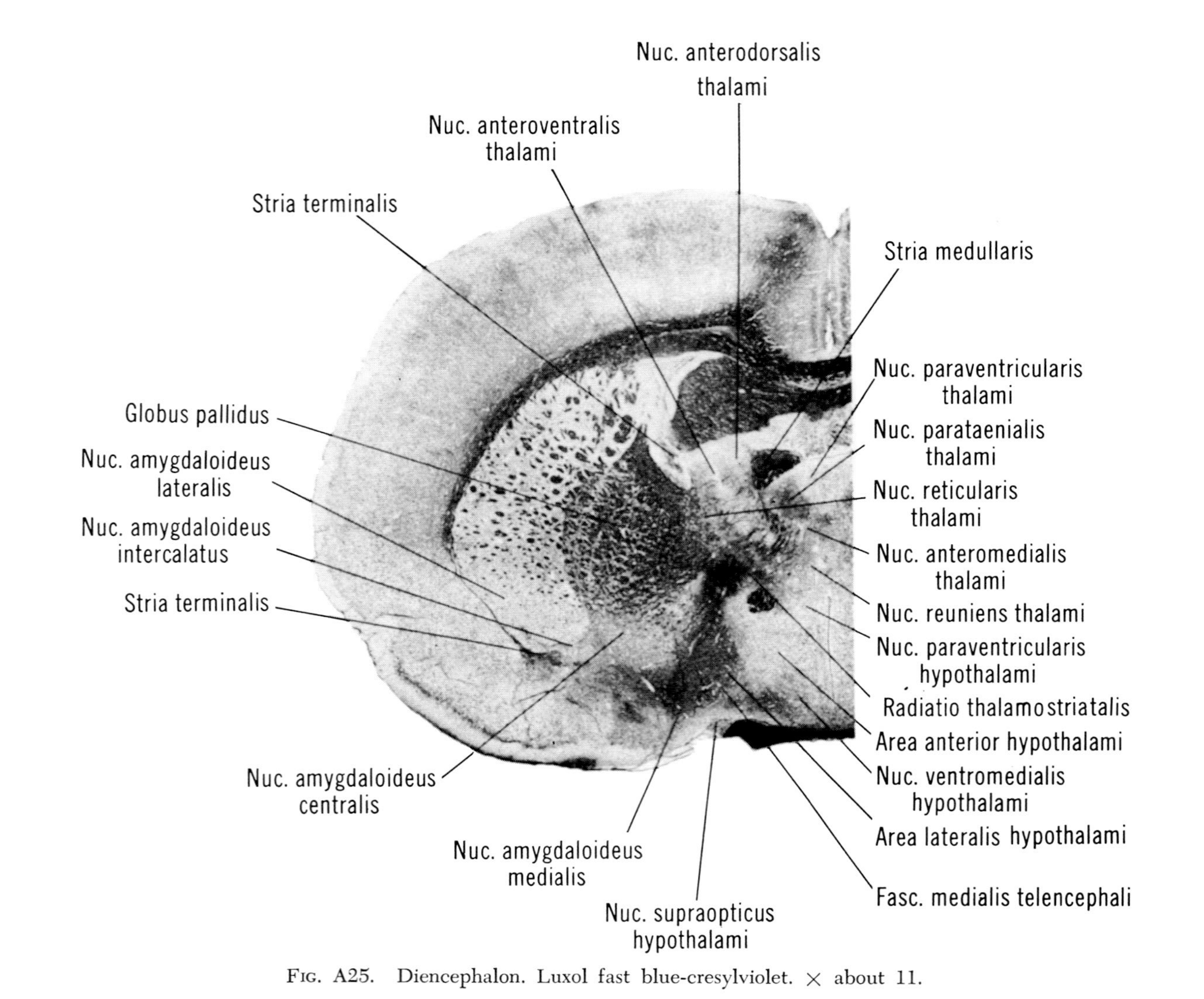

Fig. A25. Diencephalon. Luxol fast blue-cresylviolet. × about 11.

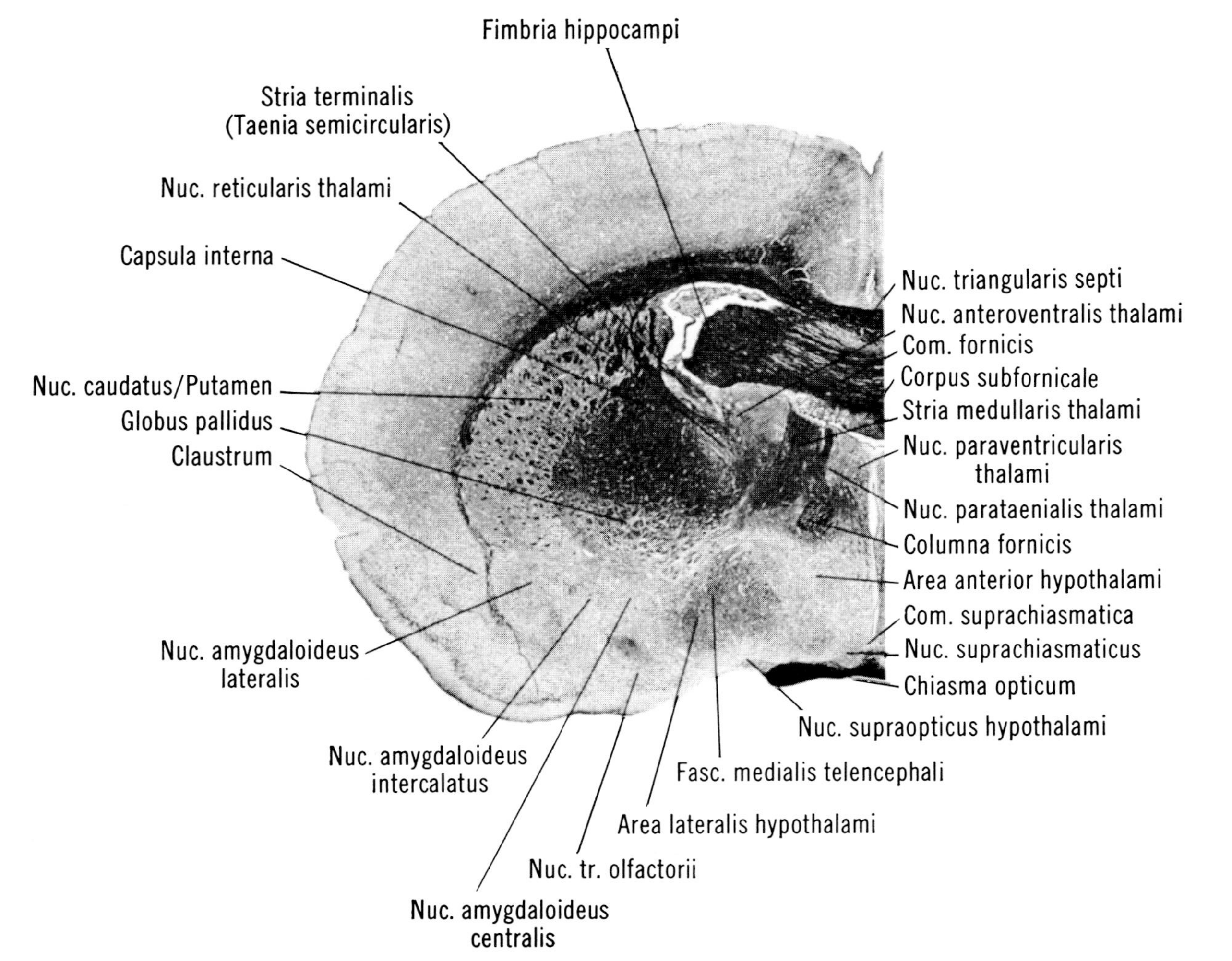

FIG. A26. Diencephalic-telencephalic junction at level of commissura fornicis. Luxol fast blue-cresylviolet. × about 11.

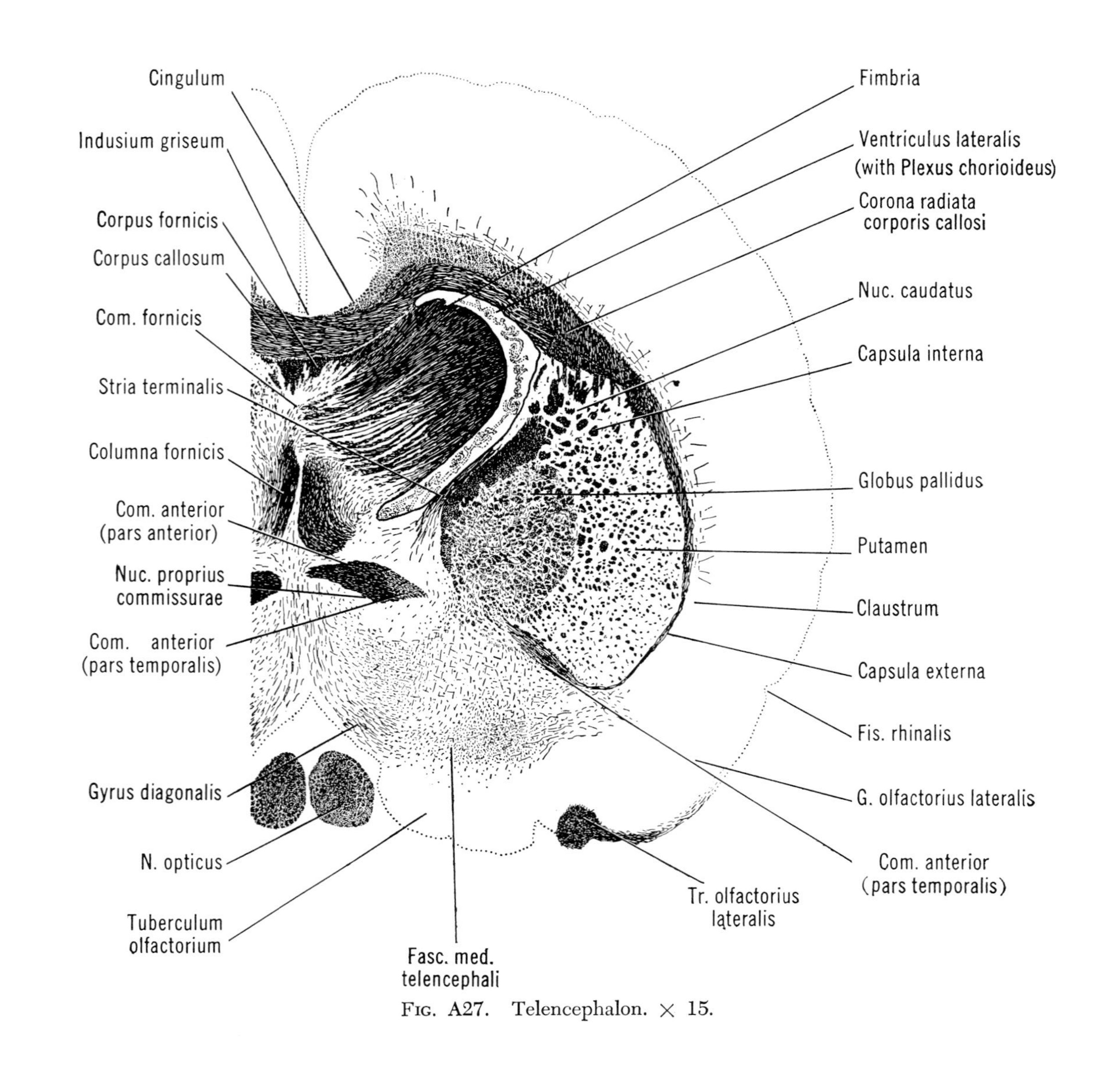

Fig. A27. Telencephalon. × 15.

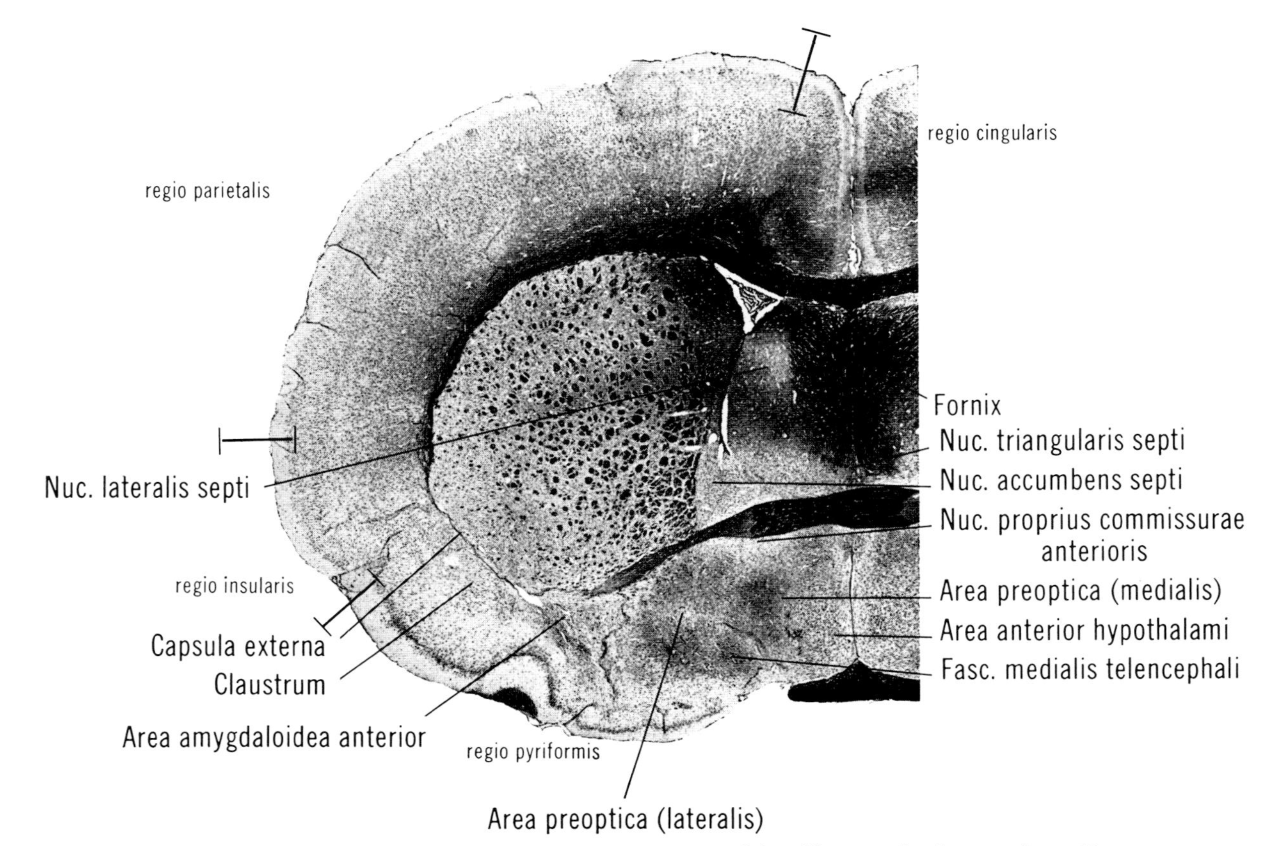

FIG. A28. Telencephalon at anterior commissure. Luxol fast blue-cresylviolet. × about 11.

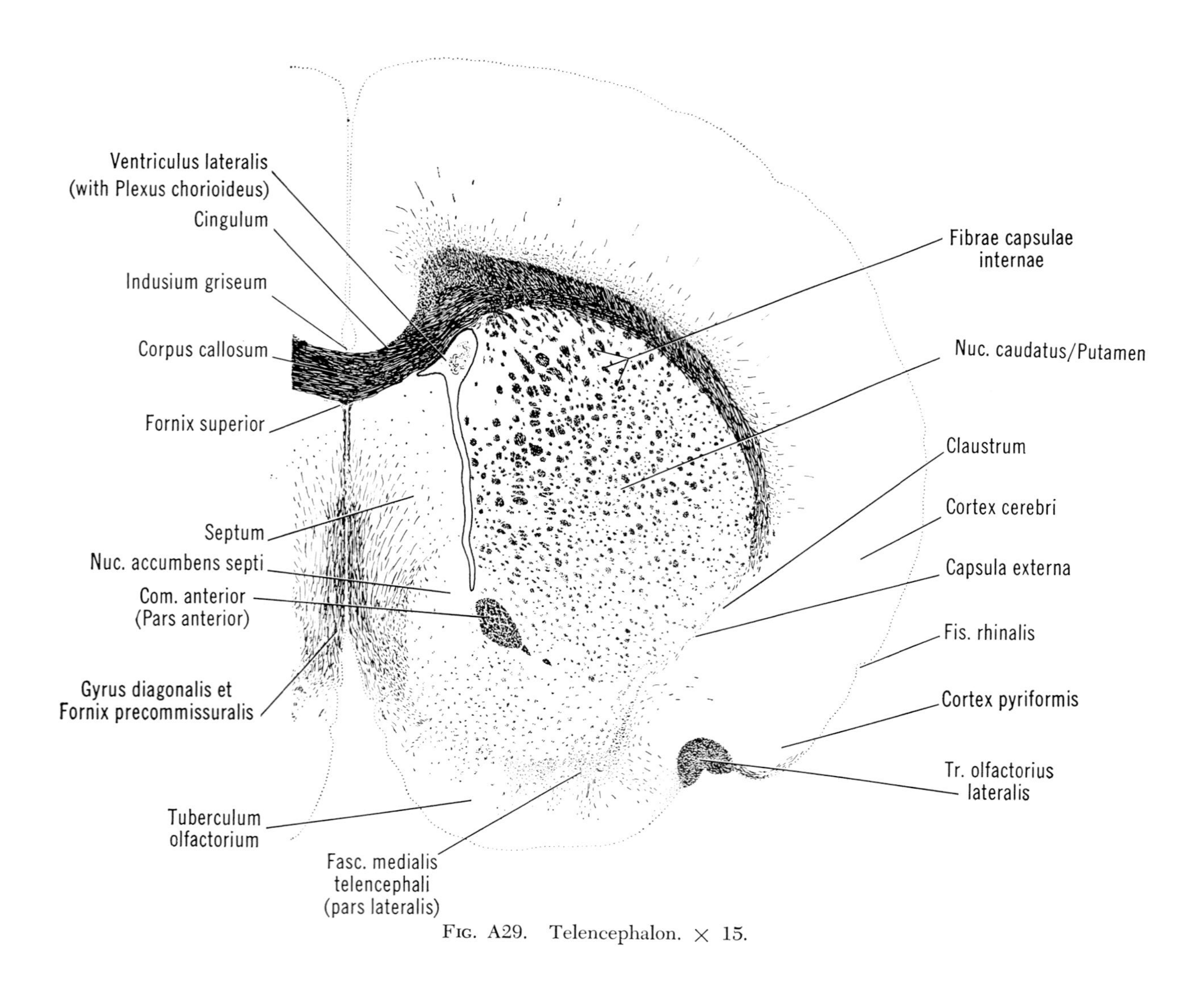

FIG. A29. Telencephalon. × 15.

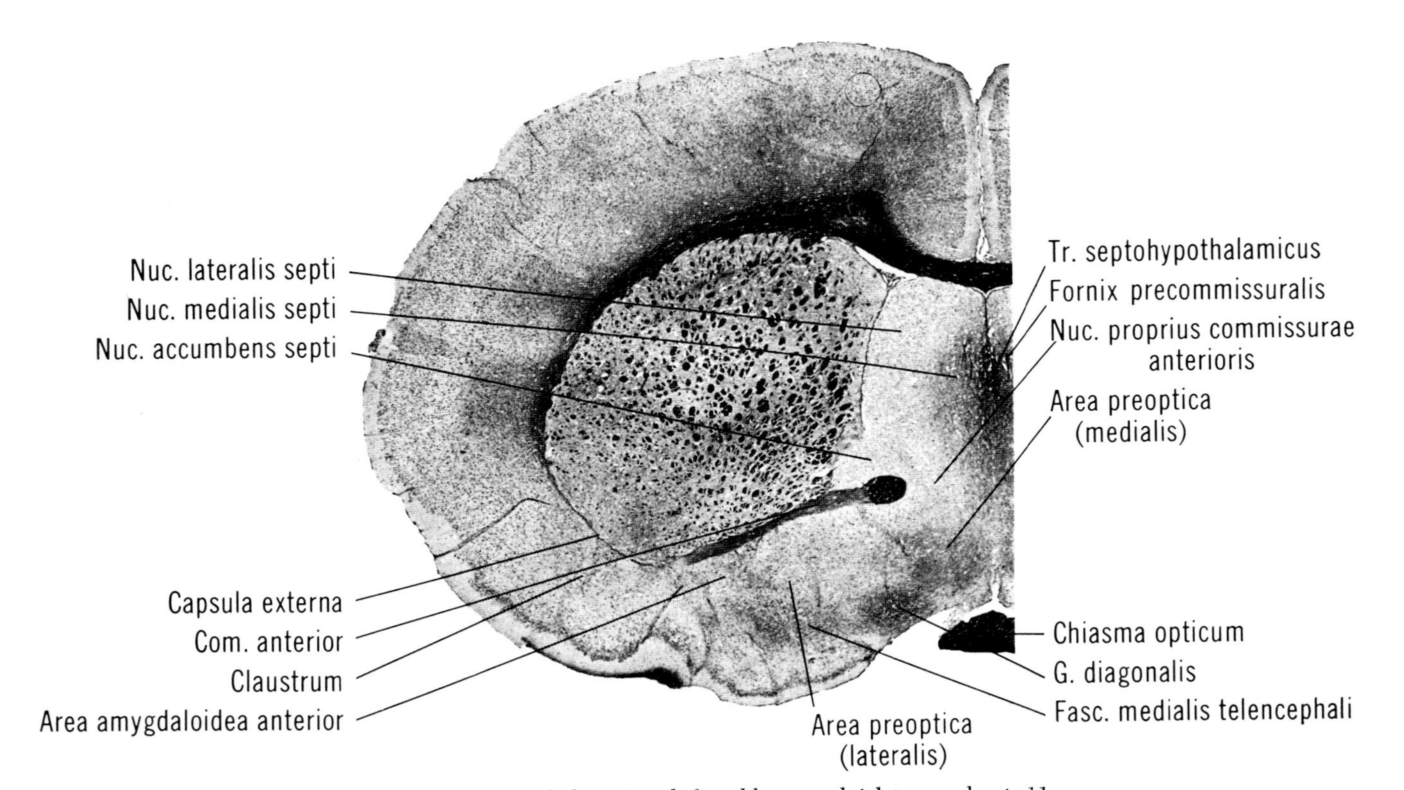

Fig. A30. Telencephalon. Luxol fast blue-cresylviolet. × about 11.

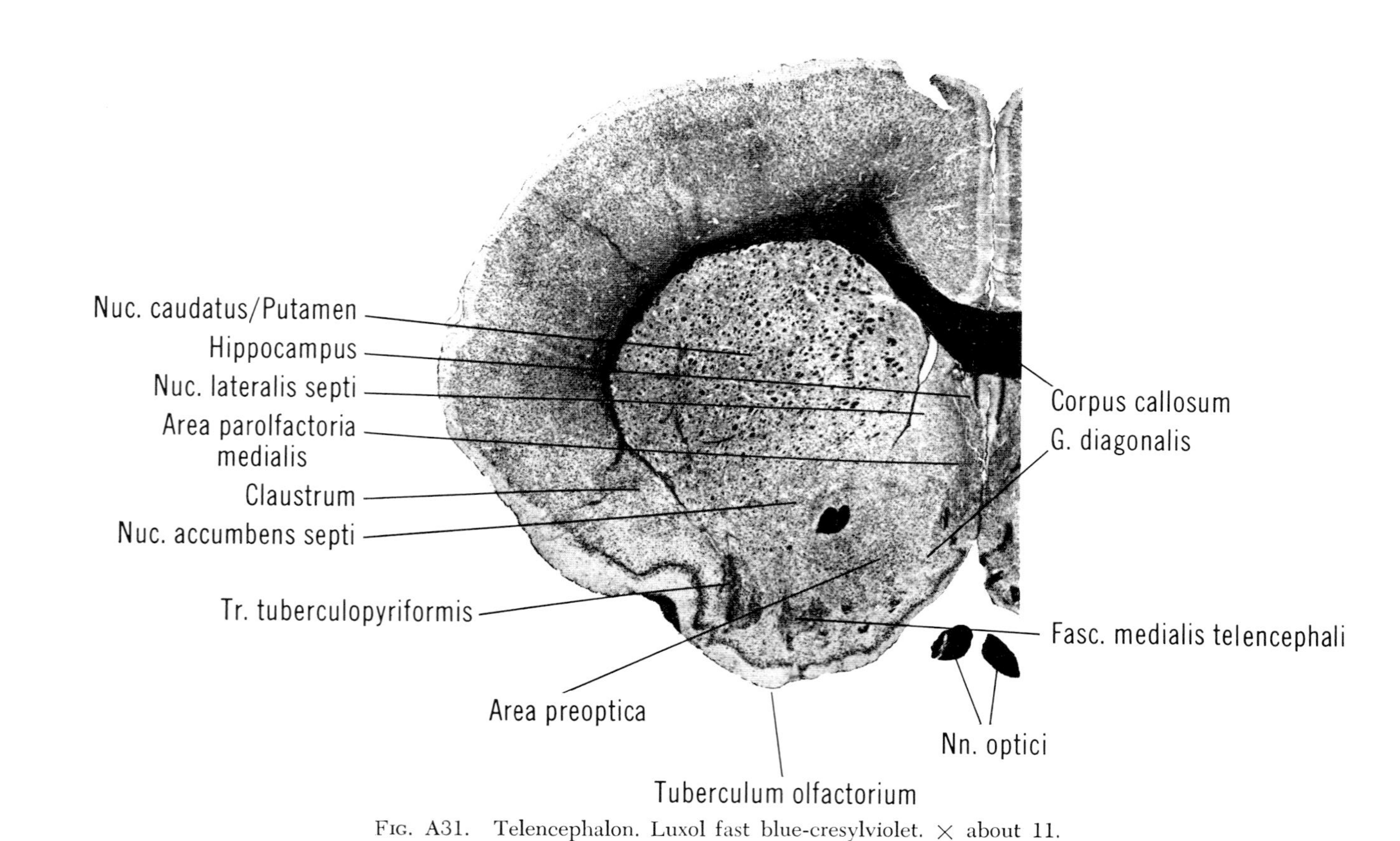

FIG. A31. Telencephalon. Luxol fast blue-cresylviolet. × about 11.

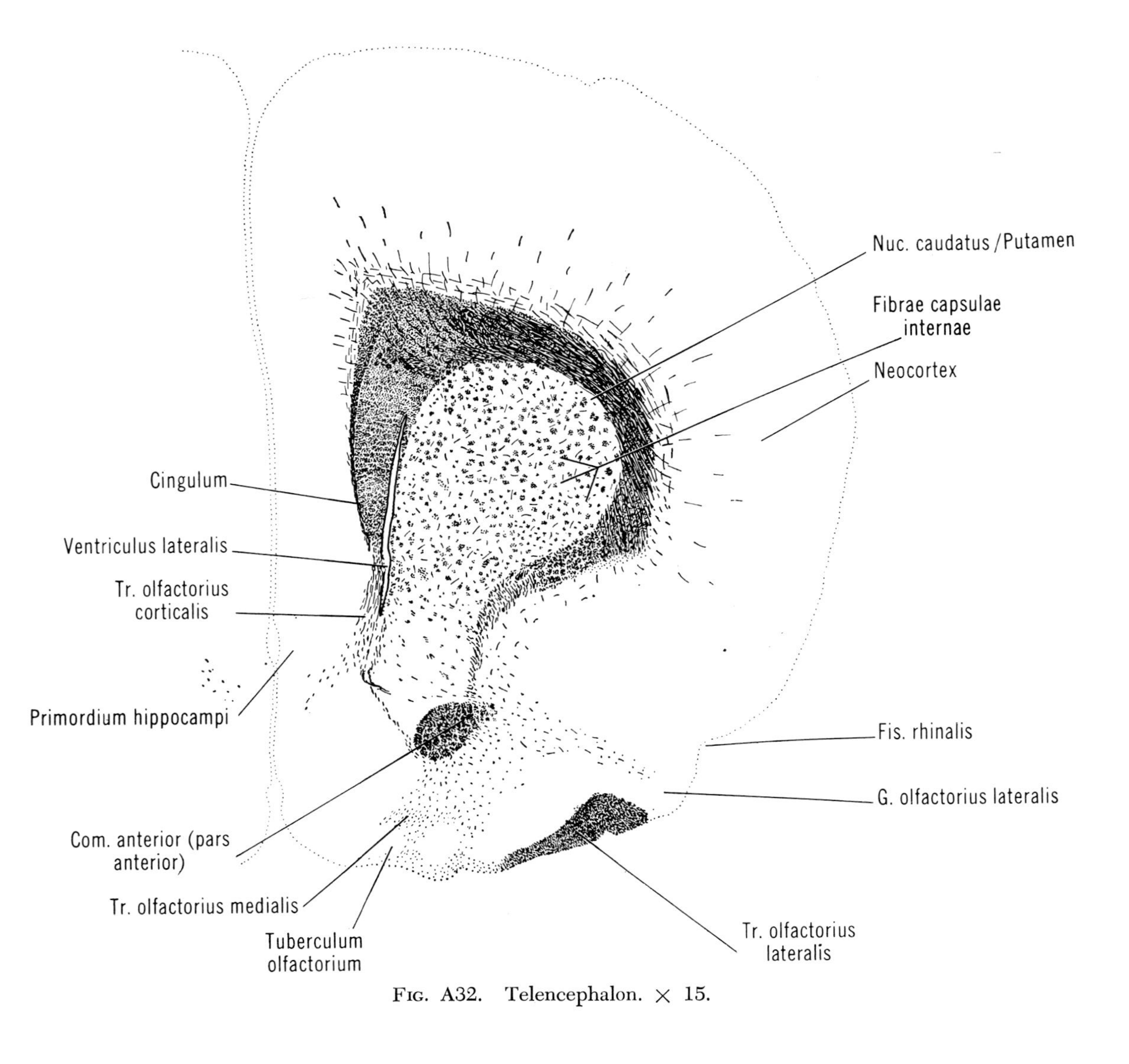

Fig. A32. Telencephalon. × 15.

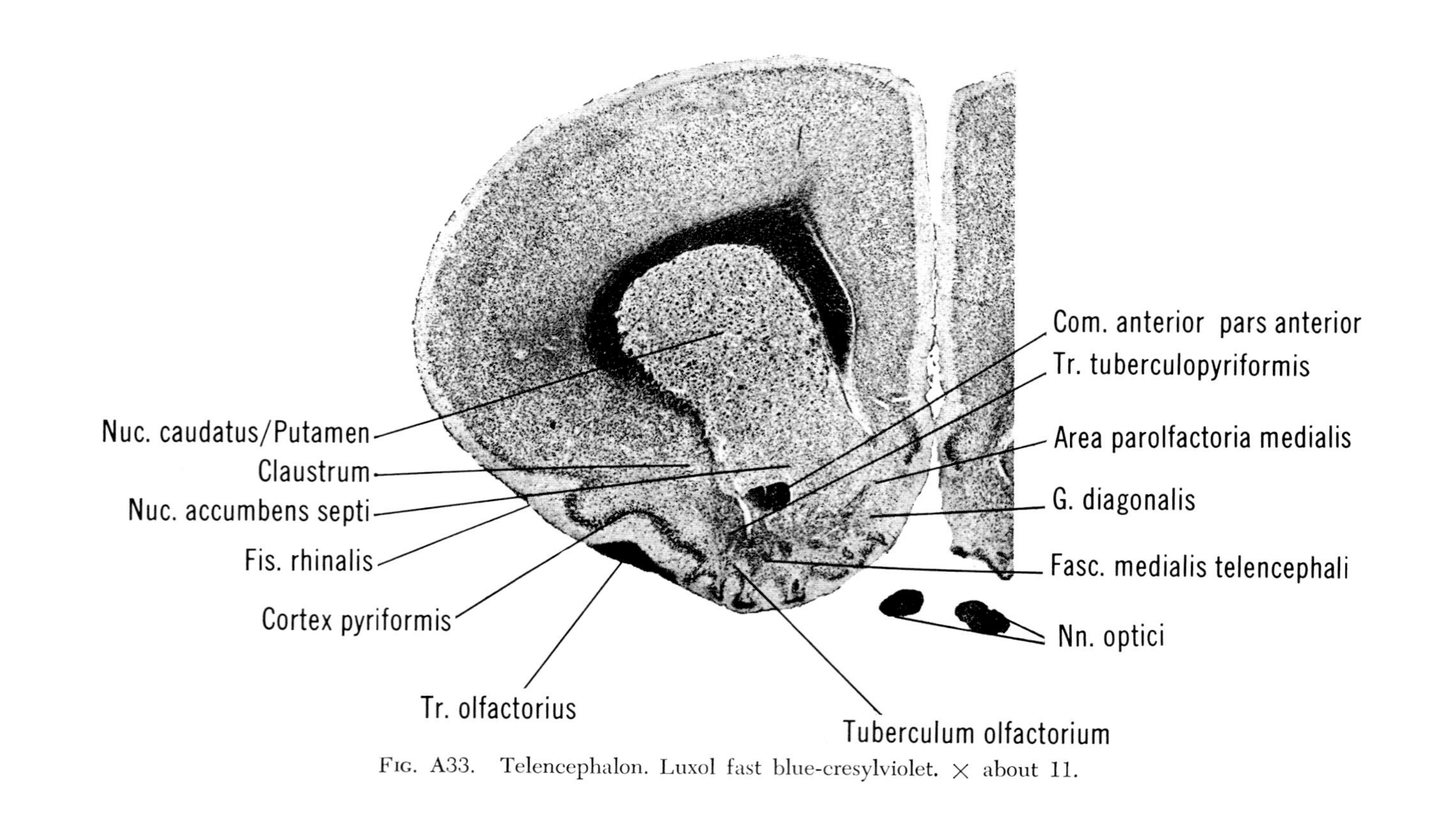

Fig. A33. Telencephalon. Luxol fast blue-cresylviolet. × about 11.

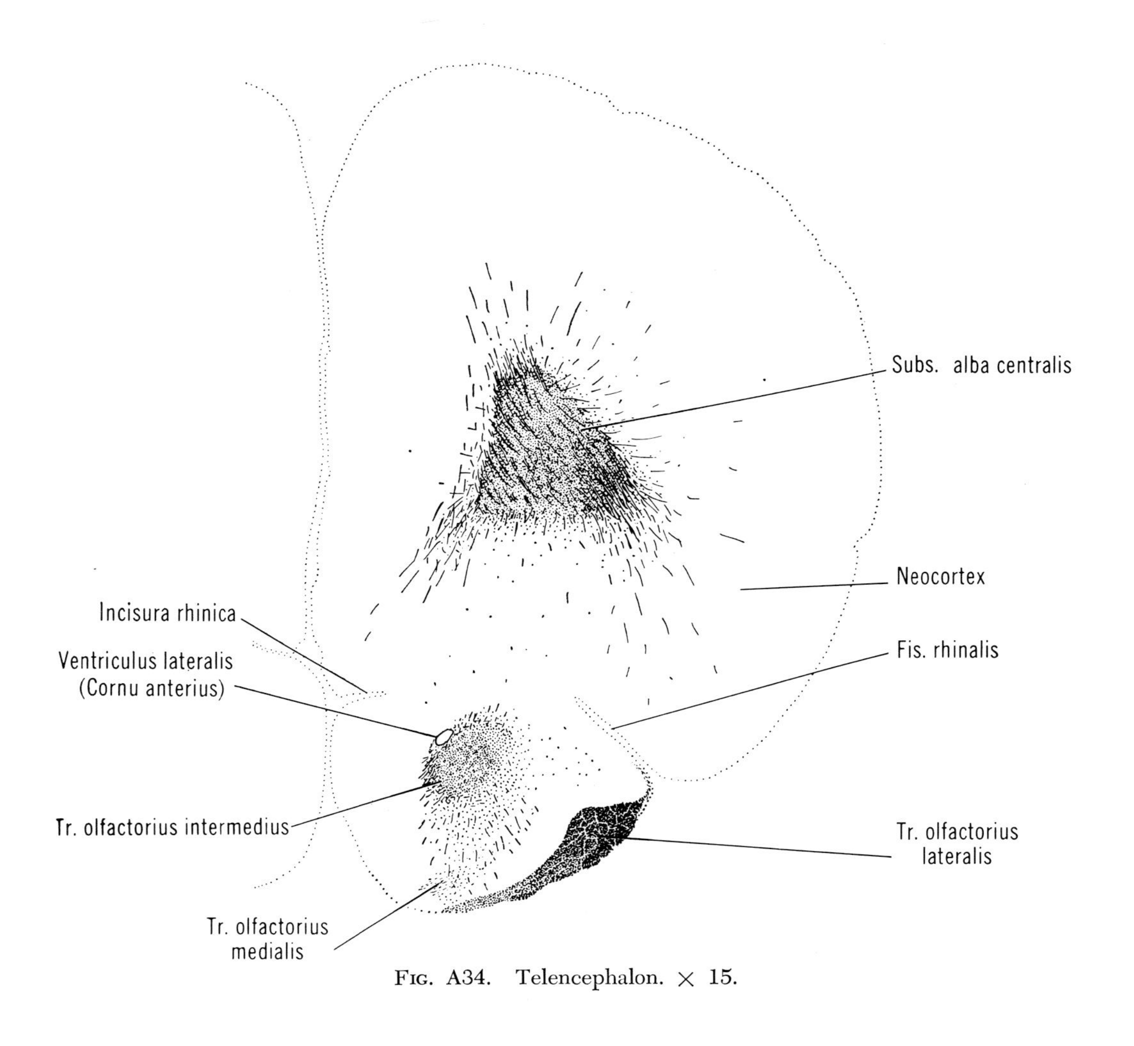

Fig. A34. Telencephalon. × 15.

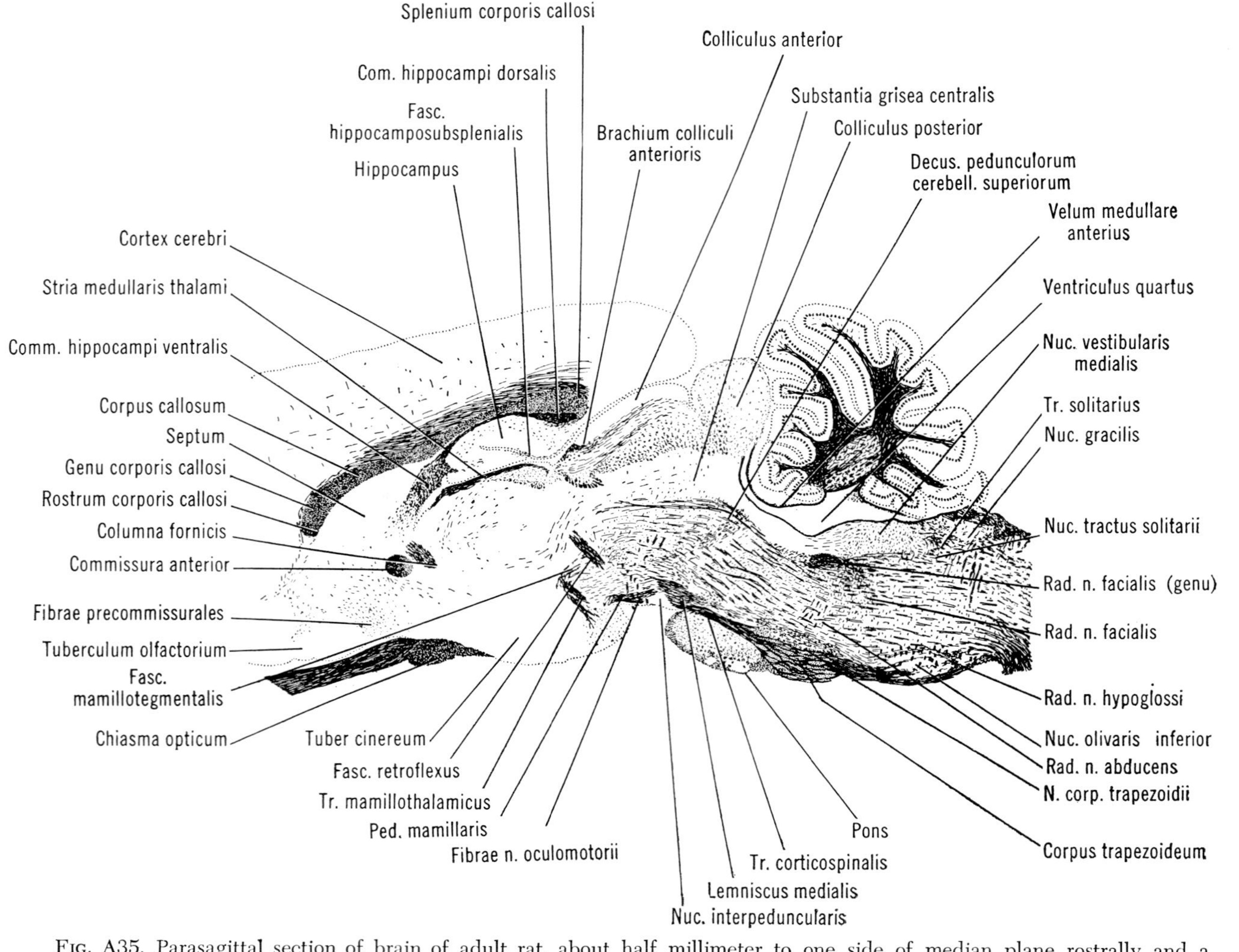

FIG. A35. Parasagittal section of brain of adult rat, about half millimeter to one side of median plane rostrally and a little further from it caudally. × about 7.

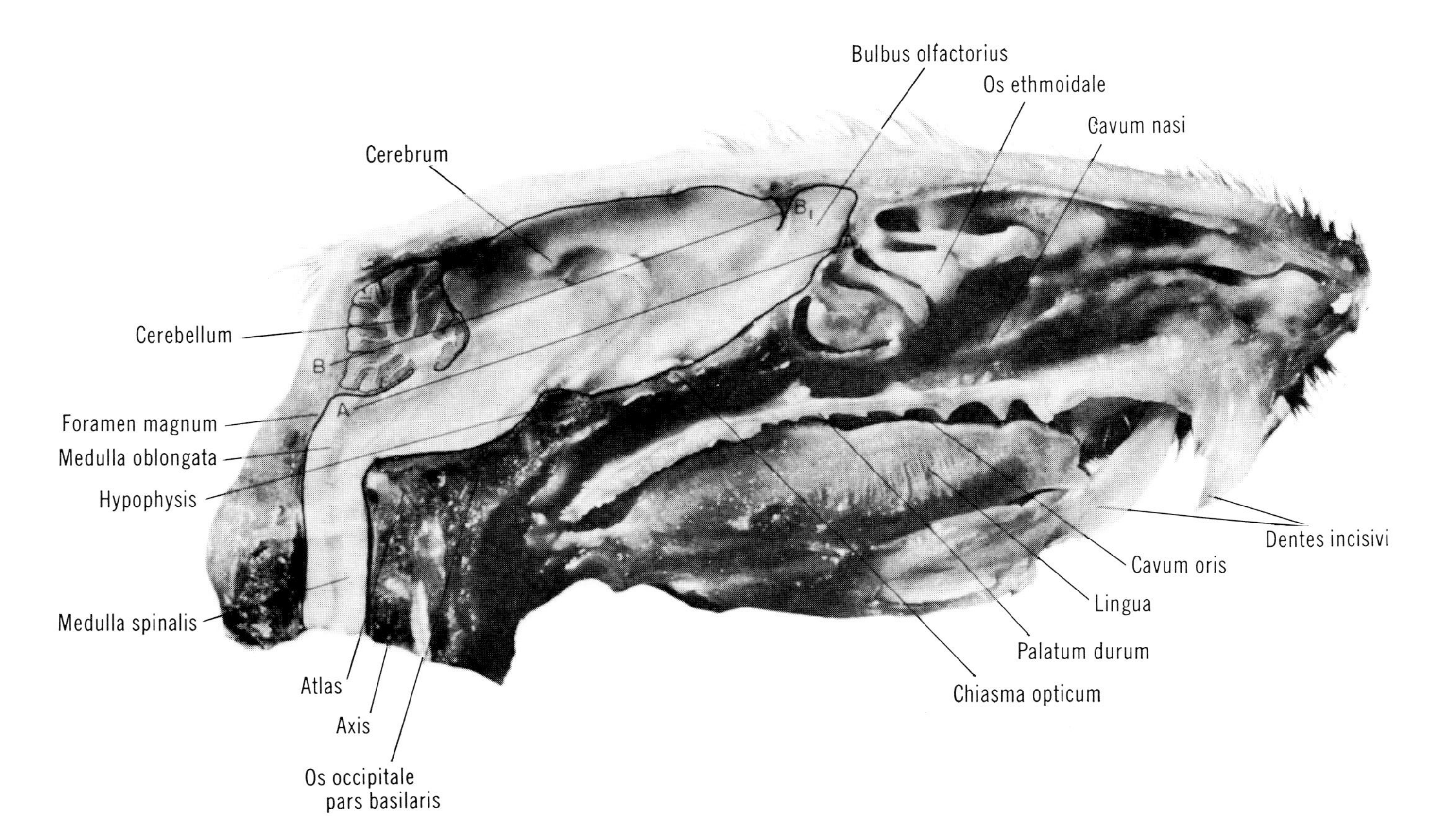

FIG. A36. Sagittal section of whole head showing anatomic relations of brain to skull. A–A_1 is the horizontal plane of section in Fig. A37. B–B_1 is the horizontal plane of section in Fig. A38. × about 3.

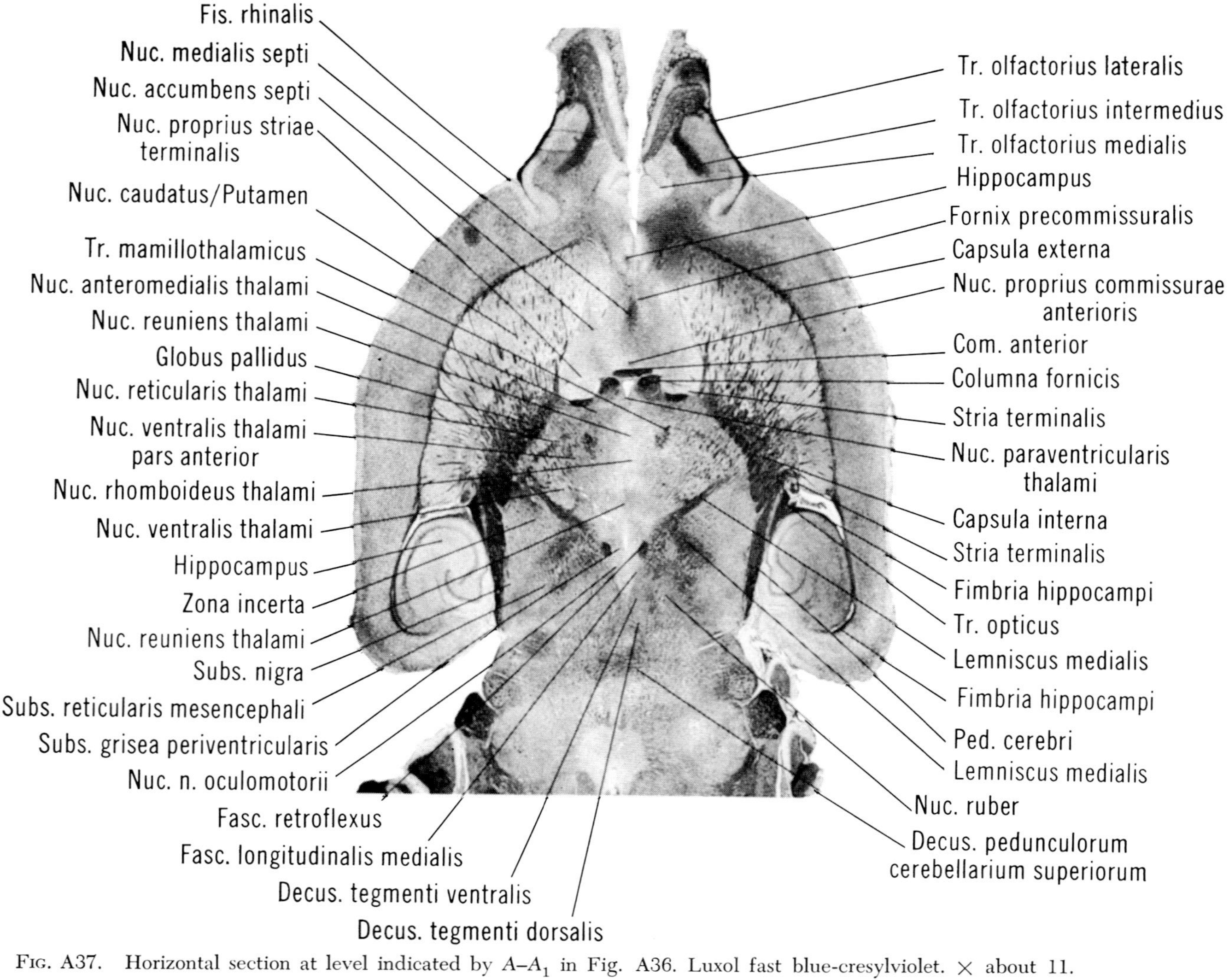

FIG. A37. Horizontal section at level indicated by A–A_1 in Fig. A36. Luxol fast blue-cresylviolet. × about 11.

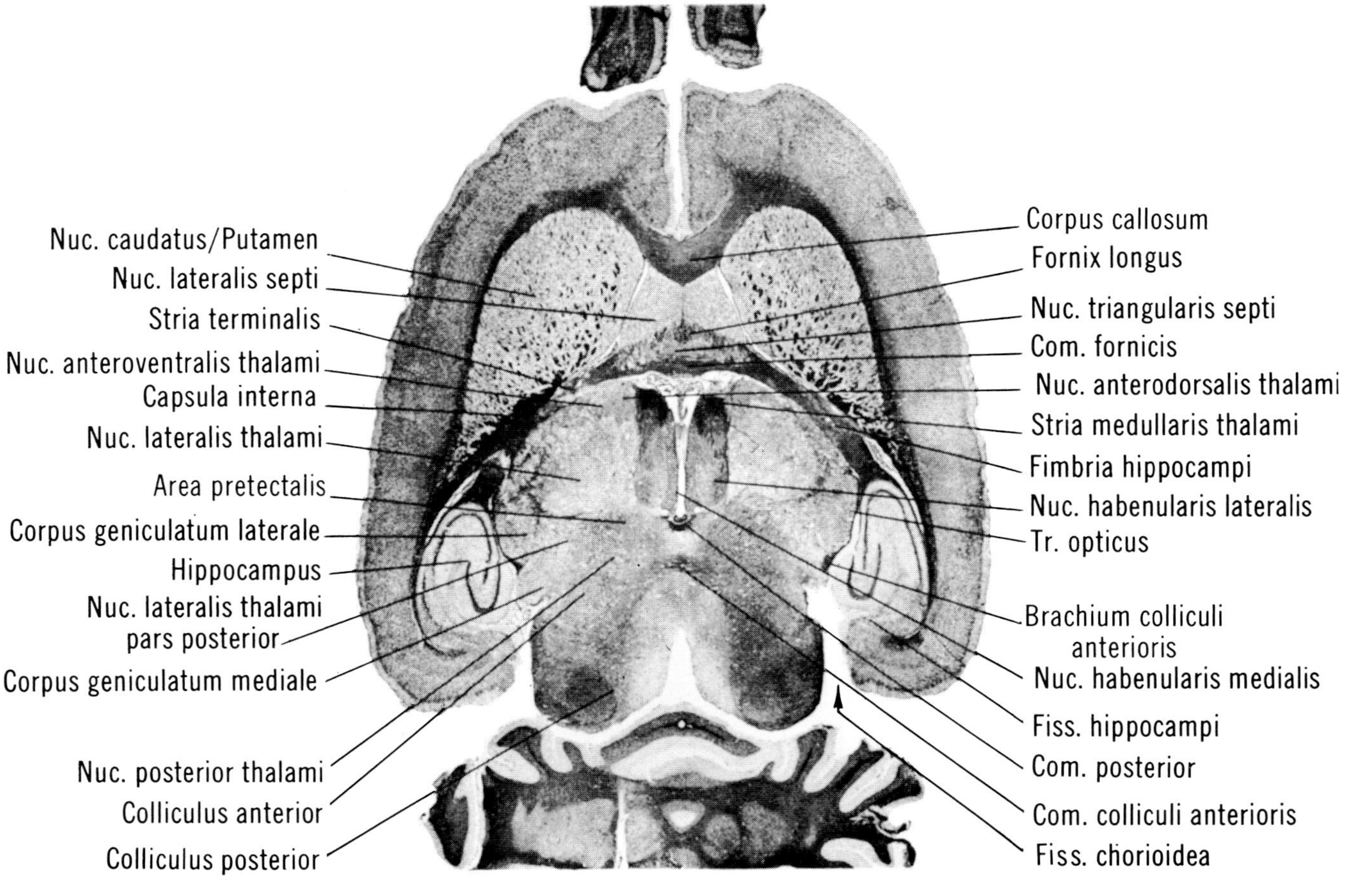

FIG. A38. Horizontal section at level indicated by *B* in Fig. A36. Luxol fast blue-cresylviolet. × about 11.

Subject Index

The page numbers in boldface type indicate that the structure is figured in an illustration. Synonyms are given in parentheses.

G

H

I

J

L

M

N

U

V

W

Z

5
6
7
D 8
E 9
F 0
G 1
H 2
I 3
J 4